THE NEW NATURALIST

A SURVEY OF BRITISH NATURAL HISTORY

DRAGONFLIES

The aim of this series is to interest the general reader in the wild life of Britain by recapturing the inquiring spirit of the old naturalists. The Editors believe that the natural pride of the British public in the native fauna and flora, to which must be added concern for their conservation, is best fostered by maintaining a high standard of accuracy combined with clarity of exposition in presenting the results of modern scientific research. The plants and animals are described in relation to their homes and habitats and are portrayed in the full beauty of their natural colours by the latest methods of colour photography and reproduction.

THE NEW NATURALIST

DRAGONFLIES

by

PHILIP S. CORBET
CYNTHIA LONGFIELD
N. W. MOORE

WITH 53 COLOUR PLATES BY S. BEAUFOY
16 PHOTOGRAPHS IN BLACK AND WHITE
200 MAPS AND DIAGRAMS
WITH KEY TO LARVAE BY A. E. GARDNER

COLLINS
ST JAMES'S PLACE, LONDON
1960

© Philip S. Corbet,
Cynthia Longfield and N. W. Moore, 1960
Printed in Great Britain
by Willmer Brothers and Haram Limited, Birkenhead
for Collins Clear-Type Press, London and Glasgow

CONTENTS

PLATES IN COLOUR

PLATES IN BLACK AND WHITE

EDITORS' PREFACE

WE WELCOME to the *New Naturalist* series a remarkable book by three distinguished naturalists. Dragonflies have been studied ever since the dawn of entomology; but a book like this, with its accent on biology—on life history, on ecology (the science of living relationships) and on ethology (the science of animal behaviour)—could not have been written until the middle of the twentieth century; the fashion to study insects as animals, and to promote fundamental research into their place in nature, though not new, has been intensified since the second world war in an unprecedented way.

Philip S. Corbet, the youngest of the three collaborators, first became interested in dragonflies as a schoolboy in 1946—partly, as he says, "because they were such good sport to catch." From 1950 to 1953 he spent three years in researches upon various aspects of the life history of dragonflies. He was specially interested in the problems of larval growth, and of seasonal regulation. In 1953 he obtained his Ph.D. degree on a thesis entitled "The seasonal ecology of dragonflies." Since 1951 a series of interesting scientific papers of mounting importance and complexity has come from him, in important entomological journals. From 1954 to 1957 he was employed as a zoologist at a fisheries research laboratory on Lake Victoria; and since then has been working on the biology of mosquitoes at the Virus Research Institute at Entebbe. Like his colleagues he is a general naturalist, and within the vast class of insects he has worked also on the biology of caddis-flies and mayflies.

Miss Cynthia Longfield is a naturalist of world repute and esteem. For thirty years, she worked in the British Museum (Natural History) on the classification and taxonomy of dragonflies. An enthusiastic all-rounder, she has watched birds and collected insects and plants in many parts of the world on many expeditions, having visited Africa, the East Indies, South America and Polynesia. Her *The Dragonflies of the British Isles*, published by Warne in *The Wayside and Woodland* series in 1949, is a standard work.

Norman W. Moore started studying dragonflies in 1938, and has published valuable papers on the subject in *Behaviour, The Journal of Animal Ecology* and *The Proceedings of the Bristol Naturalists' Society*. In 1948, with the help of the Rousse Ball Fellowship from Trinity College, Cambridge, he went to Gambia to study African dragonflies. From 1949 to 1953, when he was a Lecturer in Zoology at Bristol University, he spent about half his research time on the Odonata, and his Ph.D. degree, which he obtained in 1953, had as its thesis an essay "On the ecology and behaviour of adult dragonflies." Since then he has been the Nature Conservancy's

Regional Officer for South-west England, Like his colleagues, Norman Moore is a dedicated all-rounder. He is probably the greatest authority on the buzzard.

Apart from rare vagrants, forty-three species of dragonflies have been recorded in the British Isles. Compared with the array of species in the world this number is rather small; but it contains representatives of at least eight of the eleven largest and most widespread families. Thus, an intensive study of the British dragonfly fauna, such as has been made by our three colleagues, can throw a light upon the order as a whole, of the utmost importance; and it is an order which, from the fossil record, emerges as one of the oldest groups of insects, dating back to the Carboniferous more than 200 million years ago, when dragonflies only moderately simpler than those which fly today seem to have dominated the coal-measure forests: some of them seem to have been bigger than any insects known to science.

One of the many advantages of studying dragonflies is that to a certain extent they are as observable as birds. This makes them excellent material for the ecologist and ethologist. Our authors have produced a beautiful series of original field observations of which any naturalists could be proud. From their exploration of the life histories of some of our beautiful British species they have been able to throw light upon territorial behaviour, sexual display, dispersal mechanisms, affairs which, in so far as they are studied among insects at all, have been studied by only a few pioneers. But besides this, they have given us the precision which will enable us to identify our British dragonflies at all their very complicated stages, to understand their distribution and some of the principles that govern it; and, with a warm sense of scholarship, they have given us, too, a most useful history of the British dragonflies and their investigators as well as some sensible and agreeable conclusions about their aesthetic value, the need for their conservation and protection, and the steps that may be necessary to ensure this. This, then is the book for every kind of student of insects, from the amateur collector and insect-watcher, to the professional ethologist. Particularly may we commend the various tidy appendices, among which we are proud to include that experienced and authoritative odonatist A. E. Gardner's "Key to the larvae of the British Odonata."

For many years this book will, we are certain, be the standard work on the British dragonflies. For many years, too, it will be a source, not only of copious information, but of inspiration. So many wonderful problems and lines of research are suggested in *Dragonflies* that we confidently predict that it will give rise to a new school of odonatists, and will attract new minds into insect watching—by no means all of them from the still most necessary occupation of insect collecting.

THE EDITORS

AUTHORS' PREFACE

IN VIEW of the size and impressive appearance of dragonflies, it is perhaps surprising that our knowledge of their biology is not greater. The position at present is that although most of the world species have now been described we still know very little about the principles underlying their ecology, physiology and behaviour.

When dragonflies are compared with such groups as bees and butterflies, several reasons for our ignorance become clear. For one thing, dragonflies have no economic importance, at least none that can be easily assessed, and for another, their loss of colour after capture must have discouraged many a collector from giving them closer attention.

One thing we hope to do by writing this book is to direct the attention of more naturalists towards dragonflies. Perhaps Mr. Beaufoy's colour photographs, coupled with the recipes given for preserving colour of adults, may help in this direction.

Most books on dragonflies have dealt mainly with structure and classification. The limited extent of knowledge has made this inevitable. But in the last decade several people have paid particular attention to dragonflies as subjects for field study, and so have begun to accumulate some useful information on their ecology and behaviour. Therefore, in this book, we lay particular emphasis on these two subjects. And, in doing this, it is inevitable that we should concentrate on the aspects which are of greatest interest to ourselves. We hope that the advantages of such treatment will outweigh the disadvantages. One consequence, perhaps a disadvantage, is that several aspects of morphology are omitted or receive only passing mention. We make no apology for this in a book devoted primarily to natural history, but refer readers to the several excellent works on this subject which already exist.

One of our main aims has been to review recent work and to suggest directions in which future research may prove promising. Wherever feasible we have tried to make it clear when any piece of work has been carried out by someone other than ourselves. But limitations of space do not permit many of the older papers to be included in our bibliography, and so certain information is assumed to have become general knowledge. Readers wishing to follow up earlier references are advised to consult systematic works on Odonata, particularly Tillyard's classic book, *The Biology of Dragonflies*. We should like to mention here how much we ourselves owe to this book.

Another point we wish to emphasise is the theoretical nature of many of the ideas put forward here. This perhaps applies most of all to the ecological part of the book. Therefore, before carrying out further studies on such subjects, readers are advised to examine the appropriate references listed in the bibliography.

The full Latin and English names of all the British species will be found in Chapter 2 p. 11. Subsequently, species are referred to by their Latin names only. In the case of a genus having only one British species, such as *Anax*, the generic name only may be given; otherwise, names are usually abbreviated as follows: *A. virgo* for *Agrion virgo*. Names of non-British species are given in full on the first occasion that they are mentioned, and abbreviated thereafter.

Throughout this book, the immature stage of dragonflies is called the *larva*, instead of the *nymph* or *naiad*. This has been done advisedly, since we feel that the arguments given by Hinton (1948) are overwhelmingly in favour of such a terminology. The inclusion of a certain number of technical terms has been inevitable. Where deemed necessary, each is explained in the text on the first occasion of mention, but most of them are also defined in the Glossary on page 246.

Far too many people help to produce a book like this for us to be able to acknowledge them all individually. There are, however, several people in particular whom we wish to thank: Mr. Sam Beaufoy for the great help he has given us with the pnotographs and in many other ways; Mr. Eric Gardner for collecting many of the species for these photographs, and for drawing the wings in Appendix II from photographs kindly supplied by Mr. W. H. T. Tams; Mr. E. W. Classey and *The Entomologist's Gazette* for generously allowing us to include Eric Gardner's key to the larvae; the editors for their advice and help; those friends who read and criticised drafts of the manuscript; and those who so generously assisted with the typing.

P.S.C.
C.L.
N.W.M.

CHAPTER I

DRAGONFLIES

(N.W.M.)

We find in the Odonata a singularly isolated group, marked by very high specialisations of structure, superimposed upon an exceedingly archaic foundation.

R. J. TILLYARD (1917). *The Biology of Dragonflies*

DRAGONFLIES are an excellent group of insects for the naturalist to study. The adults are large, and fly by day, and can be observed in the field much as a birdwatcher observes birds. Many species can be identified in the field without capture; for studying the behaviour of dragonflies a pair of field glasses is much more useful than a microscope. Insects can be marked with paint, so that the behaviour, length of life and dispersal of individuals can be studied. Populations of dragonflies can very easily be determined, because dragonflies are large insects occurring in small numbers; being predators, their numbers are considerably less than those of their prey. The adults of the smaller species provide ideal material for sampling techniques. Individuals of the larger species can be counted accurately in the field without resorting to estimates based on sampling. In general, the dragonfly might be called the birdwatcher's insect.

The aim of this chapter is to introduce the dragonflies and to outline their place in the animal kingdom. Dragonflies belong to the largest single group of animals, the insects: at least a million species of insects must exist on the face of the earth. Of these only about 5,000 are dragonflies, including only 43 British species. The total population of dragonflies must form a very small part of the world's insect fauna; but dragonflies are such an interesting group, and provide such excellent opportunities for field studies, that we hope no apology is needed for writing a book about them.

Insects belong to the phylum Arthropoda, those animals covered with a hard impermeable external skeleton. The Arthropoda are an enormous group of invertebrate animals, including waterfleas, shrimps, crabs, barnacles, centipedes, millipedes, springtails, insects, scorpions and spiders. They show great diversity in colonising different environments. Yet all members of the group have a comparable plan of structure, because they are related to each other. Dragonflies are one type of arthropod; before discussing the structure and habits of dragonflies in particular, we must define the general characteristics shared by all arthropods.

Possession of an external skeleton is both an advantage and a limitation. It has allowed arthropods to live in most hostile environments, by providing a protective barrier, yet it has prevented them from evolving along other paths open to animals such as ourselves, whose skeleton is internal. The external skeleton or cuticle is given strength by a substance called chitin, and is almost impermeable to water and therefore also impermeable to gases. This means that even small arthropods can live on dry land without risk of desiccation by evaporation of the body fluids; on the other hand, respiration cannot take place through a dry outer surface, so that some special provision must be made for oxygen to enter. Because the skeleton is external the joints must be external too (the clockwork toy appearance of all arthropods is due to this), and there must be joints wherever parts need to move. The jointed appearance of the group is what struck the early naturalists—hence the term 'arthropod' ('jointed foot'). The possession of a hard outside also means that if an arthropod is to grow it must discard its old skin and grow a new one: instead of gradual continuous increase, the arthropod's growing life is punctuated by a series of moults or *ecdyses*, during which it is very vulnerable.

In insects, the problem of respiration when covered by an impermeable cuticle has been "solved" by the outside surface growing inward into the animal, and forming a large number of branching tubes or *tracheae*, along which air diffuses to all the tissues. In the adult dragonfly there are 10 pairs of openings or 'spiracles' (see Fig. 1, p. 7) leading into the tracheae which ramify until their minute end branches lie on the internal tissues. Since these tubes are really extensions of the outer surface they are partly made of chitin, and when the insect moults, it moults its tracheal lining with the rest of its skin. This method of respiration has probably prevented terrestrial arthropods from achieving any great size, for tissues above a certain size could not effectively be supplied with oxygen. In fact very few land arthropods approach anywhere near the theoretical maximum, or the size of some of the fossil forms. This is probably for an ecological rather than a physiological reason. The advantage of being big is mainly that bigness allows the animal to be more independent of its surroundings, particularly of changes in temperature. (The larger the animal the less surface area it has relative to its mass.) But competition between species and between individuals within one species also favours the bigger individuals and so many species—both prey and predator—tend to increase in size. It is particularly important to be fairly big if you control your body temperature and keep it constant, as we ourselves do. That is why there are no really minute birds and mammals. But the temperature of dragonflies, like that of most of the arthropods, follows to a large extent the outside temperature—they are warm when it is sunny and cold when it is cloudy and at night. Greater size means that body heat can be retained longer, but it also means that the animal if it is "cold-blooded" takes longer to warm up. To become quickly mobile in early morning is presumably more important to an insect than to remain warm after it has gone to roost.

It is fun to speculate along these lines, but the causes of size in each species could only be discovered by studying the ecology of insects throughout the millions of years when dragonflies were flying on the earth and there were no men to watch them.

The way of life of dragonflies must, since they are arthropods, be very different from the way of life of ourselves, as mammals. The little insect is buffeted by raindrops, even imprisoned by surface tension, while the large mammal is scarcely affected by such. Convection currents and light winds and the sun going behind a cloud may be matters of life and death to the insect, but are scarcely noticed by ourselves.

Our two ways of development are very different. Man's development is gradual, and only about a third to a fifth of his time is spent in the immature stage. But the dragonfly's is divided by sudden changes. Its immature stage is utterly unlike the adult; it even lives in a different medium, for dragonfly larvae are nearly all aquatic while the adults are all terrestrial. The adult stage often lasts less than one twentieth of the dragonfly's whole life. There are of course many other differences of anatomy and physiology: our nervous system runs along our back, the nervous system of an arthropod runs along its underside; the compound eyes of the dragonfly are built on quite a different pattern to our own eyes; although these features are less important from our present point of view.

However, the basic needs of Man and dragonflies, observer and observed, are similar. Both must perform the functions which maintain life and are characteristic of all living things. Both must eat and rest and shelter from bad weather; reproduce their kind, leave unsuitable habitats and disperse to suitable new ones. Our methods of solving these problems are vastly different because our bodies are so differently constituted. But an important similarity in method must be mentioned: in both dragonfly and Man the eye is the principal sense organ. We both live in a world of seeing. The life of a dragonfly is far more comprehensible to us than that of, say, a spider, whose world is one of vibrations.

Having indicated some of the main differences and similarities between ourselves and dragonflies, we must now in more detail compare dragonflies with other insects.

The ancestor of all insects was probably an animal whose body was divided into many segments, each with a pair of limbs to a segment. It may have looked superficially rather like the marine rag worm which is dug for bait on the English shores. In the course of millions of years the different segments became specialised for different functions. In all insects, unlike most other arthropods, they have become grouped in three regions, the head, the thorax, and the abdomen. Segmentation is only obvious in the thorax which has three segments, each with a pair of limbs (the legs), and the abdomen which has ten visible segments and vestiges of the eleventh and possibly a twelfth segment. Apart from the inferior appendage of the Zygoptera which is probably the limb of the eleventh segment, no adult dragonflies possess true abdominal limbs. The head is believed to consist principally of six segments fused together. It contains four pairs of limbs—the other segments are limbless; insects only have a single pair of antennae unlike crustacea (crabs, etc.) which have two pairs. The other three

---

Plate 1. DEMOISELLES (ZYGOPTERA: AGRIIDAE)

a. Agrion virgo, male in mature colouring. The immature male has all brown wings.

b. Agrion virgo, female. When mature the wings are tinged pinkish brown. Even when the female is immature, there is no green colour in the wings.

c. Agrion splendens, male. The coloured banding of the wings clearly distinguishes it from *A. virgo.* The band is brown in the immature male.

d. Agrion splendens, female. The wing-colour is yellow-green. When very immature the wings are colourless and it is then difficult to tell the two species of *Agrion* from one another.

a

b

c

d

Plate 1.

a. Lestes sponsa, male and female. The male is very mature and pruinose. The female shows well the slender abdomen and short ovipositor of this species.

b. Lestes dryas, female. Compare her with *L. sponsa* and the stouter abdomen and larger pterostigma are clearly seen. Note the length of the ovipositor, reaching just beyond the posterior edge of the 10th segment of the abdomen.

Plate 2. DAMSELFLIES (ZYGOPTERA : LESTIDAE)

pairs of limbs are all connected with feeding: they are the jaws—which, in the dragonfly, break up the food, the maxillae which hold it in place and push it into the mouth, and the labium which acts as the lower lip—the upper lip being the front part of the head known as the labrum. The head also bears the compound eyes and the simple eyes or ocelli when these are present. On the dragonfly, which depends almost entirely on sight to catch its prey and find its mate, the compound eyes are enormous—on some species they cover more than half the total surface of the head. Some species can be stimulated by a sudden movement 40 feet away. The antennae, which contain organs of touch and perhaps hearing and smell, are minute and poorly developed.

In common with most insects dragonflies possess wings in the adult stage. Wings have not the same evolutionary history as the limbs which have just been listed—that is they are not descended from the limbs of the worm-like ancestor of the insect. Like the tracheae they are extensions of the body wall but unlike the tracheae they extend outwards, not inwards! On all insects with two pairs of wings they are found on the second and third segments of the thorax. No insect larva possesses functional wings; in other words, wings are correlated with the adult or reproductive stage, and must be considered primarily as organs of dispersal, not of feeding or escape.

Insects can be divided into two groups—into those that possess a pupa or chrysalis stage and those that do not. Taking insects as a whole the larva, which is longlived, is primarily the feeding stage, and the adult, which is shortlived, is the reproductive and dispersal stage. It is therefore not surprising that through natural selection the two stages have become extremely unlike.

In all insects the instar before the adult acts as a mould to which the muscles can be inserted. Therefore an insect in the penultimate instar must be fairly rigid and approximately the shape of the adult. This means that in insects without a pupa, the last larval instar must bear some resemblance to the adult form which develops within it. The change from larva to adult, although striking enough, is more gradual than in the younger groups in which the pupal stage has evolved. In these the pupa bridges the gap between larva and adult and enables a far greater degree of specialisation in the larva. In particular, the development of the wings can occur much later. This enables the larvae of many species to live in the soil and in the tissues of plants and other animals—environments which cannot be colonised

D—B

by insects of the older group whose wings develop externally. Dragonflies belong to this older group—they possess no pupal stage, and their
developing wings appear externally in the larva (see Fig. 1, p. 7). In
this they resemble many others, for example, the mayflies, stoneflies,
grasshoppers, earwigs, and most bugs; but differ from the beetles, flies,
butterflies, and bees. Unlike the grasshoppers, but like the mayflies,
dragonflies have aquatic larvae.

So far we have considered the similarities with other insects; we
must now consider the unique features of the group. They are connected with feeding and with respiration in the larva, and with flight
and with mating in the adult.

First, there is the unique method of feeding in the larva. Unlike
any other insect (including the adult dragonfly) the larva has developed
a prehensile labium (see Fig. 1, p. 7). Its action will be described in
detail in chapter 6, p. 73; enough to say now that the labium or
lower lip of the dragonfly is enormously enlarged and armed with
hooks (palps)—at rest it is folded beneath the head—but when prey is
in range it is shot out by means of hydrostatic pressure; it seizes the
prey, which is drawn back to the mouth, held in the hooks of the
labium. The dragonfly larva is also unique in its method of breathing.
Most aquatic larvae have external gills. The larvae of the smaller
dragonflies—the sub-order Zygoptera or damselflies—are no exceptions. They possess three leaf-like caudal gills. The larvae of the larger
dragonflies, or Anisoptera, do not possess caudal gills and breathe
entirely through the rectum: water is pumped in and out and the
exchange of oxygen and carbon dioxide occurs through the surface or
the anterior part of the rectum. The surface is greatly enlarged by
being much folded into an elaborate organ known as the branchial
basket. The rectal pumping mechanism in the Anisoptera is also used
as a method of escape—water is squirted backwards out of the anus
and the insect glides rapidly forward: it is in fact jet propelled.
Respiration probably also occurs in the rectum of most Zygoptera but
in these there is no branchial basket.

The wings of most insects are moved in quite a different way from
the wings of birds and bats. In vertebrates muscles are attached to
the wings and pull them up and down. In most insects the main force
does not come from direct wing muscles but from muscles attached at
either end to the top and bottom and ends of the thoracic segments.
When these contract the thorax changes shape and the wings, which
are attached to the thorax but not to its muscles, are levered up and

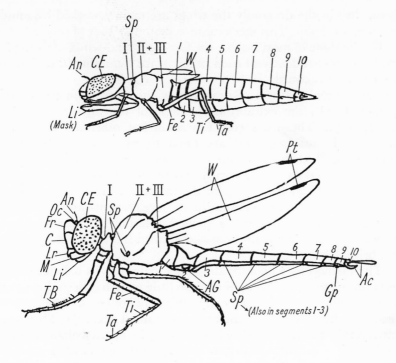

Fig. 1. Diagrams showing parts of a final instar larva and an adult male of an Aeshnine dragonfly.

Abdominal segments numbered in Arabic numerals

AG,	accessory genitalia	Lr,	labrum
Ac,	anal clasper	M,	mandible
An,	antenna	Oc,	ocellus
C,	clypeus	Pt,	pterostigma
CE,	compound eye	Sp,	spiracle (those on segs. 1–3 in
Fe,	femur		adult not shown)
Fr,	frons	Ta,	tarsus
Gp,	genital pore	Ti,	tibia
Li,	labium	TB,	tibial brush (eye cleaner)

Thoracic segments numbered in Roman numerals (I=Prothorax)

W, wings

N.B. The distance between head and synthorax (segments II & III) has been exaggerated to show relationship with prothorax (I) down. But in the dragonfly the wings are mainly worked by muscles attached to them. This mechanism is more like that of birds.

Unlike those of most insects, the fore- and hind-wings of dragonflies can beat independently of each other. Like humming-birds, dragonflies can fly backwards.

The unusual features of dragonfly wing-construction are probably connected with the extraordinary shape of the insect's thorax (see Fig. 1, p. 7). The first segment is small but otherwise normal, the second and third segments are fused together, and are relatively enormous, and furthermore the two segments have developed a skew. This has pushed the legs forward and the wings back with the result that what looks like the back of the insect is in fact the sides of the second segment. These extraordinary developments are undoubtedly connected with the dragonfly's method of feeding: it takes its prey on the wing by catching it in the basket formed by its forwardly directed and bristly legs.

The method by which the dragonfly maintains its balance in flight also appears to be unique, although so little work has been done on the way most other insects balance, that this may not be so. The enormous head of a dragonfly is attached to a very small neck. H. Mittelstaedt has recently shown that its whole head is in fact a balancing organ. Differences in position relative to the rest of the insect are recorded by sense organs in the head and the position of the insect is adjusted by appropriate action of the wings: what the halteres (modified hind-wings which act as gyroscopes) are to the fly so the head is to the dragonfly.

The external reproductive organs of the male dragonfly and the method of mating are unique in the animal kingdom. The males of all other insects and most other animals transfer sperm direct from their own sexual opening or organ into the vagina of the female. The genital opening of male dragonflies is in the usual insect position, that is on the underside of the 9th abdominal segment near the posterior end of the insect. But before mating the male dragonfly transfers its sperm to a complicated organ on the underside of the second and third segments of the abdomen. The sperm is stored here, and from there is introduced into the vagina of the female by an organ analogous to the penis of other animals.

The process of mating differs slightly in different species. In *Sympetrum striolatum*, one of our commonest species, and typical of many others, the procedure is as follows : the male pursues a flying female, lands on her back, bends his abdomen round so that the claspers at the end of his abdomen come in contact with the upper surface of the head of the female. He then releases the hold with his legs so that he is only attached to the female by the appendages at the end of his abdomen. This is known as the tandem position. Then the female's abdomen is bent downwards and then upwards so that the upper surface of her abdomen faces the ground and its under surface comes in contact with the under surface of the male. The penis of the male then transfers the sperm to the vagina of the female. The female of this species then either lays eggs, still attached to the male in the tandem position, or may lay them unattached to the male. The sequence of

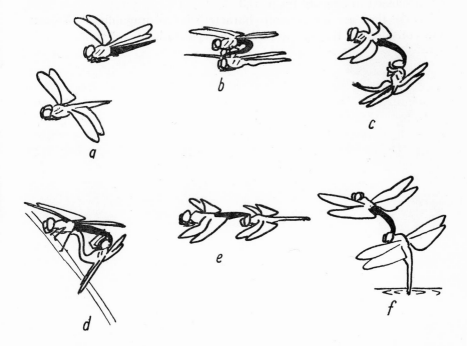

Fig. 2. The mating and oviposition of *Sympetrum striolatum*. *a.* Male pursues female. *b.* Male lands on back of female and seizes head of female with anal claspers. *c.* Pair in tandem position, male swinging female downwards and female beginning to bend abdomen. *d.* Mating-position usually achieved in flight—pair settle later. *e.* Pair return to water in tandem position. *f.* Oviposition. Male makes active dipping movements which cause the end of abdomen of the female to touch water and eggs are washed off. Sometimes eggs are dropped without abdomen touching water. Abdomen of male insect—black.

events is shown in diagrammatic form in Fig. 2, p. 9. It is interesting to note that transference of sperm to accessory genitalia does occur among some other animals although quite different organs are used. Cuttle fish and octopuses introduce sperm by means of one of their arms. In spiders, sperm is deposited on a small web, from there it is placed in a complicated organ in the pedipalps (the spider's second pair of head "limbs"). Later the pedipalps are placed into the vagina of the female spider and the sperm transferred. In the Collembola (springtails) the males smear the sperm on to their mouth parts and introduce them by this means into the genital opening of the female. The origin of the sexual behaviour of dragonflies remains a mystery; it is discussed in chapter 12, p. 158.

These then are the general characteristics of dragonflies. We can now consider the British species in greater detail.

CHAPTER 2

THE BRITISH SPECIES
(C.L.)

There are few insects in which there is so much tendency towards variation as in the Dragon Flies.

REV. J. G. WOOD (1874). *Insects Abroad*

NO ACCOUNT of the British species of these peculiar but fascinating insects, the dragonflies, can begin without a discussion of their names.

Names are exceedingly important in the Animal Kingdom, and chaos would reign, were they not applied under some rules. The reader may be referred to chapter 3, p. 25, to understand the confusion into which our few species of dragonflies were thrown, by a host of wrong or indefinite names having first been given to them. In order that all entomologists in the world should know, without any doubt, which particular insect is alluded to, its name has to be agreed on by all. This is not quite so easy as it may sound.

The dragonflies, like all other animals, have each been given a specific name made up of four parts, a generic word, a specific trivial word, an author and a date. The first word shows to which genus the insect belongs, and the second word is the species name, which is the insect's very own. Third comes the name of the author who gave it; fourth, the date on which it was first validly published. No two species of animal may bear the same combination of generic and trivial names, which should mean that there ought to be no difficulty in keeping the species name to one species: but disagreement has often arisen as to which authority named an animal first. This question of priority is settled by establishing that the naming author had correctly applied the appropriate rules for distinguishing the animal, while the date must be the first occasion on which it was published in a suitable journal on sale to the public.

Who is it who names these insects? The men or women working on the particular Order (or group) and who are called taxonomists, because they apply the laws of classification to living things. It is usual for taxonomists to be systematists in addition, because they study the evolutionary relationships while classifying the organisms. Taxonomists often get complaints from field naturalists, about what they consider frequent changes of names; and sometimes wish their friends would take into account the thousands of names where there is no difference of opinion, and where the species is immediately recognised the world over! So long as science progresses, an occasional change of generic name is inevitable, as our knowledge of the relationship of species becomes better known. Those names which can no longer be used for any species are called synonyms, and we have several for our British dragonflies, which are puzzling to many readers of old entomological books. As time goes on, names will become less frequently altered, and the International Committee for Zoological Nomenclature has the power to make final decisions in difficult cases.

In order to help make our dragonflies more popular, I gave them all, in 1937, vernacular names. These did, undoubtedly, fulfil my purpose. But since, in conversation amongst themselves, odonatists tend to use, either the generic, or merely the specific trivial name, I have decided that it is unnecessary to call the British dragonflies by the vernacular names all through this book. Frankly, my vernacular names have proved to be rather cumbersome; and the number of our species is so small that it is no hardship for anyone to learn the few scientific names involved. I am giving the complete names and authors once only in this chapter.

In the British Isles there are 43* species of dragonflies. None is endemic, that is, confined to this country alone. Seventeen belong to the damselflies or *Zygoptera* sub-order of the Odonata. The adult *Zygoptera* are distinguished by their eyes, which are widely separated on the head, and by their wings, which are partially or completely folded together over the back when at rest. The larvae, also, are quite distinctive (see p. 16). Twenty-six species belong to the sub-order *Anisoptera*, and are made up of fourteen species of Hawker Dragonflies and twelve species of Darter Dragonflies. Adult *Anisoptera* when perched hold their wings wide open, and their very large compound eyes touch each other on the top of the head—with one exception. This is our only member of the *Gomphidae*, The Club-tailed Dragonfly, *Gomphus vulgatissimus* (Linnaeus), on which the space between its eyes

*Excluding two species of Darter Dragon-fly (p. 17) which are rare vagrants.

is shorter than the diameter of an eye (Plate 13a, p. 88). The larvae of the *Anisoptera* are without the long leaf-like appendages found on those of the previous sub-order (see p. 6).

Although we have few species of dragonflies in Britain, it is remarkable that we have representatives of eight of the eleven largest and most wide-spread families. No species of the other three has ever reached either the Palaearctic or Nearctic regions; that is, Europe, northern Asia or North America. (There are also several more small and highly specialised families known in the Order.)

Among the damselflies we have species belonging to four families: *Agriidae* (2), *Lestidae* (2), *Platycnemididae* (1) and *Coenagriidae* (12). The first two are our beautiful Demoiselle Agrion, *Agrion virgo* (L.) and the Banded Agrion, *A. splendens* (Harris). The males have a deep blue or purple metallic colour on the wings when mature, or smoky brown when immature; and both sexes have brilliant emerald green or Prussian blue bodies, nearly 50 mm. long. The illustrations (Plate 1, p. 4) will show the extent of the colouring on the wings, that distinguishes the species. The females are more difficult to tell apart, but in *A. virgo* the venation has a pinkish fawn tinge, while it is yellow green in the female of *A. splendens*. These coloured wings are used in courtship by the male demoiselles, when they open and close them while facing the female (see chapter 9, p. 114).

The next two species are smaller emerald-green insects, 33-40 mm. long—the Green Lestes, *Lestes sponsa* (Hansemann) and the Scarce Green Lestes, *L. dryas* Kirby ; and their clear uncoloured wings are only partially folded back while the insects are at rest (Plate 2, p. 5).

The four species of damselflies so far mentioned have what is known as metallic colouring, produced by a certain structural arrangement of the pigment-granules splitting up the light rays and causing an "interference" effect. We get the same brilliant metallic effects in the Cordulines, and in the British species these practically permanent colours consist of green, copper, deep blue and purple shades.

Our only Platycnemid, the White-legged Damselfly, *Platycnemis pennipes* (Pallas), a little less than 37 mm. long, has the tibiae of the middle and hind-legs enlarged and conspicuously white (Plate 5a, p. 24). These white legs are made use of during pairing, as the male dangles them in front of the female before taking her in tandem. This would appear to be the only other dragonfly in the British Isles, apart from the demoiselles, that has anything resembling a courtship display.

The other twelve damselflies are all 25-38 mm. in length. The male is nearly always brightly coloured; while the female is usually more drab, or has more black on the upper surface. The Large Red Damselfly, *Pyrrhosoma nymphula* (Sulzer) and the Small Red Damselfly, *Ceriagrion tenellum* (Villers) are largely crimson in both sexes, with bronze and black markings. *Pyrrhosoma* has black legs and a very hairy face, while *Ceriagrion* has red legs and an almost smooth face. Both have female colour-varieties (Plate 3, p. 20).

The Common Ischnura, *Ischnura elegans* (Van der Linden) and the Scarce Ischnura, *I. pumilio* (Charpentier) are mostly black on top with a bright cerulean-blue patch towards the tip of the abdomen. They both have two small blue eye-spots at the rear of the head. *I. elegans* has an upstanding centre lobe to the prothorax, easily seen from the side view and absent in the rare species. In the latter, the pterostigma on the fore-wing is larger (and squarer) than that in the hind-wing. Both have female colour-varieties (Plate 4, p. 21).

The Red-eyed Damselfly, *Erythromma najas* (Hansemann) has very much the same colouring, except for having red eyes when mature, and it is a slightly longer and a much stouter insect (35-38 mm., Ischnuras 25-33 mm.). There are no blue eye-spots at the rear of the head. The female might be mistaken for a colour form of *P. nymphula* called *melanotum* Selys, but she has not got the prominently ridged and very hairy frons of the latter species (Plate 3, p. 20).

The remaining seven damselflies all have bright cerulean-blue males when mature, marked with black—and all very much alike. The Common Blue Damselfly, *Enallagma cyathigerum* (Charpentier) can be quickly separated from the others, because it has only one black line down the side of the thorax. The female has a sharp conspicuous spine beneath the 8th segment of the abdomen (Plate 4b, p. 21). (The female Ischnuras also have an apical spine, but it is pressed flat against the abdomen.) The last six "blues" are all *Coenagrion* species, with two black lines laterally on the thorax and no apical spines on the females. They are all very similar, but differ in the arrangement of the black pattern, as can be seen in the illustrations (Plates 5, 6, pp. 24, 25). These patterns do, however, vary considerably and it is advisable also to study the structure of the insects with the aid of one of the two British Handbooks on identification. Usually a hand lens is sufficient to show the shape of the posterior margin of the prothorax in both sexes and the anal appendages in the male.

Among the damselflies the female is held by the thorax while pairing; and the shape of the anal appendages of the male is modified in accordance with the shape of the prothorax of the female: so it is in only extremely closely related species that any confusion might arise. In the British Isles, the Variable Coenagrion, *Coenagrion pulchellum* (Van der Linden) might be confused with the Common Coenagrion, *C. puella* (Linnaeus) even in males; and the females are still more difficult, because where they dwell in the same habitat, they tend to resemble each other in colour pattern. The more curved and indented posterior lobe of the prothorax of *C. pulchellum* is then the only means of separation.

In the Highlands of Scotland lives the Northern Coenagrion, *Coenagrion hastulatum* (Charpentier), flying with *Enallagma* and looking extremely like it, as in both males the 8th and 9th segments of the abdomen are normally without a black pattern, and the margin of the prothorax forms a simple curve. Both the patterns and the male anal appendages are also very similar at first sight, but there is always the distinguishing second short black line on the Coenagrion's thorax. It also seems to remain, for longer in its flying season, greener about the head.

The Norfolk Coenagrion, *Coenagrion armatum* (Charpentier), as its vernacular name implies, is only known from that county. It is easily distinguished from our common Coenagrions by the extent of light green at the base of the abdomen in both sexes, and also by the very long anal appendages of the male (Plate 5d, p. 24). It has a blacker dorsal pattern than most other Coenagrions, and on that account is rather like an Ischnura, as the illustrations show. The Dainty Coenagrion, *Coenagrion scitulum* (Rambur) is only likely to be seen in Essex, although it is feared that it has been extinct there since 1953. It is very like a small-sized *Enallagma* in the pattern of both sexes (Plate 5c, p. 24), but it has a peculiar shape to the posterior lobe of the prothorax, which enables it to be recognised. This turns sharply down and under in the centre and is more the shape of that of *Erythromma* than of the other species of its own genus. Also, in the male, the upper anal appendages are longer than the lower—just the reverse of the other species.

The last of the "blues" is the Southern Coenagrion, *Coenagrion mercuriale* (Charpentier), with a scattered distribution south of the Wash. It is almost the easiest species to identify in the male, because of the planet Mercury's sign on the second abdominal segment, and by its small size, 28-33 mm. long (Plate 6b, p. 25). Otherwise it is very similar in pattern, in both sexes, to *Enallagma* and *C. hastulatum*. The female, small and dark, is best distinguished by the shallow, almost straight posterior lobe of the prothorax.

In the *Anisoptera,* the true Hawker Dragonflies in the British Isles are the species belonging to the *Aeshnidae* family: eight species in three genera. The Hairy Dragonfly, *Brachytron pratense* (Müller) and the three Aeshnas, the Southern Aeshna, *A. cyanea* (Müller), the Common Aeshna, *A. juncea* (Linnaeus) and the Scarce Aeshna, *A. mixta* Latreille, are all patterned with spots and patches of yellow, green and blue on a dark ground colour. The differences in the patterns should be studied in the illustrations; but in these cases the wing venation, or pattern of the veins in the wings, is also a good guide to separation (Plates 7, 8, 12, pp. 32, 33, 81). The long, but exceedingly narrow pterostigma of *Brachytron,* will quickly distinguish that species, and the rather short and square pterostigma of *A. cyanea* is likewise quite distinctive. *A. juncea* can be easily told apart from *A. mixta,* although the venation and the colour pattern are almost identical, by the very yellow costal vein of the former and the much smaller size of the latter species, 63-66 mm. long.

In Scotland the rare Blue Aeshna, *A. caerulea* (Ström) is found. The mature male is intensely blue, with no green in the pattern, and the insect is much smaller (63-66 mm.) than the dominant *A. juncea,* the only species of the genus that it is likely to be found with. This latter *Aeshna* is 71-76 mm. in length and one of our four largest dragonflies. Another of these, even more massive, is the magnificent Emperor Dragonfly, *Anax imperator* Leach. It can be identified, even if flying at some distance, because the entire thorax is blue-green in the male and grass-green in the female, lacking the black banding of the Aeshnas. There is a broad black stripe down the centre of the abdomen, but no definite "spotting" (Plate 10, p. 73). In some seasons "blue" females are found.

We have two more of the big Aeshnas in the British Isles, both of a brown colour: the Brown Aeshna, *A. grandis* (Linnaeus) and the Norfolk Aeshna, *A. isosceles* (Müller). The former is very common, except in the north and west, and the latter is only found in Norfolk. *A. grandis* is 74-76 mm. long, with tawny coloured wings and body. The male has blue eyes, and there are a few blue and yellow spots on the abdomen of both sexes. The rare species is 63-68 mm. long, and a yellower brown insect with green eyes. It has a bright yellow triangular mark dorsally, at the base of the abdomen, to which the scientific name is thought to refer. Both species have two yellow bands laterally on the thorax (Plates 9, 11a, pp. 72, 80).

Another large Hawker Dragonfly is quite commonly found on moorland and heaths and is very easily identified by its black and yellow wasp-like colouring (Plate 11b, p. 80). This is the very large Golden-ringed Dragonfly, *Cordulegaster boltoni* (Donovan), 76-84 mm. in length, in which the female has a unique prolongation of the ovipositor sheaths forming a hard black tail projection, a structure I have seen her use to ram her eggs into the bottom gravel of swiftly flowing streams. The uncommon Club-tailed Dragonfly, *Gomphus vulgatissimus* (Linnaeus), a shortish, stumpy insect, 48-51 mm., but a lovely green and black in colour, is also an inhabitant of running water (Plate 13a, p. 88).

Only four species of the *Corduliidae* are resident in the British Isles. One is the very rare Orange-spotted Emerald, *Oxygastra curtisi* (Dale), which has the distinction of having been first discovered in England by Mr. J. C. Dale in 1820; Dale was at last persuaded to describe it himself in 1834. As it has since been found to be quite common locally in France and Spain, it was lucky that the honour of its discovery remained for England. The only common species is the Downy Emerald, *Cordulia aenea* (Linnaeus), and even this has a very scattered distribution (Plate 13b, p. 88). It would seem to be the only one that occurs at quite large ponds and lakes, as well as canals, whereas the two rarer species, the Brilliant Emerald, *Somatochlora metallica* (Van der Linden) and the Northern Emerald, *S. arctica* (Zetterstedt) are more likely to be found hawking over bogs, although the former species can be found on canals in the south of England. In length they all range between 48-58 mm. All four males have quite distinctively shaped anal appendages, easy to see without a lens, and there are also points of difference easily seen in the pattern of the face, of the three species that are most alike. *S. arctica* has a yellow spot on either side of the clypeus, *Cordulia* has yellow only on the labrum, while in *S. metallica* the yellow stretches from either side of the frons and across the front. *Oxygastra* is quite distinct in having yellow spots all down the centre of the abdomen.

Our Darter Dragonflies all belong to the family *Libellulidae* and are divided into four genera: *Orthetrum* (2), *Libellula* (3), *Leucorrhinia* (1) and *Sympetrum* (6). The Vagrant Sympetrum, *Sympetrum vulgatum* (Linnaeus), has never bred here to our knowledge, but has been taken singly seven or eight times in widely scattered localities, the last time by C. O. Hammond in Middlesex in 1946. It is so like the Common Sympetrum, *S. striolatum* (Charpentier), that it is probably often overlooked. However, we have decided that it should not be counted as a British species, although it is included in the previous handbooks and the larval key. Another migrant species, *Sympetrum meridionale* (Selys), has been definitely taken twice in southern England, but not since 1901, and also is not yet worthy of a place on the British list. It is of a very pale red and yellow colour, almost unmarked by black, but otherwise closely resembles *S. striolatum*. The male and female genitalia closely resemble those of the Ruddy Sympetrum, *S. sanguineum* (Müller). The unmistakable Yellow-winged Sympetrum, *S. flaveolum* (Linnaeus) comes over very regularly to the south, usually in some numbers, but often only males (Plate 24a, p. 165). As adults have appeared in restricted localities, for two or more years in succession after ovipositing was witnessed, I consider that the species must have bred here, every now and then, although no larva in the wild has yet been found to prove this. The Red-veined Sympetrum, *S. fonscolombei* (Selys), arriving all along the south coast, and abundantly so at times, has been found breeding in the south of England more than once (Plate 24b, p. 165).

As recently as 1954, A. E. Gardner established that *Sympetrum nigrescens* of Lucas (1912) was a perfectly good species, not so closely related to *S. striolatum* as to *S. vulgatum*. The species had for long been considered as only a subspecies of *S. striolatum: S. s. nigrifemur* (Selys). This latter insect only inhabits Madeira Island, and Gardner established it also as a good species. *S. nigrifemur,* therefore, is not found in the British Isles or Scandinavia: the species there, with the black legs and the yellow thoracic spots, takes the name of *S. nigrescens* Lucas.

S. striolatum is a less well marked insect in most of its localities, but varies considerably in pattern between the larger, paler European immigrants to the south-east of England and our brighter and more marked resident specimens (Plate 21, p. 148). Where the range of *S. striolatum* overlaps that of *S. nigrescens,* the former species develops very similar colouring, but always remains structurally distinct. The legs are darker, the black line across the top of the frons is more pronounced, the centre band on the side of the thorax is darker with some yellow spotting and the entire insect could be taken for the rarer species without very careful examination. This resemblance in colour pattern does not indicate any probability of hybridisation, which most of us think must be very rare in dragonflies, and which possibly may not occur at all.

The Black Sympetrum, *S. danae* (Sulzer) is an abundant species where both the dark form of *S. striolatum* and *S. nigrescens* are found, and although the mature male is black with either no yellow markings or very few (according to the age of the specimen), the female and the immature male are very like the other two species (Plates 22b, 23b, pp. 149, 164). Especially deceptive is the black band with yellow spots, on the side of the thorax. There is, however, one infallible point of distinction: every *S. danae*, of whatever age or sex, has a dark brown or black triangular patch on the dorsal surface of the thorax just behind the prothoracic upstanding posterior lobe (which forms a raised collar with a hairy border). Some other *Sympetrum* species have black across the neck, but none has the triangular dorsal thoracic mark.

S. danae and *S. sanguineum* have a club-shaped abdomen in the male. This latter *Sympetrum* is crimson-red, when mature, and not scarlet, like all the other "red" species (Plates 22a, 23a, pp. 149, 164). This red colour is only fully acquired by the mature males, but very old females will develop some red pigment. The abdomen colours develop first, then the head and thorax, and the depth of the colour appears to depend on temperature and exposure to the sun. *S. fonscolombei* also has the wings mostly red when mature, whereas in *S. flaveolum* the most conspicuous part about the wings is the bright yellow or saffron patch of colour at the base of the hind-wing. Some yellow is at the base of the wings of most of the species, being especially marked in the females; but it covers only a small area compared with that on *S. flaveolum*. Besides the colour differences shown in the illustrations here, there are quite marked differences in the structure of the genitalia in both sexes, which can be studied in the handbooks.

Very like *S. danae*, and an insect that might be mistaken for it at a distance, is our only species of *Leucorrhinia*, *L. dubia* (Van der Linden) the White-faced Dragonfly, of a black ground colour and 38 mm. long, and therefore only slightly larger than the *Sympetrum* species, which range between 30-35 mm. The white face in front view, or the yellow or red spots on the abdomen, will distinguish this species when it is seen close to; and the small dark patch of colour on the hind-wing base is a further guide (Plate 20, p. 113).

The three British species of *Libellula*, the Four-spotted Libellula, *L. quadrimaculata* Linnaeus, the Broad-bodied Libellula, *L. depressa* Linnaeus and the Scarce Libellula, *L. fulva* Müller, also have a dark patch at the wing base. *L. quadrimaculata* is so named because it has in addition a dark spot of pigment at the front border of each wing in the centre (Plate 17a, p. 104). Libellulas are large dragonflies, 44-50 mm. in length, and very much bulkier than *Leucorrhinia*. Indeed, *L. depressa* is the stoutest dragonfly we have, measuring 10 mm. across the abdomen

at its widest part. The female and the young male are a tawny
brown all over, with bright chrome-yellow spots along the edges of the
third to the sixth abdominal segments (Plate 19b, p. 112). Mature males
become a beautiful light blue on the abdomen, though the yellow
spots usually remain (Plate 17b, p. 104). Of an even brighter tawny
colour is *L. fulva*, with no yellow on it, but a black dorsal stripe down
the centre of the abdomen, partially obscured in mature males by the
light blue pruinescence that spreads over it (Plate 18, p. 105). *L.
quadrimaculata* is always of a much more drab brown colour, and never
becomes bright blue in the male—only a slaty grey. It has some
yellow spots along the side of the abdomen and yellow on the side of
the thorax. In both *L. fulva* and in a colour variety of *L. quadrimaculata,
praenubila* Newman, there are tawny brown patches to the wing tips
(though not in all *L. fulva* males) (Plate 19a, p. 112).

Just as big and very like the Libellulas is the Black-lined Orthetrum,
Orthetrum cancellatum (Linnaeus), especially when the mature male
becomes bright blue on the abdomen (Plate 14, p. 89). However, the
wing has no dark patch at the base. When immature, it is conspicuous
by having a wide, festooned black stripe on either side of the centre
dorsum of the abdomen. This is also present in the female (Plate 15a,
p. 96). The "blue" male has the last 3-4 segments black. The other
species, the Keeled Orthetrum, *O. coerulescens* (Fabricius), also turns a
bright light blue in the mature male and also has no dark wing base
(Plate 16, p. 97), but the female often has the upper border of the wing
streaked with golden-yellow. This little species, 5 mm. shorter than *O.
cancellatum* and proportionately smaller, resembles the *Sympetrum* species
in size, and also in appearance when they are all in immature colouring. There is no red pigment in *O. coerulescens* and almost the only
black colouring is on the leg. The best separation character is the
presence of two wide cream-coloured stripes on the top of the thorax
(Plate 15b, p. 96).

It should be realized that when the dragonfly first emerges as a
winged adult, it is still immature with respect to its gonads and colours.
The maturation period is discussed in chapter 8, p. 100. But the
primary colours—dark brown or black, some yellows and some reds—
appear first, to be followed by greens and blues. Most of the body
pigments are sub-cuticular, being deposited in a fatty layer beneath
the cuticle; but melanins and some basic flavins are laid down in the
cuticle itself.

Very few of the pigments involved are yet known, because those of

a *b*

a. Pyrrhosoma nymphula, male. Note the red thoracic stripes, dark bronze on the last segments of the abdomen, and the black legs.

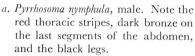

b. Pyrrhosoma nymphula, female. The normal British form, with the narrow dorsal bronze line down the abdomen.

c

c. Erythromma najas, male. Showing the mature red eyes, unmarked thoracic dorsum, and the blue at the extreme tip of the abdomen. The female is very dark on top, but then resembles a dark form of *P. nymphula* female. The immature male and female have green eyes.

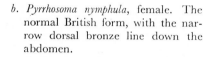

d

d. Ceriagrion tenellum, male. Clearly distinguished from *P. nymphula* by the red legs, the all-red abdomen, and no red thoracic stripes. The female, which has thoracic stripes and bronze on the abdomen, is best identified by the red legs.

Plate 3. Damselflies (Zygoptera : Coenagriidae)

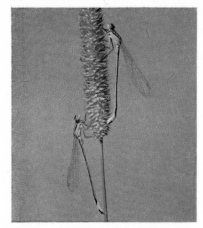

a. Ischnura elegans, male and female. Both are fully mature and are distinguished by the 8th segment of the abdomen entirely blue, and the rest of the dorsum black.

b. Enallagma cyathigerum, male and female *per collum*. They are fully mature, a typically marked male and the normal British grey-green coloured female. The prominent spine beneath the 8th abdominal segment of the female can be clearly seen.

c. Ischnura pumilio, male. Distinguished from *I. elegans* by structure of prothorax and pterostigma, and smaller size. Also by all the 9th abdominal segment blue, and only part of 8th.

d. Ischnura elegans ♀ f. *rufescens*. Even when teneral is differently marked to the normal female. All light colour is orange, except for the blue 8th abdominal segment. The distinguishing character from the orange form of *I. pumilio* is the prominent projection on the prothorax.

Plate 4. DAMSELFLIES (ZYGOPTERA : COENAGRIIDAE)

the dragonflies have scarcely been investigated. Certainly the melanins and possibly the flavins are well represented. A further kind of coloration gradually develops on the surface of the cuticle, as an exudation of the hypodermal cells. It is most prominent in mature males, although very old females often acquire quite a lot. It is called "pruinosity" or "pruinescence," from its resemblance to the "bloom" on a plum. The form it takes in dragonflies is either white or pale blue, and it will completely alter the appearance of a mature male in those species which develop it plentifully. Study the pictures of the males of our two *Orthetrum* species and of *Libellula fulva*, and it is hard to believe that they are the same species, when immature and mature in colouring.

I have already spoken of the structural or "interference" colours, and will only add here that in the wings of dragonflies there are other colours which are formed by oxidation of pigments of protein origin. These are usually yellow, brown or black patches or flecks at the base of the hind-wing, or sometimes elsewhere. In most cases this wing coloration deepens and extends with age, but in a few of the *Sympetrum* species, the bright amber-yellow or saffron colour is of greater extent when the insects are extremely immature or even "teneral," and largely disappears when fully mature. A teneral stage follows emergence and is easy to recognise, because the dragonfly is then exceedingly soft in the cuticle, and its wing membranes have not fully coalesced, so that blood-plasma still lies between. This plasma is then usually of a milky colour, but sometimes, in some species, gives a greenish gold or coppery tint all over the wing. This golden phase in the wings seems to be more noticeable in the populations in the north of the British Isles. The pigments involved are likely to be temporarily in the blood-plasma and are possibly caused by waste products derived from the metabolic processes of metamorphosis. They completely disappear in some hours or a few days at the most.

It will be seen that all dragonflies pass through two, three or more stages of colouring during a few hours, days or weeks. Those I have mentioned here are only some of the many stages they may be seen in; a state of affairs which renders keys to identification difficult and descriptions lengthy. A few of the British species are shown in two forms of coloration in the unique set of photographs from life in this book, and every opportunity has been given to compare with each other those species most likely to be confused.

Melanism, though liable to be found anywhere, often occurs in an abnormally high proportion of individuals in isolated populations; it

D—C

is also pronounced in the north or west of the British Isles. It may take the form of an enlargement of the existing black pattern, or of a spreading of dark pigment on to areas of no previous pattern. It will occur most markedly on the segments nearest the organs of reproduction in the males. In some cases there will be a reduction of the black pattern, but this would appear to be unusual in the British Isles. The dragonflies principally affected in this way are *Enallagma, C. puella, C. pulchellum* and *L. quadrimaculata*.

A much greater contrast is afforded by the many female colour-forms, occurring in some of the species. Those which differ from the male pattern are known as heteromorphic; whereas the females resembling the males are called andromorphic. In some populations the heteromorphic females predominate. There are also very many intermediate forms, preventing these heteromorphs being classed as true varieties. Among the Ischnuras there is a fairly plentiful form which is mostly orange and black (*I. elegans* ♀ f. *rufescens* (Stephens), *I. pumilio* ♀ f. *aurantiaca* (Selys)). This colour, and the pattern which goes with it, are also found as a female colour-form in several related tropical genera, and are likely to represent an ancestral colour pattern (Plate 4d, p. 21). I think it is convenient to use the names that have been given to those heteromorphic females that appear regularly. In the two colour forms in the Ischnuras mentioned above, the normal blue band on the 8th segment of the abdomen is present; but in another heteromorph of *I. elegans* (*I. elegans* ♀ f. *infuscans* Campion) the pattern resembles that of the male, though the blue is entirely replaced by dark olive-green on the head, thoracic stripes and the base of the abdomen, and dark orange-brown on the 8th segment. This is also the colouring in a further heteromorph (*I. elegans* ♀ f. *infuscans-obsoleta* Killington), but in this case the dorsal thoracic stripes are missing. The last two seem to be the common forms in the British Isles, and the least abundant are the andromorphic females (Plate 4a, p. 21). Very occasionally one may see two exquisitely beautiful colour stages in either females, or males of *I. elegans*. In one, the whole thorax is a bright rose-pink, and this would seem to be a teneral stage of the form *rufescens;* it is very rarely seen. The other can occur both in males and females and is also a teneral stage, but not the normal one. Here the sides of the thorax are a vivid violet, and it was named *violacea* by Selys. The violet turns to the normal blue of maturity, but without going through the usual emerald-green stage.

In *I. pumilio* the andromorphic females are the most abundant;

and so far only the one heteromorphic form is known in the British Isles. In *Pyrrhosoma* the normal form of female is a heteromorph, with a black-bronze line down the dorsal centre of the abdomen, spreading out into a roundish spot at the joint of the first seven segments. The last three segments are mostly bronze all over (Plate 3b, p. 20). The other two forms are rare and have been named *P. nymphula* ♀ f. *fulvipes* (Stephens) and ♀ f. *melanotum* (Selys); the first is the andromorph, having very little bronze and being a very red insect; and the last is a hetero-morph with yellow in place of the red thoracic stripes and eye-spots, and a very black abdomen. It could easily be confused with a female *Erythromma*, as I have previously stated. Similar forms are found in the rarer Ceriagrion, *C. tenellum* ♀ f. *erythrogastrum* (Selys) and ♀ f. *melanogas-trum* (Selys); the first is the andromorph with an all-crimson abdomen, and the last has an entirely black-bronzed one. I believe the first is fairly plentiful in the Cornish populations, but the heteromorphs are the usual females found in the New Forest.

When we come to the "blue" damselflies, we encounter fewer female colour-forms and much more variation in the black pattern. Normally the females are much blacker than their males and their pattern is of a different design. In *Enallagma* the female is normally of a greyish green, heavily marked with bronze-black on the upper surface (Plate 4b, p. 21). Sometimes we get the female type-form of Charpentier (the French author of the species), in which the light colour is as blue as in the male. The black pattern in the male sometimes extends over the 2nd and 8th segments to a variable degree, too indefi-nite for these forms to have been named. Some of the *Coenagrion* species are so scarce in the British Isles that we have not, as yet, distinguished any named forms; but undoubtedly the small Essex colony of *C. scitulum* was very variable in pattern, especially in the male.

In one of the two largest and commonest species, *C. puella* ♀ f. *annulatum* Selys is fairly plentiful, at any rate in certain years, and mostly where the species is flying together with *C. pulchellum*. This form of female shows conspicuous blue rings round the abdomen at the segment joints, whereas the normal British female of *C. puella* is very black above from the 4th segment to the tip of the abdomen (Plate 6c, p. 25). A form is found in *C. pulchellum* (♀ f. *nigrescens* Puschnig) which is practically ringless on the abdomen, whereas the normal female is nearly as blue as the male (Plate 6d, p. 25). In both species the male varies considerably in the extent of the black pattern, but in *C. puella* less than in *C. pulchellum*. The former is normally marked with a fine-lined U on the 2nd abdominal segment. This U is sometimes without the side pieces and then more nearly resembles the mark on *Enallagma;* or more often, it is thickened and joined to the segment's apical black ring, when it exactly resembles the normal marking on *C. pulchellum.* The shape of the black pattern on the 9th segment also varies. In *C. pulchellum* there are similar variations to the abdominal pattern, and considerable variations in the two narrow blue dorsal thoracic stripes. Our commonest form appears to be the "dot & dash," in which the blue stripe stops short at half or two-thirds of the length and finishes with an unattached blue spot near the wings. Still quite abundant is the form with the stripe entire (Plate 6a, p. 25). A form often seen in the Norfolk Broads is the "4-spot," where nothing is left of the blue stripe, except a minute spot at either end (Plate 6a, p. 25).

Platycnemis has a very white teneral stage in both sexes, but normally this soon turns turquoise-blue in the male and yellow-green in the female, marked longitudinally by narrow black stripes down the abdomen. In form *lactea* (Charpentier), the damselfly remains white, except for a rusty yellow tinge on its head, thorax and wings; also there is less black on its abdomen (Plate 5b, p. 24). This form is not uncommon with us, especially in the female.

In the British species of *Anisoptera,* colour-forms are never sufficiently marked to justify naming. Two named forms have, however, been created for variations in wing patterns. One is *Libellula quadrimaculata* f. *praenubila* Newman, with its wings extensively pigmented, but with a great deal of variation in the amount of extra colour present (Plate 17a, p. 104). There is also, very rarely, a specimen of this species minus the four centre wing spots. The second named pattern-form is that of *Leucorrhinia dubia* ♀ f. *lucasi* Fraser, with wings infused with grey and with amber-yellow basal patches, rayed with black. As yet, only one specimen has been met with, although a very similar female is in A. E. Gardner's collection, taken in Surrey during the hot summer of 1955.

a

b

a. Platycnemis pennipes, male. Mature blue colouring and clearly showing the wide, white legs.

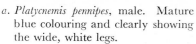

c

b. Platycnemis pennipes f. *lactea*, female. Fully mature, with tinged wings, and rusty on thorax and tip of abdomen.

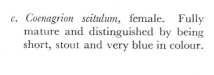

c. Coenagrion scitulum, female. Fully mature and distinguished by being short, stout and very blue in colour.

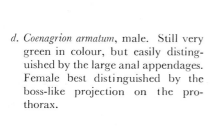

d

d. Coenagrion armatum, male. Still very green in colour, but easily distinguished by the large anal appendages. Female best distinguished by the boss-like projection on the prothorax.

Plate 5. Damselflies (Zygoptera : Platycnemididae and Coenagriidae)

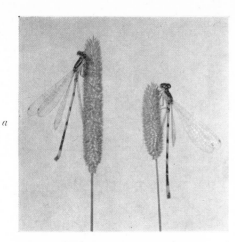

a

b

c

d

a. Coenagrion pulchellum, males. Both are mature. The left-hand male shows the typical form, with thoracic stripe entire, and the right-hand male, the " 4-spot " form.

b. Coenagrion mercuriale, male. Distinguished by the characteristic black mark on the 2nd abdominal segment, small size and very blue colouring. The small female is very like *C. puella* in appearance.

c. Coenagrion puella, female. Fully adult and the normal form. Compare her with the female *C. pulchellum*, with which she often flies. In her uncommon " blue " form, she can only be distinguished by the less scalloped shape of the prothorax.

d. Coenagrion pulchellum, female. The normal form, showing much more blue than the normal *C. puella* female. The males are so variable in pattern, that they are best distinguished by the structure of the prothorax and appendages.

Plate 6. Damselflies (Zygoptera : Coenagriidae)

CHAPTER 3

HISTORY OF THE BRITISH
DRAGONFLIES
(C.L.)

*L'établissement comme règle générale du droit de priorité
était bon et juste.*
DE SELYS (1890). *Causeries Odonatologiques, No. 2*

NYONE who reads the names of the authorities for our 43 British
dragonflies will see that only six of them are Englishmen. This
is not because our entomologists paid no attention to dragonflies, but because they were slower in adopting the system of naming
each species with a scientific name derived from Latin or Greek, used
by Linnaeus, and adopted by all future generations. It was the 10th
edition of Linnaeus' book *Systema Naturae* which standardised this
system in 1758. (See chapter 2, p. 11 on naming of species.)

Carl Linné, the great Swedish zoologist and botanist, known to the
world as Linnaeus, was the first author of eleven of our species of
dragonflies, all of which are also to be found in Sweden. All were
given the same generic name of *Libellula*, although one of them was the
beautiful Demoiselle *virgo*. It was Fabricius, a Dane, who in 1775
created two more genera, in effect distinguishing the long-bodied
Hawker dragonflies with the name *Aeshna*, and giving the name
Agrion to all the small, slim-bodied species then known.

As early as 1634, the posthumous work of Dr. Thomas Mouffet,
called *Insectorum Theatrum*, had been published in Latin. This book
incorporated, amongst those of others, the 16th century entomological
notes of Conrad Gesner, the famous Swiss zoologist. Mouffet mentioned
three categories of dragonflies, *maxima*, *media* and *minima*, and used the
names *Libella* and "dragonflies." But he gave no individual names to
the quaintly drawn specimens shown, although it is possible to recognise
Libellula depressa and *Agrion splendens* amongst them. Both Fabricius
and Linnaeus had taken this latter species of demoiselle to be merely

a form of *virgo,* and Moses Harris was the first to correctly name it, although he followed Linnaeus in calling it a *Libellula.* Harris was the first British entomologist to produce really identifiable coloured illustrations. He engraved these himself and also invented and published the first colour chart.

Dru Drury, a wealthy goldsmith, had written in 1770 on dragonflies in English, in his book *Illustrations of Natural History,* and had made some quite good observations on the larvae of the British species. However, the descriptions, and the illustrations by Moses Harris, are all of foreign species from Drury's collection. Harris, on the other hand, wrote a book entirely on the British insects, published in 1782 or possibly earlier. It was called an *Exposition of English Insects* and in it he included seven plates of sixteen different kinds of dragonflies. Some were found later to be different ages or sexes of the same species; some were only given English names; some had already been validly named by previous workers and some have never been definitely identified. One of Harris' illustrations is of a female *Cordulegaster boltoni,* but he unfortunately mistakenly named it *Lib. forcipata* L., which is the name of a species of *Onychogomphus.* Although Harris is left as the author of only one species of dragonfly, he undoubtedly did a fine piece of pioneering work, which inspired others.

Edward Donovan, the next British author and artist to illustrate dragonflies, gave us the first correctly named illustration of *C. boltoni,* again under the generic name of *Libellula.* In the *Natural History of British Insects* published between 1792 and 1813 in sixteen volumes, Donovan also named and illustrated a pair of *Sympetrum danae,* calling them *Libellula scotica,* and some odonatists are of the opinion that his name is the correct one, while others of us attribute the first valid name to the Swiss Dr. Sulzer, who in 1776 had five named dragonflies illustrated in his *Abgekürtzte Geschichte der Insecten . . . ,* three of them foreign and the other two, *Pyrrhosoma nymphula* and *S. danae,* from Swiss localities. Admittedly they might have been better portraits, but they could not have been any other species. It is curious that with very few exceptions, the illustrations of dragonflies, whether in colour or not, were of such indifferent quality and accuracy right up to the twentieth century.

One of the exceptions to this generalisation was the printer and engraver John Curtis who, owing to his life-long work in entomology, gave additional care to the exact rendering of his subjects. His *British Entomology* in sixteen volumes (1823-40) has only one small part on

Neuroptera, in which the dragonflies were always included in the early books. This part, published in 1836, contains only three plates of three species of dragonflies and all had been named before. However, Curtis made the first portrait of his friend Mr. Dale's *Oxygastra curtisii,* discovered in Hampshire and called by them *Cordulia,* a generic name of William Elford Leach.

Leach worked on zoology in the British Museum and published many works on classification. In 1815, in the section on entomology in *Brewster's Edinburgh Encyclopedia,* he produced the first classification of the known British species of dragonflies. He was responsible for dividing the Order into three families, *Libellulida, Aeschnides* and *Agrionida.* He separated *Gomphus, Cordulia* and *Cordulegaster* from *Libellula;* he adopted Fabricius' name *Aeshna* and separated *Anax* (and was himself author of *A. imperator*); and he took *Lestes* away from *Agrion.* Leach was also author of the name *Calepteryx* (emended by Burmeister to *Calopteryx*) for our coloured-winged species of *Zygoptera* and thereby started a long and continuing dispute as to the correct generic name of our demoiselles. Leach's name was adopted by the entomologists of the period, who were writing on the dragonflies. They were the Englishman James Francis Stephens, the German Hermann Burmeister, the Belgian Edmond de Selys-Longchamps and the Frenchman Toussaint de Charpentier. All of them ignored the fact that *virgo* had been fixed as the type of the genus *Agrion* by the French entomologist Pierre Latreille. This rendered *Calepteryx* a synonym of *Agrion,* as was pointed out by W. F. Kirby in 1890.

J. F. Stephens was a Civil Servant at the Admiralty, but was sent for a time to the British Museum to help Leach arrange the entomological collections. He was himself a great collector of entomological specimens and the literature on them. In his own publications: *Illustrations of British Entomology* in twelve volumes produced between 1827 and 1846, and the *Systematic Catalogue of British Insects* (1829), he did not illustrate any new species of dragonflies, but he did list the known British species, describing several and briefly giving the taxonomy. He attempted to disentangle the complicated nomenclature, adopting Leach's families and genera, and he also added very brief notes on distribution. He brought the list of British species to 48, but only 32 of these are now known to be British. He included, and had illustrated, the male specimen of the continental *Gomphus flavipes* (Charp.) which he captured himself near Hastings on 5 August 1818 and which can still be seen in his collection at the British Museum

(Natural History). Amongst the other 47 species, only fourteen bear the same scientific names today, although half a dozen more of the names are still in use on foreign species, but were misapplied by Stephens.

A collector friend and Admiralty colleague, Mr. W. F. Evans, illustrated a small volume in colour, either from specimens captured by himself or in Stephens' collection and applied the latter's names to the species. This helps us to distinguish those pictured, but some are on too small a scale to allow for certain identification. The book was privately circulated in 1845 and is not a valid publication according to the rules of nomenclature. Evans added a further three species to the British list, but described 55 altogether, which just shows the amount of synonymy that has had to be sorted out.

It was not until 1840 that a real advance was made in fixing the correct scientific names and their original authors to the correct species. This was done with the help of Charpentier's large clear illustrations in *Libellulinae Europaeae* and de Selys' minute interpretations of the species concerned, more particularly in his *Monographie* (1840) to be followed by the *Revue* ten years later. Charpentier made great advances with the *Zygoptera* in particular. Both he and the Belgian Professor Van der Linden had already created many new species in their monographs on the dragonflies published in the year 1825. Charpentier, in addition, was the author of several new genera.

This process of settling the synonymy should also have been largely helped by William Forsell Kirby's valuable *Synonymic Catalogue of Neuroptera Odonata* published in 1890, but unfortunately de Selys and others refused to abide by Kirby's conclusions. Many of these conclusions have since been upheld by the International Committee on Zoological Nomenclature. Kirby, however, did make a bad decision on both *Aeshna* and *Gomphus,* which de Selys quite rightly condemned. Kirby gave us the generic name of *Coenagrion* for the little damselflies, a further bone of contention amongst odonatists, but one which de Selys had no right to contest after publishing the remark quoted in this chapter heading.

Baron E. de Selys-Longchamps, author of the sub-orders *Zygoptera* and *Anisoptera,* also of many families and some of the genera which contain British species, was a brilliant taxonomist, possessing a vast collection of species from all corners of the globe. He says himself that he was greatly helped by his collaborator Dr. Hermann Hagen and by the two scholarly works of Professor Burmeister (1839) and Dr.

Rambur (1842). De Selys came on a visit to the British Isles in 1845, and personally examined most of the national and private collections in England, Scotland and Ireland, besides doing some collecting himself during his stay. He published the results of his investigations in 1846 in volume 18 of the *Annals and Magazine of Natural History*. He named 46 species in all, one being only a synonym; five were single vagrants and two very doubtfully taken in Britain, but he added three more good species to the British list. These were *Coenagrion mercuriale*, *Somatochlora arctica* and *Sympetrum fonscolombei*.

One of the well-known Scottish collectors of this period was Dr. Buchanan White. He captured *Somatochlora metallica* in Inverness-shire in 1869 and Mr. J. J. F. X. King of Glasgow re-took the species there in 1880. The famous British trichopterist and neuropterist, Robert McLachlan, was a young friend of de Selys and also collected and wrote on the World Odonata later in the same period. He it was who found *Aeshna caerulea* and *Somatochlora arctica* established in Perthshire in 1865. The former species was previously known from Britain only by Mr. Wilson's one specimen from the north of Scotland, given to de Selys in 1845. Mr. Birchall subsequently gave McLachlan a specimen of *S. arctica* taken in 1862 at Killarney. Nearly forty years after de Selys' British list, McLachlan published his, in volume 20 of the *Entomologist's Monthly Magazine*. He severely pruned the list of British resident species and, following de Selys' opinion at that time, amalgamated the two allied species *Sympetrum vulgatum* and *S. striolatum*. He took out eight species that he considered only casual visitors, but mentioned how they had been captured or reported. Of the species that we now regard as British, McLachlan lists forty.

He was very sceptical about the reputed record of a Mr. J. Sparshall who, during a collecting trip with friends to the Norfolk Broads in 1823, was said to have captured a dragonfly, later named *Libellula sparshalli*, but which turned out to be a specimen of *Pantala flavescens* (Fabricius), a purely tropical species, as then supposed. In 1884, when McLachlan published his disbelief that *Pantala* had ever reached the British shores, the species was already known from all over the world, with the exception of Europe. Up to 1955 no one else had ever seen one alive in the northern region, but in this latter year, I was sent by Mr. O. G. Watkins of Plymouth, an unknown dragonfly that had been found flying in the wardroom aboard one of our warships, two to three days before reaching Devonport Harbour. The ship was returning from Singapore, and the dragonfly was a male *Pantala flavescens*. As this was definitely a case of assisted passage, the species cannot yet be added to the European list.

McLachlan was responsible for adding *Coenagrion hastulatum* to our resident species, by so determining a male from Aviemore, collected in 1900 by T. W. Yerbury, and this brings us to the beginning of the 20th century.

In 1900 a schoolmaster and an ardent naturalist, W. J. Lucas, published the first completely illustrated handbook on the British Dragonflies, each species being portrayed in colour, drawn and painted by himself. Thirty-six species were known to him to be residents and a further three as frequent immigrants. Lucas' work is unsurpassed even to-day, and in some cases the egg, larva and adult were described for the first time. All the larvae were not then known, but in 1930 the Ray Society published an illustrated volume on them by Lucas, giving descriptions of the final instar based on either personal knowledge, loaned specimens in spirit or on exuviae. Lucas' handbook gives the synonymy of each species, some notes on biology and behaviour and all the distribution in the British Isles that he could gather together. Two of his correspondents, Messrs. King, and K. J. Morton of Edinburgh, supplied him with rare species and data from Scotland and Ireland.

Kenneth Morton was a life-long student of the *Neuroptera* and the *Odonata*. He it was who first established that *Lestes dryas* was a British resident, by finding a colony near Cambridge in 1893 (although one female had been taken in Essex in 1891 by Mr. C. A. Briggs). He also found the first English bred *Sympetrum fonscolombei* at Ruislip in 1922. With this kindly Scot, I too exchanged correspondence during my early studies of the dragonflies, and to Lucas I gave one of the first pairs of *Sympetrum sanguineum* to be found in Ireland, where I discovered a breeding colony on my father's property in Co. Cork in 1928. It was Lucas in 1912, who described the new species *Sympetrum nigrescens* from Stornoway, but was later persuaded that it was only a form of *S. striolatum*.

From 1906 for three years, Prof. Frank Balfour-Browne studied the life-histories of a few species of *Zygoptera*. He was the first to breed and describe in detail *C. pulchellum* and *I. elegans* from egg to adult and to obtain pairings in captivity. He established the probability of a pronymphal (*i.e.* prolarval) stage in all species of Odonata, previously only described for *Lestes viridis* by Abbé Pierre, in 1904. Balfour-Browne's *The Life-History of the Agrionid Dragonfly* (1909) was for forty years the only paper dealing with this subject, and will always remain a classic.

During all this time a brilliant entomologist and morphologist, whose especial interest was the Odonata, was working on the Order in Australia. This was Robin John Tillyard, the author of *The Biology of Dragonflies* (1917), still in world-wide use. Alas, I never met him, although I know several men who knew him well. He was intensely interested in phylogeny, and his active brain was for ever questing after new theories of origin. He left an uncompleted classification of the Order, based on his great knowledge of wing venation and the fossil species. This was completed by his friend F. C. Fraser in the years 1938-1940*. Colonel Fraser, who often argued contrary theories on the origin of certain veins and the consequent origin of the species themselves, must have been of great help to Tillyard, as there is nothing like good argument to stimulate ideas. Fraser, for years in the I.M.S., produced the standard work on dragonflies in the *The Fauna of British India*, in three volumes, and has also described a vast number of new species from many parts of the world.

Lucas' book had been long out of print, and the dragonflies neglected in this country, when in 1937 I was able to revive interest in them by my handbook on identification, published in Frederick Warne's *Wayside and Woodland* series. This was unusual in its format, but had an instant success. An enlarged second edition was brought out in 1949 and this incorporated the coloured portrait and a full description of *Coenagrion scitulum* found resident in Essex by Mr. E. B. Pinniger and myself in 1946.

In 1949 was also published F. C. Fraser's part on the Odonata in the *Handbooks for the Identification of British Insects* sponsored by The Royal Entomological Society of London. These greatly needed volumes, full of keys and diagrams, were launched after a successful appeal from me at a very full meeting of the Fellows of the Society. I was naturally delighted that the section on the dragonflies, with Fraser's invaluable, enlarged figures of the genitalia, should be one of the first parts to be produced.

There still remained the need for a volume dealing with the natural history of dragonflies. This was now possible owing to recent advances in our knowledge of the Order. Both my colleagues have spent many months intensively studying them in the field—in fact, both received their Ph.D. degrees as a result of their work on dragon-

*Revised and re-published by Fraser, 1957.

flies. By the combination of our publisher's generosity and Sam Beaufoy's beautiful pictures, this volume is well illustrated with photographs from life of thirty-seven of the British species, all in colour.

We are also incorporating Eric Gardner's illustrated *Key to the British Larvae,** much more detailed than any previous one. Gardner has been, and still is, in the process of rearing every species from the egg and describing it through every instar. This is exceedingly valuable work which has never been undertaken since Balfour-Browne, and for which Gardner is eminently suited by virtue of his skill in rearing larvae, his patience and regard for detail, and the excellence of his drawings. The late W. J. Lucas' mantle seems to have fallen on him.

*Published in *Entomologist's Gazette,* 1954, 5:157-71, 193-213.

a. Bràchytron pratense, male. Note the hairiness of the thorax, and the very narrow pterostigma, which distinguish it from other Aeshnines. The abdominal spots are more pear-shaped than in most Aeshnas. Female very similar.

b. Aeshna mixta. male. The dark costa, distinguishes it from *B. pratense* and *A. juncea*, also the pattern on 1st and 2nd abdominal segments is quite different. It is very much smaller than *A. juncea*.

Plate 7. DRAGONFLIES (ANISOPTERA : AESHNIDAE)

Plate 8

CHAPTER 4

DISTRIBUTION OF
THE BRITISH SPECIES

(C.L.)

It is remarkable that of the emigrating insects here enumerated, the majority—for instance, the lady-birds, saw-flies, dragon-flies, . . . etc., are not usually social insects, but seem to congregate, like swallows, merely for the purpose of emigration.

KIRBY AND SPENCE (1823). *Introduction to Entomology*

A s WE have no endemic species of dragonflies in the British Isles, their distribution naturally tends to depend rather closely on their countries of origin. For instance, the Arctic element is to be found in North Britain and the Mediterranean in the south, but this rough division still leaves many problems unsolved and poses many further questions. Which are likely to be the oldest-established? Which are relict Ice Age species? Which are most probably comparative new-comers?

The answers to these questions are still undecided, but some light may be thrown on these problems by the known distribution of the species in the British Isles and elsewhere. There are several difficulties to overcome. We still do not know every reason for the restricted and very local occurrence of certain species. One of the factors involved may simply be that a species may be either difficult to see or to recognise, and that its distribution may very well be wider than we know at present. Another factor involved would seem to be suitability of habitat, but here we do not know why some species are extremely adaptable to greatly varied conditions, while others are not.

Plate 8. DRAGONFLY (ANISOPTERA: AESHNIDAE)

Aeshna juncea, male. Fully mature. Distinct from *A. cyanea* by the yellow costa, 2-celled anal triangle in wings, and divided blue spots on 9th and 10th abdominal segments. Distinct from *A. mixta* by the first two characters, and the larger size.

Temperature tolerance is discussed in Chapter 11 (p. 145), but is also approached in this chapter, from a different and partly ancestral angle.

It is impracticable by statistical methods to say which are the most abundant species, but I believe that all odonatists would agree that *Enallagma, I. elegans* and *Pyrrhosoma* are the most abundant species that we have and the most widespread (Figs. 44, 46, 52, pp. 182 to 184). Opinions differ concerning the species of Anisoptera, but I believe that *S. striolatum* should head the list (Fig. 70, p. 189), although other species would be far more abundant in certain regions. *S. danae* would undoubtedly come first in the Scottish Highlands (Fig. 76, p. 190), whereas in the south of England this might be true of our two commonest Libellulines or even of *O. cancellatum*. All of them are also occasional or even frequent immigrants. On certain rivers and streams in early summer, the demoiselles are more abundant than any others, and *C. puella* and *C. pulchellum* may often be swarming in the Fenlands.

A thrilling sight, but one seldom witnessed, is a mass immigration of species such as *A. mixta* or *S. flaveolum* to our southern ponds (Fig. 11, p. 51). Twice within recent years a mass movement (?immigration) of *S. striolatum* has been witnessed in Eire, and in previous years England was one of the termini for some spectacular cross-continental migrations of *L. quadrimaculata*. Migration will be further discussed in Chapter 10 (p. 131).

When every dragonfly may be a potential migrant and in a few genera migrations seem to be the rule, the status of the British species is hard to define. Breeding has not yet been established for all the species in all the probable counties and, in any case, it may frequently be only intermittent, but much progress has been made in the last twenty years. The best discovery of recent years was the confirmation in 1954 of W. J. Lucas' species of *S. nigrescens* in the north and west of Scotland and in Ireland (Fig. 71, p. 189). So far it has been found to be a coastal species, both in the British Isles and in Norway, where it occurs in the south and south-west. This is probably an interglacial relict of the Ice Age, and perhaps was unable to advance southwards against the dominant Mediterranean species *S. striolatum*, which was pushing rapidly north following the retreat of the ice. Where *S. striolatum* overlaps the range of *S. nigrescens*, the former very closely resembles the latter in colour-pattern and appearance, and it was previously supposed that these "intermediate" specimens might possibly be hybrids. However, structurally they remain two distinct species.

Another Ice Age relict is perhaps *Cordulia* (Fig. 62, p. 187), a Palae-arctic species found quite commonly in the south and south-east of England, two widely separated localities in the west and north, two even more widely separated counties in Scotland, and in Kerry in Ireland. What must surely be an arctic-alpine interglacial relict is *S. arctica*, locally plentiful in a few counties in the Highlands of Scotland and also in Kerry (Fig. 64b, p. 187). It is a boreo-alpine (northern and highland) species in north and north-east Europe and still survives quite plentifully in the high mountain ranges of Central Europe and in the Caucasus.

S. metallica should probably be placed amongst the Ice Age relicts, although it has a much wider range than the other Cordulines, both in the British Isles and in Europe. With us, its distribution may indicate two, quite separate colonisations (Fig. 63, p. 187). In Inverness-shire and Argyll, wherever found, the species breeds in and frequents the acid-type bogs and tarns of moorland country. In south-east England four to five localities are known where it breeds fairly plentifully in quite base-rich canals and ponds. Dr. Valle said that it is equally adaptable in Finland and can also breed in quite brackish water. It is curious that it is not more common in the British Isles, but it may have to compete with the more successful *Cordulia,* which might have been established in the south of England before *S. metallica* arrived.

F. C. Fraser has introduced the Corduline species, *Somatochlora alpestris* (Selys) into the British list in his *Handbook* (1949 and 1956), on the basis of a single specimen given him by the late K. J. Morton. This was a male found to be labelled "Inverness, 7.7.1926." Mr. Morton, however, did not visit Inverness-shire in 1926 and spent July of that year in the Pyrenees. He collected *S. alpestris* in the Austrian and Italian Tyrol in the year 1928. This species inhabits exceedingly high latitudes in Scandinavia, or altitudes in the mountain ranges of southern Europe, and no habitat that we could provide in the British Isles would really be suitable. Only Shetland comes within its latitudinal range. I consider that there must have been a mistake made in labelling this specimen, and in any case one immigrant does not make a British species. If it did, then we should add the following list:

Lestes viridis (Van der Lind.) 1 ♂ captured 11 August 1899 flying by a lake at Shenley, Herts (E. R. Speyer).

Aeshna affinis (Van der Lind.) 1 ♂ taken 5 August 1952 on Romney Marsh, Kent (W. Edwards Dyson).

Hemianax ephippiger (Burm.) 1 ♀ captured 24 February 1903 in
Devonport (J. H. Keys), and 1 ♀ captured 12 October, 1913
in Dublin (A. Douglas). Both these may have been on ships
from the Far East.
Gomphus flavipes (Charp.) 1 ♂ taken by J. F. Stephens 5 August 1818
near Hastings, Sussex.

All the above specimens are preserved in the National collections
in London or Dublin.

As you can read in Chapter 9 (p. 118), the distribution of *Leucorrhinia*
depends on a suitable habitat (Fig. 77, p. 190). Probably for the same
reasons of habitat preference, as was found in Germany, it is confined
to those bogs in which sphagnum moss grows. It extends north-east
into Siberia but, although found as far south in Central Europe as the
Pyrenees and the Alps, it is also found in the countries between and to
the east. It is not therefore simply another boreo-alpine relict species,
but one with a restricted habitat.

The sphagnum-type habitat linked with geographical latitude,
would seem to be the limiting factor of a rare species confined to
Scotland (Fig. 61a, p. 186). This is *A. caerulea* which more nearly conforms to a boreo-alpine relict, although again found in several Russian
localities, but I believe all near the Arctic Circle. *C. hastulatum*, although
previously called a boreo-alpine species, and exceedingly common up
to and above the Arctic Circle, with a southern range in the Pyrenees
and the Alps, is also found in between these regions and into Mongolia
and Turkestan. In the British Isles it is only found in Highland
Scotland (Fig. 50a, p. 184), but is not confined to sphagnum bogs, and
in none of its European colonies is it particular about the kinds of
waters it inhabits. What limits its spread is very difficult to say.

O. coerulescens, mostly a moorland and marsh-dweller with us,
would seem to be confined to the acid waters in the milder parts of our
land (Fig. 65, p. 187). In Fennoscandia it is said to prefer to stay by
running water, and it does sometimes breed in streams in the British
Isles. The truly Mediterranean and Asian species, *O. cancellatum*, has
adapted itself very well in southern England (Fig. 66, p. 188) and
southern Scandinavia, being equally common in brackish and alkaline
water, in marshes, pools, lakes, pits and ditches. It is very widespread
from Spain and Portugal to as far east as Russia, Turkey and Asia Minor,
but is always rather local (Fig. 13, p. 52). Why these two most adaptable species have not reached further north is probably due to climate.

A. mixta has become a successful colonist of southern England from its Mediterranean headquarters and is also probably a fairly recent resident, although it has possibly been an immigrant for centuries (Fig. 60, p. 186). In the last twenty years we have witnessed a steady northerly extension of the species. As it has a life-history which is completed in one year, and as its final instar larva is possibly intolerant of low temperatures, Münchberg has suggested that climate is the principal barrier.

In the north and west of the British Isles, *A. juncea* is the dominant species of the genus (Fig. 59, p. 186), but in the south and east of England, it can only hold its own on the acid waters, *A. cyanea* being dominant on the base-rich ponds and lakes. In Fennoscandia, as in Scotland, it breeds in moorland marshes and peat bogs, often in pine woods, and I believe also in the rest of the Palaearctic Region, although it tends to keep to the higher plateaus and mountainous districts.

A. cyanea, although breeding commonly in the southern English counties (Fig. 58, p. 186), is only an occasional migrant in Scotland and has not yet been seen in Ireland, although it is known from most Welsh counties. Many of its more northern records are of recent date, but there has always been a strong Yorkshire colony, successfully competing with *A. juncea*, and this might suggest its origin in northern Europe dating from the Pleistocene second glaciation, when Yorkshire escaped the ice. It is one of the Mediterranean and Middle East species, common in Central Europe, but not reaching far to the north. It has a less specialised mode of egg-laying than most species of the genus. It has the complete ovipositor of the endophytic (inside-plant) layer, but instead of always placing each egg in a slit cut in a plant tissue, the eggs are more often pushed haphazardly into mossy banks, floating masses of submerged weeds, tangled tree roots or submerged logs.

A. grandis often places its eggs in the crevices of submerged logs and is a common breeder in any base-rich waters of any size, including slow moving canals or rivers. It is found throughout south and central England and most of Ireland (Fig. 57, p. 185). A. W. Stelfox tells me that it has become increasingly abundant in the Dublin district, where it seems to be replacing *A. juncea*. It is not established in Scotland, although there have been two authentic records from there. Considering the powerful flyer that it is and the wide selection of habitats that it resides in, it is puzzling that it does not spread north. It is too conspicuous to have been overlooked and, as it is abundant in Fennoscandia and in large tracts of Russia from above the Arctic Circle to

D—D

Mongolia, it is difficult to understand why it is not equally common in Scotland.

Anax seems to have a somewhat similar distribution pattern here (Fig. 56, p. 185). It is, however, scarcely recorded from Wales, not at all from Scotland and only twice, possibly, from Kerry. In Europe and Asia it stretches from the Azores to well into eastern Russia and the North-West Provinces of India, and south to the N. African coast, Egypt and Arabia (Fig. 12, p. 51). This species also occurs in Tropical Africa where it has been given the status of a sub-species—*A. i. mauricianus*. However, although no clear morphological difference has been recognised, it is very likely that this difference would be justified on physiological grounds (see Chapter 11, p. 139). This, or another sub-species, occurs in S. Africa.

Brachytron, with very much the same European distribution, is also scarce in Wales, but is common in Ireland (Fig. 55, p. 185). As it is not known in Scotland and appears to avoid the Welsh uplands, as *Anax* does, the limiting factor for these two Mediterranean (or southern) species may still be one of climate. All that is written on the latter species in Chapter 11, p. 138, has a definite bearing on the above remarks.

Erythromma, in the British Isles, has a distribution closely similar to that of *Anax*, but extends abroad further to the east, from southern Siberia and Turkestan (Fig. 42, p. 182). Dr. Valle said that it will breed in brackish water, but I have no evidence that it will do so in the British Isles; on the contrary, it would seem to need clear water with either floating water-lilies or *Potamogeton* spp. On the whole it frequents large shallow lakes, but is often quite common on smaller ponds and on canals. With its preference for the type of waters that are abundant in the British Isles, it can only be supposed that there are some other factors limiting its spread westward and northwards. Perhaps the limiting factor is an inability to circumambulate the acid water regions, as it appears to be common in Finland up to the 66th parallel, showing that climate is not the only barrier.

S. striolatum and *S. sanguineum* (Fig. 73, p. 189), both regular breeders in the British Isles as well as immigrants, and the two frequent migrants, *S. flaveolum* (Fig. 74, p. 190) and *S. fonscolombei* (Figs. 14, 75, pp. 52, 190), are all Mediterranean species. *S. striolatum* in all the British Isles, usually has a normal breeding population which is more strongly marked and is slightly smaller than the typical European form. *S. sanguineum* is an inhabitant of ditches and ponds where the Great

Reedmace (*Typha latifolia*) and Horsetails (*Equisetum* spp.) are growing, and so far the larvae have only been found on the roots of these
plants (Fig. 3).

S. *vulgatum,* being very hard to differentiate in the field from S.
striolatum, may quite well be a more frequent immigrant than the
seven recorded instances suggest (Fig. 72, p. 189). It has a very wide
range in north and east Europe and in Asia and may, possibly, be
established here before long. It has formerly been included in the
British list, but we think it is better to leave it out until it is proved to
be able to breed here. There were previously four records of single

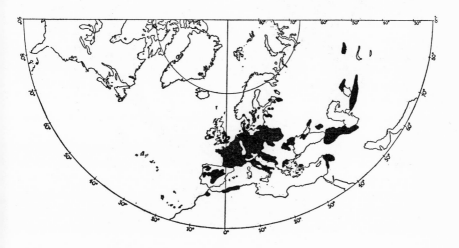

Fig. 3. *Sympetrum sanguineum* (Müll.). A partial migrant, and a resident in *Typha-* and
Equisetum-filled waters. Perhaps restricted in numbers by its specialised habitat.

occurrencies of the Mediterranean and Asian species *Sympetrum meridionale,* but only two of these have proved to be correct. They are a
female taken in Surrey in 1847 and now in the Dale collection in the
Hope Department at Oxford, and a male taken by H. J. Turner in
1901 at Dawlish and now in the Gardner collection.

S. *danae* is both an abundant breeder and a migrant. It needs
boggy or acid marsh conditions, with plenty of growing vegetation,
although it can breed also in brackish water. It is equally common
just below the Arctic Circle right round the World, south to the

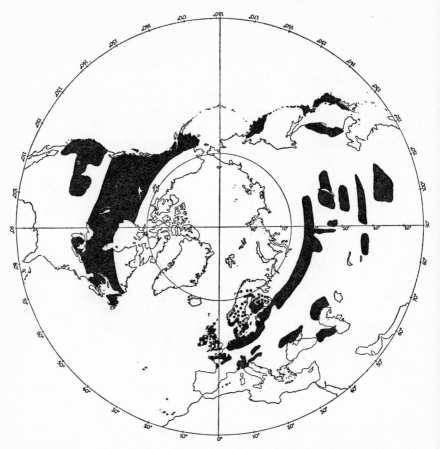

Fig 4. *Sympetrum danae* (Sulz.). Circumboreal. No doubt largely spread by migra
tion, helped by a wide choice of habitats.

Italian Alps, China, Japan and British Columbia (Fig. 4). In the
British Isles it has lately been seen accomplishing some quite spectacular migrations northwards. The most notable result has been the record
as first Libellulid to reach Orkney, where it was found in 1951 by S. B.
Hodgson. Previously, the only dragonflies known to inhabit the
Orkney Islands were *Enallagma, Pyrrhosoma* and *I. elegans,* all three
being extraordinarily adaptable and capable of breeding in brackish
water.

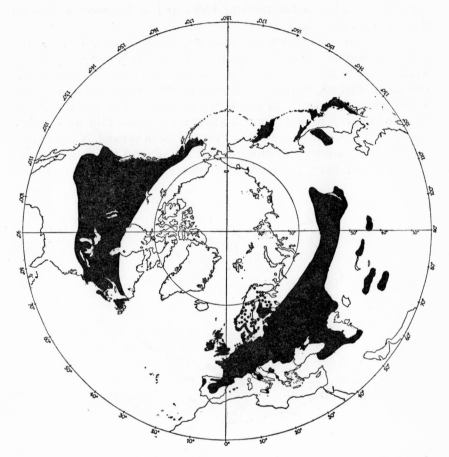

Fig. 5. *Libellula quadrimaculata* L. Circumboreal. It sometimes migrates in swarms, but is not normally extremely abundant.

Also capable of breeding in brackish water and probably a frequent immigrant, is *L. quadrimaculata*. It would appear to breed in most of the British Isles, although it has seldom been recorded from the northeast of England and Scotland, and also from the Scottish Lowlands. It is very tolerant of water conditions and is adaptable in its habits (Fig. 67, p. 188). Like *S. danae* it is a circumboreal species, being very abundant in Europe, northern Asia and in North America. It covers a broad belt of country between the latitudes 40° and 65° N., and sometimes reaches as far south as India and as far north as beyond the Arctic Circle (Fig. 5, p. 41).

Apparently less climatically adaptable, is the beautiful *L. depressa*, very common in southern England and the Midlands, and which would seem to be slowly pushing further north, particularly up the east coast (Fig. 68, p. 188). As it is certainly a migrant at times and is found quite abundantly in southern and eastern Europe, also in the Middle East, it is probably only a wanderer to some of the more northern localities, where breeding has yet not been proved. Valle gave a similar steady advance northwards in Finland, and also to westwards, since the year 1917. It would therefore seem that climate must have

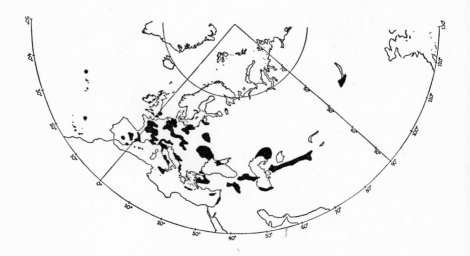

Fig. 6. *Ischnura pumilio* (Charp.). A Mediterranean species, colonising northwards and eastwards, the former only in favourable seasons.

been the previous barrier to its extension northwards. It can surely not be specialised habitat requirements that restricts its spread, because it can breed in still and slowly flowing water and in slightly brackish, but not, it would seem, in definitely acid water. It can survive in the most crowded conditions of bomb-crater pools and small garden ponds, where it has been as successful a breeder as it is in the wide ditches of the Fenlands.

What factors govern the range of *L. fulva* are difficult to decide.

In the British Isles it inhabits the Fens on the east coast in both still and moving waters, and also dykes, bog-pools and streams along the south coast, but only in widely separated localities (Fig. 69, p. 188). It seems to live in the same assortment of habitats in Central and South Europe and yet is rare and local everywhere.

Other Mediterranean species that just hold their own in the south of the British Isles, are *I. pumilio, C. mercuriale* and *C. scitulum*. The latter species may now be extinct in the British Isles (Fig. 51B, p. 184). It was discovered by myself and E. B. Pinniger in one low-lying corner of Essex in 1946, and watched as a flourishing colony until 1953, when it was drowned out by sea floods. *I. pumilio* would appear to fluctuate in numbers according to the temperature, as it completely vanishes for one or two years and then reappears in a favourable season. It is not, as yet, found far inland, but goes considerably further north in Ireland (W. Donegal) than its Norfolk limit in England (Fig. 45, p. 182). It inhabits the seepages of both peat bogs (probably the less acid) and marshes. It has not yet been found in Scandinavia, but extends into eastern Europe (Fig. 6). *C. mercuriale* has penetrated even less far and only inhabits the English south-west regions covered by the previous species (Fig. 50B, p. 184). It is mainly found in running water in peat bogs. It would appear from this distribution that the above species are comparative new-comers to the British Isles. Perhaps the winter temperature north of a given latitude is below their critical survival value, and therefore the factor limiting their distribution.

Two more Mediterranean species are locally abundant (Fig. 7, p. 44). *Platycnemis* is restricted to flowing water, and is not yet found above the latitude of the Wash in England, but is very plentiful in suitable localities in all the southern counties (Fig. 43, p. 182). It has reached to 65°N. in Fennoscandia, but is considered as a southern species there. *Ceriagrion* breeds only in acid bogs and runnels in south and south-west England and Wales (Fig. 47, p. 183). It is still being discovered in new localities and is evidently much more abundant than originally thought. However, I would say that it is distinctly intolerant of cold, as it fluctuates considerably in numbers according to the temperature.

I do not suppose reasons of temperature apply entirely to the very local Norfolk habitat of *A. isosceles*, another Mediterranean species (Fig. 61B, p. 186). On the contrary, I think that it is more likely from its being confined to the Fenland, to be a very ancient colonist, prevented from spreading by a specialised mode of life. Is this also the case for *C. armatum* (Fig. 51A, p. 184), equally confined to the Norfolk Broads? I think it may be so, because it is a north European species with a very local and scattered distribution even there.

Both the above cases are pure speculation, but I believe we do know some of the factors limiting the distribution of our two demoiselles. *A. splendens* is not found in Scotland, is scarce in the north-west of Ireland and very local in most of Wales (Fig. 39, p. 181). It is, otherwise, very common on all our large and small quietly flowing rivers (if unpolluted), on slow-flowing streams and canals. It will also breed freely in certain ponds. It requires a muddy bottom, emergent or floating water weeds and surroundings of open meadow or park-land.

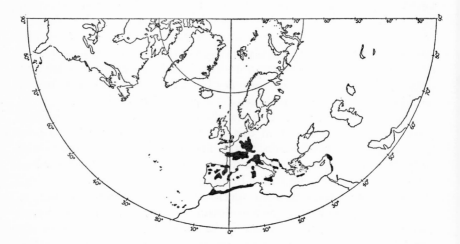

Fig. 7. *Ceriagrion tenellum* (Vill.). A Mediterranean species, more restricted in its advance northwards than *I. pumilio,* possibly by reason of its more specialised habitat.

Where the rivers and streams are more swift or the water more acid, it will not be found. It requires the same conditions in Fennoscandia, and is found up to the 66th parallel, so it cannot be wholly climate that limits its distribution but mainly type of habitat.

A. virgo prefers just the opposite conditions and is therefore found in Scotland and the north of England, all over Wales and in many Irish counties, though absent from most of the centre (Fig. 38, p. 181). It is also scarce in or absent from most of the east of Scotland and England—in fact it keeps to rivers and streams that flow fairly rapidly and have sand or gravel bottoms. It also favours trees along the banks and moderately acid water. However, in the south of England, it is quite common to find the two species breeding in the same rivers and streams. As this has been disputed, I will list some of them: Exe (Devon); Bristol Avon (Wilts); Severn (Salop, Worcs, Glos.); Stour, Avon (Hants); Thames, Evenlode (Oxon); Colnbrook (Bucks); Wey, Mole (Surrey); Rother, Arun (Sussex); Medway, Darent (Kent); Roding (Essex); Stour (Suffolk) and many others.

This can be quite consistent with their preference for different habitats because so many of our southern rivers and streams originate from below the chalk Downs, flow through fields and woodlands, gathering momentum and loam in some places, and in others mineral salts. Many rivers of southern England consist of long meandering stretches of steady flow, alternating with faster stretches with sandy bottoms, thus providing suitable habitats for the two species respectively. Where they are found together in the same counties in Wales, they also sometimes inhabit the same rivers. Identical conditions have been noted in some slow-flowing Irish rivers.

It is difficult to compare the habitats of the two species abroad, owing to the amount of subspeciation there would appear to be in these very widespread Palaearctic species. The Fennoscandian form is the same, I believe, as ours and there, according to Valle, they do not overlap in Finland, and *A. splendens* is never found on small streams, but can exist in brackish water. The species is not a resident of Norway, but is quite common in Finland up to the 64th parallel and fairly plentiful in south-east Sweden up to 60°N. Here, Sømme says it is common on the same streams as *A. virgo*. The latter species is much more abundant and extends to north of the Arctic Circle, but is uncommon in Norway, even absent on the western side. I suspect, owing to this distribution in northern Europe, that the two species originally reached us from the Mediterranean region, but owing to their sedentary habits, they must have done so many centuries ago, to have spread so far by now.

L. sponsa has a very similar, wide distribution abroad (Fig. 15, p. 53). It is quite widespread in the British Isles, but less common in the higher counties than in the low-lying. As it breeds in most types of still water, including very acid bog-pools, quite brackish water, and in ditches, canals, ponds, lakes and reservoirs, it probably has a wider distribution than recorded for it (Fig. 40, p. 181). It always needs a thick growth of

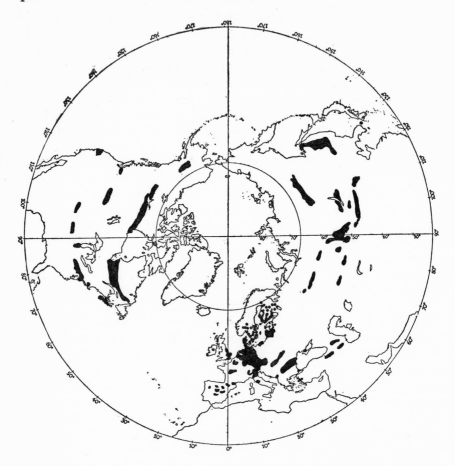

Fig. 8. *Lestes dryas* Kirby. World-wide, but keeps almost entirely between 40° and 60° N. Lat. Not very abundant anywhere, and perhaps a relict species.

emergent reeds and rushes where it breeds. It also often seems to move from one area to another, although it does not appear to be a migrant in the true sense. Owing to this disposition, it may not have taken anything like as long to have spread into northern Europe as the demoiselles.

The much rarer *L. dryas* is not usually so abundant anywhere, although it is a circumboreal species (Fig. 8). It is mostly found in Fenland conditions, which it only gets along the coast of east and southeast England (Fig. 41, p. 181). It is only found in Norway about the

Oslo district and in Denmark, south Sweden and Finland equally in the same type of habitat. It is very local throughout the rest of its range to Japan, presumably being limited by its habitat preference. In North America it is said to breed often in small ponds which dry out completely in the summer, but it must have clumps of emergent vegetation to oviposit in.

Our *Gomphus* is rare in England, although abundant extremely locally (Fig. 53, p. 184). It has a distribution abroad which is rather similar to that of our *Cordulegaster*, although the latter is more abundant, and is also found in Spain. Both species would seem to be restricted by the nature of their habitat, which is well aerated flowing water with a lot of silt on the bottom. This they find in both big and small rivers and streams, and *Cordulegaster* is also an inhabitant of mountain becks, which is no doubt why it is the more abundant of the two in the British Isles (Fig. 54, p. 185). It is found from the north of Scotland to Cornwall and the Isle of Wight, on mountain uplands, heather moors and rough heath lands. It is not known in Ireland and although it reaches the 66th parallel in Sweden and Finland, it is very scarce in the west of Norway and is not known in Russia. *Gomphus* is not known in Spain south of the Pyrenees, but has reached Russia as far as the Ural Mountains. Both species are found in northern Italy and *Cordulegaster* has reached northern Africa. In Asia Minor both species are known by sub-specific forms. They are both considered to belong to families very ancient geologically. It is difficult to understand why they have been so long in extending their range, unless perhaps they are species which may be dying out.

This surely must be the case with *Oxygastra* (Fig. 64A, p. 187), one of the rarest species in the south of England, a little more abundant in France "Midi" and locally common in Spain, but not known as a resident from anywhere else. It has turned up on rare occasions in Portugal, Italy, Switzerland, Germany, Holland and Belgium, but is only recorded as having bred in Switzerland once and in Germany twice. It appears to be restricted to a riverine habitat, but nothing is known of the factors which limit its extension, nor why it should have such a curious distribution, but perhaps it was much more abundant and widespread in past centuries.

Another particularly interesting problem is the distribution of *C. puella* and *C. pulchellum*, which needs to be solved. The former species is widespread and is always said to be very common in most of its range both in the British Isles and elsewhere in the Palaearctic

(Fig. 16, p. 53). *C. pulchellum* is equally widespread in the Palaearctic Region (Fig. 9), extremely abundant where found, but is always very local. The two species sometimes replace each other, but at other times breed in and frequent the same waters. *C. pulchellum* (Fig. 48, p. 183) is found at slightly brackish habitats, and is more of a fen-dweller, I believe, than *C. puella*, but there is so much overlapping in habitats, even in the case of mildly acid conditions, that the only essential so far known for both species is the presence of plenty of emergent vegetation (Fig. 49, p. 183). Abroad they mostly have a very similar distribution, from Spain to western Russia and Asia Minor. *C. pulchellum* is the only one found in Finland (Fig. 9, below), and neither species is

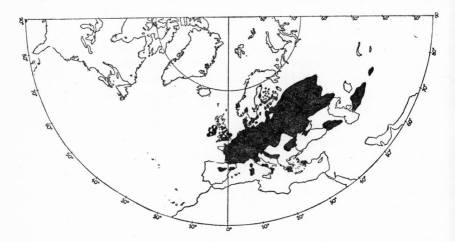

Fig. 9. *Coenagrion pulchellum* (Lind.). Almost entirely confined to the Palaearctic and always rather local. Why?

common in Norway or Sweden. In Fennoscandia, according to Sømme, they would appear to be entirely restricted to the marine clay sediment country. *C. puella* would therefore appear to be the latest comer to these regions, as it has spread less far. On the other hand, perhaps it is more successful and is gradually ousting *C. pulchellum*, except from certain strongholds. In Germany, Schmidt and May have stated that *C. puella* is the most abundant species they have; nevertheless, according to the distribution already given, it

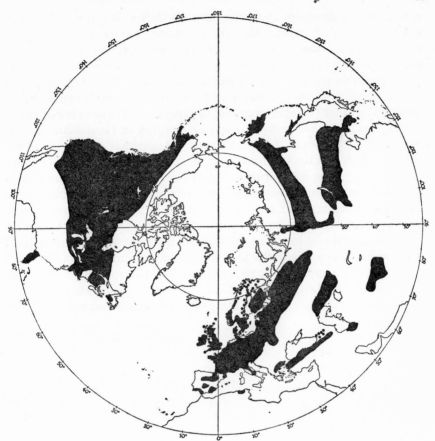

Fig. 10. *Enallagma cyathigerum* (Charp.). Circumboreal and perhaps the most abundant species of dragonfly in the world.

would not seem to be anything like as adaptable as the three species still to be mentioned.

These three species which are resident in nearly every vice-county in the British Isles (or, in all probability, in all on the mainland), are *I. elegans, Enallagma* and *Pyrrhosoma*. All three species are exceedingly adaptable with regard to type of habitat. They will be found in both acid, alkaline or brackish, still or moving water. *I. elegans* frequents more brackish habitats, and needs more emergent vegetation, I believe, than the other two. *Enallagma* prefers large lakes with floating vegetation, if these are available, and *Pyrrhosoma* is quite at home in swift rivers and streams, which the other two species do not frequent to any extent. These also seem to be the only differences between the species in other lands, but the range of distribution differs considerably. *Enallagma* is the only one of the three that is circumboreal (Fig. 10, p. 49), so perhaps that would establish it as the most abundant dragonfly in the world. The other two species extend in range from Spain to Iran. In the north, *Enallagma* has reached the 70th parallel in Fennoscandia, and Shetland in the British Isles, whereas *Pyrrhosoma* has only reached the 66th parallel, and the Orkney Isles. *I. elegans* keeps even further south (Fig. 17, p. 54), as it is not recorded in Norway north of 61° or in Finland 64°, but is in Orkney. *Enallagma* reaches south to the latitude of the Mediterranean and Korea, *Pyrrhosoma* to about the same degree south, and *I. elegans* to further south still and east to Japan, but in all these south and east localities this *Ischnura* has been divided into several sub-species. Does this mean that it is more ancient geologically than *Pyrrhosoma*, or younger, but more successful? The species of the genus *Ischnura* are found right round the world, even to the scattered islands of the Pacific Ocean, whereas the genus *Pyrrhosoma* has never left the Palaearctic.

Fig. 11. *Aeshna mixta* Latr. A known migrant and also a recent resident in its northern range.

Fig. 12. *Anax imperator* Leach. A resident in the temperate and sub-tropical zones. It has a different life-cycle in its tropical habitats, but no structural differences can be found in the adults.

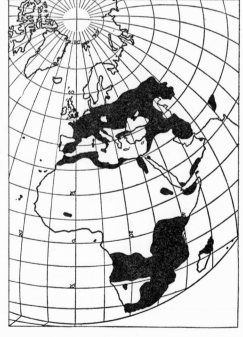

Fig. 13. *Orthetrum cancellatum* (L.). Possibly a relict species, but more probably only now advancing northwards.

Fig. 14. *Sympetrum fonscolombei* (Selys). A species centring on the Mediterranean and also a resident in S. Africa and India. It would appear to be only a migrant through the Tropics.

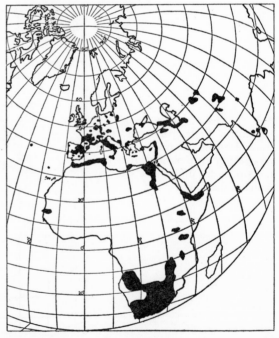

Fig. 15. *Lestes sponsa* (Hans.). A species with a wide Palaearctic distribution. It is probably a partial migrant, but does not seem to like extremes of temperature.

Fig. 16. *Coenagrion puella* (L.). A species almost confined to Europe, but occasionally found on the North African coast, in Turkey in Asia (Anatolia) and in Iran.

D—E

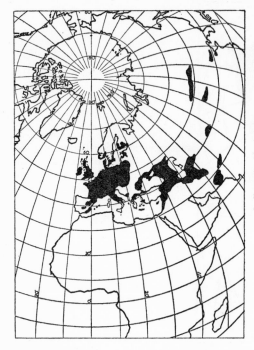

Fig. 17. *Ischnura elegans* (Lind.). A
very widespread resident (no doubt
far more common than the map
indicates). It does not migrate in
the usual sense, but is continually
spreading to fresh habitats. Wafted
on the wind ?

CHAPTER 5

THE EGG AND EGG-LAYING
(P.S.C.)

*The female (dragonfly) being thus impregnated, after some time dips
her tail into the water, and throws her eggs into it. How long such an
egg remains in the water before the Worm is produced from it, is as
much unknown to me, as how long it is increasing from that time until
it changes its skin; but I should think two years are necessary for this
purpose, since I have observed that these Worms were at the end of the
summer very far from a state of perfection.*

J. SWAMMERDAM (1758). *The Book of Nature*

THE FACT that dragonflies have eggs and larvae which live and
develop in water seems to have been known for about three
hundred years. The great Dutch naturalist, Jan Swammerdam,
may well have been the first to discover the connection between the
aquatic larva and the aerial adult. Before the first publication, in
1669, of Swammerdam's famous book on insect metamorphosis,
Johann Jonston (1657), one of the later and less scrupulous encyclo-
paedists, was illustrating both the larvae and adults of dragonflies
without recognising that they represented different stages of the same
animal.

The larvae Jonston figured probably belonged to the Aeshnidae.
He called them "water-lizards," and remarked briefly on their
significance as the food of fish, and on their habit of living amongst
rocks and stones. It is hardly surprising that he had nothing to say
about their means of reproduction!

The association of larva with adult, which we tend to take so much
for granted nowadays, was probably one of the many significant
discoveries made during the second half of the seventeenth century, a
period made richer by the contributions of scientists such as Ray,
Swammerdam and van Leeuwenhoek, and distinguished by the
foundation of the Royal Society of London.

Although the general plan of the dragonfly life-history has been known for so long, it is only recently that workers have paid attention to some of the details which make its study so fascinating. One of the principal reasons for this delay has probably been the difficulty of assigning larvae to their appropriate species. Progress in Britain has been as rapid as in most other countries in this respect, yet it was not until 1930 that the first set of larval descriptions was published by Lucas. Even then, these descriptions referred only to the final instar, and diagnosis of closely-related species often remained difficult and, in some cases, impossible. Nevertheless, an important step forward had been taken, and a foundation laid for the careful work of Gardner (1950 *et seq.*) which, in recent years, has done so much to increase our knowledge of the immature stages.

One of the more valuable results of Gardner's work is that ecological studies can now be undertaken on the life-histories of dragonflies in nature; and recently several British species have been investigated in this way. In the next three chapters I propose to use the information which has been obtained to describe the dragonfly life-history from egg to adult, I hope in greater detail than has been possible hitherto.

It is hardly necessary to mention that the life-histories of all species are not identical. On the contrary, different dragonflies vary considerably in this respect, even in Britain. Since, however, the life-histories of only a few British species are known in detail, it will be necessary in the following account to call repeatedly on these for illustrative examples. Amongst these species, I shall rely mainly on the Emperor Dragonfly, *Anax imperator,* which has so far been studied in the greatest detail. In the Odonata, as in most other animal groups, not all species are equally suitable for study, and it is often necessary to draw most of our conclusions from the few which yield their secrets fairly readily.

The development of a dragonfly egg is determined to a large extent by the way in which it is laid. It has been known for a long time that dragonflies may lay their eggs in one of two ways. The Zygoptera, the Anisozygoptera (now only represented by *Epiophlebia* in Japan) and, amongst the Anisoptera, the Petaluridae and Aeshnidae, all insert their eggs into the tissues of water-plants, floating débris, or the bark of trees, by making incisions with a serrated ovipositor. This method of oviposition is considered to be the more primitive of the two.

The other dragonflies, which comprise the remaining families of the Anisoptera, lack a fully-developed ovipositor, and lay eggs freely on the water surface. As a rule they do this by washing off the eggs accumulating at the tip of the abdomen; but sometimes they may let the eggs fall to the water without touching it with the abdomen at all. In most species the eggs are laid singly and sink slowly to the bottom, but in a few (*e.g. Epitheca* and *Tetragoneuria*) they are extruded in a gelatinous mass. This expands rapidly on contact with water, and adheres to submerged plants in the form of an egg-string, not unlike miniature toad-spawn in appearance.

Two terms have been coined to describe the different methods of oviposition. Dragonflies which lay their eggs in plants can be said to oviposit *endophytically*, and those which lay them freely, *exophytically*.

Endophytic species show considerable variation in the methods they employ, but all are obliged to alight on the substratum in order to obtain sufficient purchase to insert the eggs (Plate III *a*, p. 84). This means that while ovipositing they tend to be exposed to attack by fishes, newts and frogs; the latter, especially, have on several occasions been observed to catch egg-laying females. The habit which some Zygoptera have of ovipositing in tandem, the male retaining his grip on the female's thorax after copulation, may help to reduce the female mortality at this time by increasing the speed of take-off and acceleration. This habit would, of course, also increase a female's chances of survival were she to become waterlogged.

Most endophytic species tend to lay in water-plants or débris at the surface. Amongst floating aquatics, the leaves and stems of *Potamogeton, Myriophyllum* and *Glyceria* are frequently used, whereas amongst emergent plants eggs are often laid in *Alisma, Sparganium, Menyanthes, Juncus* and *Typha*. Sometimes the egg-laying activities of dragonflies may have severe effects on the plants themselves: Needham (1900) has reported that about a quarter of the fruiting stems of a certain iris may be killed annually in this way by two species of North American Lestidae.

Many Zygoptera actually descend beneath the water to lay their eggs, and often remain submerged for a considerable period. At this time the male and female dragonflies are usually in the tandem position. For an observer who is unfamiliar with this behaviour, it can be a remarkable experience to watch two adults alight on a reed stem and then slowly disappear beneath the surface. While they are underwater their bodies have the appearance of being silvered, because of the film of air which clings to the hairs on the thorax. It is quite possible that this air may assist in the process of respiration while they are submerged. Probably some such system must be operating, because sometimes two adults may remain submerged for fifteen minutes or more before returning to the surface. The film of air in this case may serve the same function as it does in certain aquatic bugs and beetles, in which the oxygen in the bubble is replenished by diffusion from the water.

A pair of damselflies may descend to a depth of a foot or more below the surface, far enough, in a muddy pond, to disappear from sight. When they climb slowly into view again—two silver spots against a dark background—the female is usually laying eggs as she comes.

Underwater oviposition occurs in all the families of British Zygoptera except the Platycnemididae, and the species in which it has been observed include *A. splendens, A. virgo, L. sponsa, C. pulchellum, E. cyathigerum* and *E. najas*. It is difficult to imagine what adaptive significance, if any, this remarkable specialisation may have, although we should bear in mind two circumstances which may have some connection with it. First, eggs laid some distance below the water surface will be unaffected by drying up of the habitat, save at a fairly late stage in the process. This consideration will of course apply only to species which oviposit in standing reeds or rushes; those which do so in floating weed are automatically insured against all but extreme desiccation. In this connection, it is interesting to remark that those species which lay their eggs *above* the water, such as *A. mixta*, often do so in late summer or autumn, shortly before the seasonal rise in water level may be expected. The second circumstance which may be associated with underwater oviposition concerns the vertical temperature gradient which is liable to develop in small pools in warm weather. This may involve a daily range of from 16° to 30°C in the surface water. If, for any reason, temperatures of this level and variability were unfavourable for the development of the eggs of certain species, the habit of underwater oviposition might be of considerable advantage to them, since it might reduce the average summer temperature experienced by the eggs by at least 5°C. As we shall see later in this chapter, this may be an important consideration in the life-history of *L. sponsa*, a species which not only inhabits small, moorland pools but also frequently lays its eggs beneath the surface.

Before leaving the subject of endophytic oviposition, we should mention the anomalous methods which are encountered among members of the genus *Lestes*. Although *L. sponsa* often lays its eggs under the water, *L. dryas* seems to lay in reed stems a few inches above the surface (rather like *A. mixta*), and a European species, *L. viridis* (Van der Lind.), first studied by Pierre (1904), oviposits in the branches of sallow bushes overhanging the water. Certain tropical species appear to oviposit in desiccated sites just before the seasonal rains are due, and in this way ensure that the hatching larvae will enjoy a fair chance of survival. Unfortunately, very little accurate information exists on the life-histories of tropical and subtropical species of *Lestes*. But it may well be that the diverse types of egg-laying behaviour in *Lestes* all represent methods of colonising temporary pools. Future work on this genus should greatly increase our understanding of the adaptations which have been evolved to secure survival in these precarious habitats.

Most Anisoptera belong to the group of dragonflies that lay eggs freely, or exophytically. In Britain, these comprise *Cordulegaster*, *Gomphus*, and the Corduliidae and Libellulidae. These dragonflies fly down close to the water and make rapid dipping movements with the abdomen, thereby washing off the eggs which have accumulated at the genital opening. However, Gardner (1950) has watched female *S. sanguineum* actually dropping eggs on to the water from just above the surface. In this group the male is even less consistent about accompanying the female (there seems to be less need for him to do so) and, in the same species, females may sometimes be seen ovipositing singly, and at other times in tandem. The mortality of exophytic dragonflies during oviposition is probably considerably less than that of endophytic species, since, in nearly all cases, they remain in flight throughout the process.

One might expect exophytic species to breed in standing water, where their eggs would not be carried away by currents. In general, this expectation is confirmed, but there are two outstanding exceptions, *Cordulegaster* and *Gomphus*, both of which breed in swiftly-flowing streams. *Cordulegaster* seems to have solved the problem by plunging its eggs into sediment near sheltered banks in shallow parts of the stream. This is doubtless the function of the formidable-looking structure at the end of its abdomen. *Gomphus*, on the other hand, seems to lay its eggs freely on the surface. It is still not known how it manages to prevent the eggs being swept downstream, but an interesting discovery made recently in West Africa by Gambles may throw some light on the matter.

Gambles (1956) found that a stream-dwelling Gomphid, *Lestino-gomphus africanus* Fraser, lays eggs which possess coiled terminal filaments. On coming into contact with water, these filaments expand rapidly and unite the eggs into small clusters. Similar structures are known to exist in certain rheophilic mayflies, where they probably serve to entangle the eggs amongst the stones of the stream bed. It is therefore possible that *Gomphus vulgatissimus* may make use of a similar device. But this question can only be answered by obtaining its eggs, an achievement which has so far proved exceptionally difficult.

Perhaps the most remarkable exception to the rule that exophytic dragonflies oviposit in standing water is the Ethiopian Libellulid, *Zygonyx natalensis* (R. Martin). This species, together with other members of the same genus, breeds in waterfalls, often under torrential conditions that no other dragonfly can withstand. The eggs are laid on rocks or other surfaces within the spray zone. To achieve this, the female alights near the edge of the waterfall and sticks her eggs, singly or in small clusters, on to mats of roots or algae. While ovipositing she often keeps her wings fluttering, perhaps to shake off the drops of water which are continually falling on her.

Although mortality of females during oviposition is probably less amongst exophytic, than endophytic species, the death-rate is likely to be greater afterwards among the eggs, since they will be far more exposed before they hatch. We might therefore expect exophytic dragonflies to lay greater numbers of eggs, on the whole, than endophytic ones, an idea supported by the fact that certain exophytic species (*e.g. Libellula depressa*) have broad, spacious abdomens.

Exophytic and endophytic species are also likely to differ considerably with respect to the rate of egg development. The eggs of Zygoptera and Aeshnidae are laid and develop in the region of highest temperature, light intensity and oxygen concentration, factors which doubtless have an important effect on rate of development. The surroundings in which eggs of pond-dwelling Libellulidae find themselves, however, are quite different, and in nature they probably hatch much later than those of endophytic dragonflies. The egg-strings of such species as *Tetragoneuria*, which adhere to water-plants near the surface, will of course provide an exception to this statement. Very few records exist concerning the duration of egg-development in nature, although it is known that eggs of *Anax* in the south of England hatch about three weeks after having been laid. The following table gives the durations of the egg stage of certain species which have been reared in captivity.

TABLE OF EGG DEVELOPMENT

Species	Duration of egg stage in captivity (days)	Authority
A. isosceles	36	Gardner
A. imperator	30	Corbet
	(24 in nature)	
B. pratense	35	Gardner
C. aenea	13	Gardner
L. dubia	26	Gardner
L. depressa	13, 27	Gardner
L. fulva	11	Gardner
L. quadrimaculata	29	Gardner
O. cancellatum	28	Gardner
O. curtisi	22	Gardner
S. metallica	38	Gardner
S. flaveolum	31–41	Gardner
S. fonscolombei	21	Gardner
S. sanguineum	22	Gardner
	129–149	Longfield
S. striolatum	14	Corbet
	24	Gardner
	48	Hall (in litt. to Longfield)
C. armatum	19	Gardner
C. hastulatum	17	Gardner
C. mercuriale	about 21	Corbet
C. puella	29	Gardner
C. pulchellum	28	Gardner
E. cyathigerum	20	Gardner
I. pumilio	23	Gardner
P. nymphula	18	Gardner and MacNeill

This subject of egg development is in fact more complex than these remarks indicate, because in some dragonflies the eggs spend the summer and the succeeding winter without hatching. From an ecological point of view, this phenomenon is a very important one, and will be best illustrated by an example.

In the damselfly, *Lestes sponsa*, oviposition occurs from July to September. As soon as the eggs have been laid, the embryos develop rapidly up to a stage where all the appendages are differentiated and clearly visible. This stage is reached in less than six weeks. But then, just before the embryo would otherwise have hatched, it stops growing and remains in this condition throughout the winter, not hatching until April of the following year.

In the laboratory it is known that eggs of *L. sponsa* can hatch without difficulty at 20°C, and in nature in April they may well be able to hatch at lower temperatures. Therefore the inability of eggs to hatch during the summer cannot be due merely to temperatures being unfavourable for hatching at this time, but must have some more deep-seated physiological cause.

A wide variety of cold-blooded animals, particularly insects, have been found to possess a stage in the life-history in which growth is interrupted in a similar fashion, and this condition of arrested development has been given the name of *diapause*. It must be realised that diapause is a physiological state quite distinct from *dormancy* or *quiescence*, in which growth and activity are depressed as a direct result of unfavourable environmental conditions. Low temperature is the commonest cause of dormancy, and the lethargy of tortoises and lizards in winter provides a well-known example of its effects. In these animals, if the temperature is raised to a sufficient extent, the condition of torpor is brought to an end, and normal activity is gradually resumed.

Another very important respect in which dormancy and diapause differ is that, whereas dormancy can occur in any stage of development, whenever environmental temperatures are low, diapause is typically found in one stage only. So that when this stage is reached growth is arrested, whether the environmental conditions happen to be favourable or not. The stage in which a diapause occurs is characteristic of a given species: thus in some species it is always in the egg, in others the last larval instar, and so on. In *A. cyanea*, for instance, the egg is always the diapause stage, and this means that whenever this stage is reached, growth is arrested for a considerable time, long enough in practice to make the egg the overwintering stage.

A great deal still remains to be learnt about the nature and operation of diapause in different animals, but the experiments which have been carried out so far show that it is intimately bound up with temperature.

Andrewartha (1952) has pointed out that diapause should not be regarded as a complete cessation of development, but as a *different kind* of development. He has suggested that it is correct to regard the diapause as differing from other stages in the life-history in having a considerably lower optimum temperature for development. Thus, whereas most developmental processes respond positively to *increasing* temperature, diapause is liable to respond positively to *decreasing* temperature. Another way of expressing this would be to say that the diapause stage has a negative, not a positive temperature coefficient for development, within the range normally experienced by the species. A recent review of diapause undertaken by Lees (1955) cites several examples which strongly support Andrewartha's interpretation, and this is the theory that I shall follow in this book.

Let us now consider what the practical effect of this negative temperature coefficient is in *L. sponsa*. During the summer, embryonic development will proceed rapidly until the diapause stage has been reached, after which it will slow up very considerably. The optimum temperature for diapause development in this species is about 10°C, although it can proceed extremely slowly at other temperatures between 5 and 20°C. This means that in nature diapause is completed rapidly in autumn, before temperatures have fallen to less favourable winter values. Thus, by the time winter comes, the embryos are actually ready to hatch, but are prevented from doing so by the prohibitively low temperatures. The fact that the optimum temperature for diapause development lies below that which permits hatching, results in hatching being postponed until temperatures rise in the following spring.

The diapause in *L. sponsa* can therefore be seen as a physiological device ensuring that the egg is the stage which overwinters. A similar arrangement is found in several other British species, particularly among the Aeshnidae.

BRITISH SPECIES KNOWN TO HAVE
OVERWINTERING, OR DIAPAUSE, EGGS

Species	Authority
A. cyanea	Münchberg
	Hall (*in litt.* to Longfield)
A. juncea	Münchberg
A. grandis	Münchberg, Corbet
A. mixta	Münchberg, Gardner
S. danae	Gardner, Corbet
	Hall (*in litt.* to Longfield)
L. dryas	Gardner
L. sponsa	Corbet

In general, eggs of species which fly in spring or early summer develop directly, without delay, whereas those of species flying in late summer or autumn show diapause. Several exceptions to this statement exist, but it holds good often enough to indicate that the stage most vulnerable to cold is probably the young larva. In cases where there is a regular possibility of newly-hatched larvae being overtaken by the winter, a diapause in the egg is found. The British members of the Aeshnidae provide a good illustration of this point: those species which fly earliest in the year (*Anax, Brachytron* and *Aeshna isosceles*) lay non-diapause eggs which hatch in about three weeks; the remaining species all lay diapause eggs, in which hatching is postponed until the following spring. An interesting possibility which needs to be investigated is that certain species with long flying seasons may lay non-diapause eggs early in the year, but diapause eggs later on. So far there is no clear evidence in support of this idea in dragonflies, although there are indications that under certain circumstances it may occur in *S. sanguineum* (see table on page 61). Such an arrangement is by no means unusual among arthropods. Certain mites, studied by Lees (1953), were found to begin laying diapause, instead of non-diapause eggs in autumn as soon as the daylength fell below a certain value. And an analogous situation exists in certain butterflies which may hibernate either as larvae or pupae, according to which has been reached by a certain date in late summer.

Of all the stages in the life-history, there can be little doubt that the egg is the one best suited to over winter. It is well-protected by its hard chorion, and often by the plant tissue in which it has been laid. It is inconspicuous and therefore unlikely to attract the attention of potential predators. Its metabolic rate is probably very low, particularly if almost the whole of the embryonic growth has been completed before the diapause stage; and, finally, its volume/surface-area relationship is such as to impose very modest respiratory demands.

A hazard which non-diapause eggs of endophytic dragonflies are obliged to face is the possibility of being imprisoned by the closing-up of the plant tissue in which they have been laid. In the case of diapause eggs, this danger is probably avoided by the annual decomposition of plants during winter, but it must be particularly serious in eggs with direct development, which are laid during the season when plant growth is most rapid.

A feature which may have been evolved to avoid this risk is found in *Anax imperator,* and also in other species of the genus *Anax* elsewhere in the world. At the anterior end of the egg is a blade-like structure which, being an extension of the chorion, has the form of a cone. This helps to anchor eggs which have been laid in thin floating leaves, such as those of *Potamogeton natans* L., but it also serves the more important function of preventing the sides of the incision from healing over in the case of eggs laid in stems. When the egg hatches, the larva passes between the two layers of the cone, and in this way is also protected from abrasion by the plant tissue.

It seems that other species must solve this problem in different ways, for there are several Coenagriidae, apparently with ecological demands similar to those of *Anax,* which nevertheless lack this cone or any structure like it. The egg of *Coenagrion hastulatum* has a small extension on the anterior end which may perhaps serve a function similar to the cone in *Anax,* but the resemblance is far from being convincing. It is of course possible that, in some species, the egg itself prevents the incision from closing, by protruding slightly from the stem. For the present we must regard this matter as being in need of clarification.

The egg is perhaps the least interesting stage of the life-history, in as much as it exhibits no behaviour. But from what has been said it will be clear that the study of its biology raises many fascinating problems. A sound knowledge of its physiology and rate of development is fundamental to an understanding of the dragonfly life-history.

CHAPTER 6

THE LARVA
(P.S.C.)

. . . and under a bank he saw a very ugly, dirty creature sitting, about half as big as himself, which had six legs, and a big stomach, and a most ridiculous head with two great eyes, and a face just like a donkey's. "Oh!" said Tom, "You are an ugly fellow, to be sure!"

CHARLES KINGSLEY (1863). *The Water Babies*

THE CREATURE which hatches from a dragonfly egg differs greatly in appearance from the later larval stages with which many people are familiar. In form, it is very similar to the pupae of wasps and beetles, having the separate, non-functional appendages lying closely along its ventral surface. As in these pupae, its movements are restricted to convulsive wriggles, and are probably concerned solely with escaping from the egg-shell and the surrounding plant tissue. Unlike succeeding larval instars, the first is of very short duration, and seldom lasts for more than five minutes. Sometimes it may even be completed in a matter of seconds.

This stage has previously been known as the *pronymph*, but it is less confusing and more consistent to follow Gardner's recent lead and call it the *prolarva*. Such a name emphasises its status as a true larval instar, and in addition draws attention to its resemblance to the prolarva of certain Orthoptera.

A prolarval stage has been encountered in all dragonflies which have been reared in captivity and observed to hatch from the egg. Despite the wide differences in form which may develop later on between species with different larval habits, the prolarvae of all dragonflies are extremely similar. There can be little doubt that (as is the case in locusts) the main function of this strange stage in the life-history is to provide a means for escaping easily and safely first from the egg-shell and then from the tissue or sediment surrounding it. The exposed, spider-like appendages of the second instar larva could be considered a severe handicap in such a process.

This interpretation of its function is supported by the fact that the prolarval stage seldom lasts longer than would appear to be necessary. Thus, in an exophytic species, *Sympetrum striolatum*, it may only last a few seconds, whereas in the endophytic *Anax* it may have a duration of several minutes while the hatching larva pushes its way through the passage afforded by the cone, and then out of the plant tissue. What is probably an extreme example is found in the European dragonfly, *Lestes viridis*. As we learnt in the previous chapter, this dragonfly lays its eggs in willow branches overhanging the water. When an egg hatches, the prolarva drops into the water, and the next moult occurs a few moments later. But occasionally a prolarva falls on the bank or on a floating leaf; it then wriggles and skips about until it reaches the water, postponing moulting until it does so.

In many species, particularly those which oviposit exophytically, the first moult takes place before the prolarva has completely left the egg. In these cases the prolarva appears to use the egg-shell as a support in order to brace itself for ecdysis. For the first moult, as for succeeding ones, the cuticle splits dorsally along the middle of the head and thorax, and transversely between the eyes.

After the first moult it takes about five minutes for the body and appendages to expand to their proper shape and size. While this is happening the liquid which fills the internal breathing tubes, or *tracheae*, is replaced by gas. This occurs very suddenly, although the larva is under water at the time and has no access to the air. It will be remembered that the tracheal system of the larva is secondarily closed, and that functional openings to the exterior develop only in the last few instars.

Tillyard (1917) suggested that the filling of the tracheae with air is brought about by the absorption of the liquid in them, and by the subsequent liberation of carbon dioxide into the system from the tissue fluids in the region of the mid-gut. After this, the composition of the gas in the tracheae is presumably adjusted by simple diffusion through the gills or cuticle when the respiratory mechanism becomes fully functional. We really know very little about the physiology of this process, and a comparative study of it in other aquatic insects would be of great interest, particularly in view of their probable terrestrial origin.

Although it is often difficult to distinguish closely-related species in instar 2, it is nearly always possible to tell families apart and often to recognise genera. This is true of the Anisoptera more often than of the

Zygoptera. This instar possesses certain remarkably constant characters which have, I believe, been found in all species so far investigated. Among these are an undivided tarsus, a three-segmented antenna, and a single seta on each palpus near the base of the movable hook.

During instar 2, the prominent yolk sac is retained in the mid-gut, and consequently it may not be necessary for the larva to feed. Indeed, this stage may only last a short time: in *Anax*, it can be completed in nature in three days. Once the reserves of yolk have been used up, the young larva is thrown upon its own resources to obtain food, and from the third instar onwards it may be said to have embarked upon its normal larval existence.

Almost all dragonfly larvae live in fresh or brackish water, although the actual habitats and microhabitats which they colonise vary greatly from one species to another. For example, larvae of certain tropical families live in the water which collects among the leaf-bases of forest trees. These, however, provide exceptions, and nearly all other dragonflies inhabit streams, rivers, ponds or lakes.

The diversity of form exhibited by dragonfly larvae is closely related to the niches they occupy in their fresh-water habitats. By using such guides as shape, colour, form of the legs and degree of hairiness, one can usually determine at a glance whether a given larva customarily lies buried in mud, sand or débris on the bottom, or whether it lives among water plants near the surface.

The larvae of *Cordulegaster* and *Orthetrum* in Britain are mud-dwellers *par excellence*. Some of the features possessed by larvae of this type give them an appearance which is very grotesque to the human eye. The body, usually a uniform dark-brown (even after having been cleaned with a paint-brush!), is short, thick-set and covered with a dense pile of hairs to which particles of mud adhere. The eyes form conical projections on the top of the head at either side, and usually it is only these and the tip of the abdomen that are visible above the surface of the mud in which the larva lies buried. Often

---

Plate 1.a. Above. The Fish Pond, Wokefield Common, Berks; 26 May, 1953. This pond, made over a century ago by the damming of a small stream, supported a large population of *Anax imperator:* in 1952 more than four thousand three hundred individuals of this species emerged from it. At least twelve other species of dragonfly bred regularly in the Fish Pond. (*S. Beaufoy*)

b. Below. The Oberwater, New Forest, Hants. The breeding place of several of our rarer stream-dwellers. (*S. Beaufoy*)

Plate II

(especially in *Cordulegaster*) the hinder part of the abdomen is curled dorsally in order to protrude above the mud, thus preventing sediment from being drawn into the rectum during breathing. In some tropical genera of Gomphidae this requirement has resulted in the elongation of the last abdominal segment to form a respiratory tube.

While on the subject of the appearance of mud-dwelling larvae, we may perhaps be excused a light-hearted digression concerning the quotation at the beginning of this chapter. On several counts it is likely that the species Tom was dealing with was *Cordulegaster boltoni*. He was in a stream (a trout-stream actually) at the time, and was talking to a larva which was fairly large when full-grown. Both *Gomphus* and *Cordulegaster* suggest themselves on these counts, but two further clues make the latter seem far more likely. Firstly, the creature was evidently ugly enough to elicit the rude comment from Tom; and secondly, we learn later that its labium extended upwards and forwards to cover part of the front of its head: ". . . all the thing's donkey-face came off in a moment, and out popped a long arm with a pair of pincers at the end of it, and caught Tom by the nose." This description could not apply to *Gomphus,* in which the labium is flat, rather than spoon-shaped, and lies inconspicuously beneath the head. However, we should beware of setting too much store by our diagnosis, because a few lines further on Kingsley makes full use of his artistic licence. We are told that, almost immediately after releasing Tom's nose, the larva climbed out of the water and emerged. As we shall see later on, the larval labium is non-functional for at least two days before emergence can first occur! This is because the adult organ has already been formed by this time, and being very much smaller than that of the larva and also being non-extensible, it finally occupies only a part of the base of the larval labium. However, allowance for this in-consistency would have to be made whatever species of dragonfly were involved; so there is considerable justification for assuming that Tom's companion on this occasion was a final instar larva of *Cordulegaster*.

The legs of mud-dwelling larvae are usually short and robust, and are fashioned for digging. When placed in water, such larvae make

---

Plate II. a. Above. The Byfleet Canal, Surrey, before development. It has been famous up to recent times, for its interesting species. (*S. Beaufoy*)

b. Below. In the Norfolk Broads. Areas like these, partially choked by reeds, still produce some rare species. (*C. Longfield*) energetic digging movements, even if they are on a surface of smooth glass. These movements involve the legs being bent inwards and underneath the body, and then extended, so that they push outwards. In this way sediment is removed from directly beneath a larva, and pushed to each side, so that the creature's body sinks quickly out of sight. In doubtful cases, it is helpful to be able to use these reflex movements as a guide to a larva's micro-habitat.

Among the British fauna, the most highly-specialised mud-dwellers all belong to the Anisoptera, *Cordulegaster*, *Gomphus*, *Orthetrum* and *Libellula* being good examples. Zygoptera which are often found in muddy situations include *Agrion*, *Platycnemis*, *Pyrrhosoma* and *Ceriagrion*, but these seem to live on the mud surface amongst roots and débris, and not to burrow down into it.

Bottom-dwelling larvae appear to have a low metabolic rate, to move slowly and to show little capacity for colour change. So far, their habits have made it difficult to obtain large enough samples for the estimation of growth-rates. But what information is available indicates that they tend to grow more slowly than larvae living in other situations. This is perhaps to be expected if we bear in mind that, like the eggs of exophytic Anisoptera, they live in that part of a habitat which experiences the lowest temperature, oxygen concentration and light intensity.

A few dragonflies have larvae which lie flat on the bottom but which do not burrow. It is characteristic of such larvae to have broad, flat abdomens and long spidery legs, and the tropical genus *Macromia* provides some fine examples of species which have evolved along these lines. Such larvae have a pale, mottled pattern when they live over a sandy bottom, but a dark colour when they are on mud. Some other species which live over soft mud (the African *Ictinogomphus ferox* (Rambur) is a good example) tend to develop long, curved lateral spines on the abdomen, presumably to prevent the body from sinking.

The only British species which appears to resemble these in body form and behaviour is *Cordulia*, but so far this resemblance has been observed only in aquaria. It is known that, at the time of meta-morphosis, larvae colonise muddy shallows near the shore in some numbers, but they are seldom found earlier in life. During a period of three years, during which I collected more than twelve thousand larvae of British dragonflies, I obtained only fifteen larvae of *Cordulia* that were not full-grown!

Larvae which live among water plants near the surface are by far the most active and interesting to watch. Hence they are in much greater demand as demonstration pieces in aquaria.

One of the most highly-specialised weed-dwellers is *Anax*. Its smooth, lithe body and its formidable jaws give it the same status amongst aquatic insects as the pike holds among fishes. In *Anax* the eyes have come to occupy the whole of the side of the head, thus permitting the maximum range of vision and, as if this were not sufficient, the head can be moved slightly to left or right. Larvae of *Anax* move readily and fast, and are prepared to escape promptly or to defend themselves vigorously if the occasion arises. They thus provide the antithesis of the sluggish mud-dwellers.

Another marked difference between the two types of larvae concerns their colour and their ability to change it. The ground colour of weed-dwellers is usually green, yellow or light brown, and appears to be produced by pigments in the deeper, hypodermal part of the cuticle. Superimposed upon this is a mottled pattern of dark brown or black spots representing positions in the superficial exocuticle where melanin has been deposited. The distribution of melanic spots tends to be characteristic of a genus or species, but in a given species the overall shade of colour can be varied considerably by the intensity of each spot and the area covered by it being altered. Thus many larvae of this type have the ability to change both their colour and its shade to match their background. Larvae of *Enallagma,* for instance, can be found in almost every colour from black to light ochre, passing through dark brown, olive and green.

Anax is adept at changing its colour to match its surroundings, but can do so only at the time of a moult. Then, as a rule, it will assume the colour of the background it has experienced during the three days immediately preceding the moult. In producing a wide range of colours, there is a complex interplay between the light hypodermal browns and greens and the dark melanic spots in the superficial cuticle. The former can probably be changed to some extent during an instar, but the latter, once laid down after a moult, seem to be immutable.

Dragonfly larvae provide very suitable material for a study of colour change, and it is to be hoped that they will receive attention from this point of view in future.

Most of the British dragonflies are weed-dwellers of one sort or another but, as is to be expected, not all species can be assigned easily to one of the three habitat-types we have recognised. Some may live among sticks, débris or matted roots beneath overhanging banks, and these sometimes become so dark that their basic pattern becomes obscured. Certain Zygoptera, such as *Agrion* and *Platycnemis,* have already been mentioned in this connection, and among the Anisoptera *Brachytron* and *A. grandis* provide good examples. The activity of these larvae tends to give them a position intermediate between bottom and surface-dwellers.

The most extreme examples of specialised weed-dwellers in Britain are species of *Lestes* and *Erythromma,* and we may also note in passing that their growth is unusually rapid. Other dragonflies of this type are most of the Coenagriidae, certain Aeshnidae, *Sympetrum* species and *Leucorrhinia.*

It is interesting to note that the taxonomic unit, the genus (which is, of course, based on adult characters), seldom cuts across the larval habitat classification. This suggests that the larval habitat represents a primitive and stable character in the life-history.

It is usually with respect to an animal's food that judgement is passed upon whether it is beneficial or injurious to man. The natural food of dragonflies, especially of the larvae, has received very little attention so far, and until it has we must deduce much of our information from a study of the habits and mechanism of feeding, both of which can be studied in captivity.

Our ignorance of the food of dragonfly larvae is a palpable demonstration of the maxim that a horse can be led to water but not necessarily made to drink. Nature has 'laid everything on' to ensure that such a study is as simple as could be wished. At frequent intervals, usually every night, larvae expel the remains of their last meal enclosed neatly in a transparent capsule formed by the sloughed peritrophic membrane. Thus, larvae can be collected in the afternoon, confined in separate dishes during the night, and released the following morning. If, in addition, their lengths are recorded, the food of different size-groups can be studied. Despite these attractive features, however, such work has not yet been undertaken systematically, and we must hope that some naturalists will see their way to tackling it fairly soon.

Plate 9. DRAGONFLY (ANISOPTERA: AESHNIDAE)

Aeshna grandis, male. The largest of the tawny Aeshnas and the only one with blue on the abdomen. When fully mature the wings are yellow all over, but without any deeper colour at the bases. Note the white membrane, the blue eyes and the yellow costa. The female is very similar.

Plate 9

Plate 10

In their feeding habits, dragonfly larvae are not unlike spiders. Both groups of animals wait, inconspicuously, for their living prey to arrive, and then catch it with speed and skill. But whereas the spider usually constructs a web to entangle its prey, the dragonfly grabs its victims with the extensible mask or labium, which is shot out from beneath the head. Predators which feed in this way, by awaiting the chance arrival of their prey, must be adapted to survive long periods of fasting, and to make good use of occasional heavy meals.

Voinov (1898), who made a careful histological study of the process of digestion in *Aeshna* larvae, found that the longer the period for which a larva is obliged to be without food, the greater becomes its capacity for dealing with the next meal. After a period of rest following a meal, the epithelial cells of the mid-gut become swollen with digestive products. These accumulate at the internal ends of the cells and come to lie beneath the porous peritrophic membrane. They continue to be produced until food enters the mid-gut, when the epithelial cells and their contents are discharged. Some epithelial cells, however, although they may burst, retain their nuclei and remain in the gut wall. These cells are presumably capable of taking part once again in the cycle of quiescence and activity. There are other cells in the mid-gut which can selectively absorb the products of digestion.

The use of an extensible labium to catch prey is a feature which distinguishes dragonflies from all other insects. The actual extension of the labium at the moment of catching the prey is extremely rapid, and is brought about by a kind of hydraulic mechanism involving controlled blood pressure. A muscular diaphragm across the anterior region of the abdomen appears to contract suddenly, forcing the blood forwards into the base of the labium. At the same time extensor muscles open the two palps. Retraction of the labium, once the prey has been grasped, is muscular. A convincing demonstration of this mechanism can be given by taking a recently-dead Anisoptera larva, and compressing the abdomen as one might a concertina. If internal decomposition has not proceeded too far, the labium can be made to shoot out in a very life-like manner.

Plate 10. DRAGONFLY (ANISOPTERA: AESHNIDAE)

Anax imperator, male. Fully mature. Note the distinctive rounded inner lower edge to hindwings, which is angled in the male Aeshnas. The different type of colour-pattern, also to be found on the female, is clearly seen. The female is usually much greener.

To qualify as prey—that is, to stimulate extension of the labium—an object must be moving, must be within a certain distance of the larva, and must lie between certain limits of size. These attributes of prospective prey are far from restricting, and therefore we may expect larvae to show catholic tastes, and to feed on whatever happens to be nearest, easiest to catch and most abundant in their particular environment. Under natural conditions, there seems little doubt that this is so, since the faecal pellets of a single species in one habitat have contents which vary greatly with the different seasons. Such catholic feeding habits must have considerable ecological advantages by buffering larvae against the effects of sudden fluctuations in the numbers of any single element in their prey.

An illustration of the part played by movement in eliciting feeding is provided by putting small tadpoles in an aquarium with an *Aeshna* larva. If *Aeshna* larvae (and sometimes those of other weed-dwellers) are very hungry, they will sometimes abandon their natural dignity and stalk their prey. Now tadpoles have an intriguing habit of swimming a little way and then remaining motionless for a few seconds, then swimming again, and so on. *Aeshna* larvae will respond promptly to the movement while the tadpoles are swimming, but as soon as they stop, the larvae "lose" them, and have to wait for the next wriggle. This game of hide-and-seek may continue for some minutes, and must doubtless prove very frustrating for the dragonfly.

Some attempts have been made to analyse this response in the Anisoptera by moving striped screens in front of larvae and by determining their "flicker threshold," the minimum dark interval which will enable two light impressions to be perceived separately. Salzle (1932) and Crozier *et al.* (1937) found that the flicker threshold in *Aeshna* and *Anax* larvae was about 60 stimuli per second. Thus these larvae are slightly more sensitive than man, in which the corresponding value is between 45 and 53 stimuli per second. In *Anax* the flicker threshold appears to vary with the intensity of illumination and with temperature.

Accurate use of the labium demands an ability to estimate three-dimensional space. Therefore there must exist in dragonflies a mechanism analogous to stereoscopic vision. Baldus (1924) demonstrated this by showing that a larva will wait until its prey is in approximately the correct position before striking. It now becomes clear why certain larvae (particularly weed-dwellers) turn their heads towards a moving object: this can be regarded as a necessary preliminary to optical fixation. Baldus found that this localisation is purely visual and that it is effective through glass. When orientating itself, a larva will always turn towards an object in such a way that the visual axes of corresponding ommatidia in the compound eyes intersect on the object.

In the Zygoptera, responses concerned in feeding may be rather different. It appears from the work of Alverdes (1924) that in *Agrion* the tactile perceptions of the antennae also play an important part in localisation of prey. Nevertheless, larvae which had the antennae removed were able to seize objects accurately fourteen days after the operation, and so it is clear that the eyes may sometimes assume an important role in Zygoptera also.

The size of prey that larvae will tackle seems to depend on circumstances. Hunger has a good deal to do with it, and the threshold response for attempted feeding ("courage" to the anthropomorphic) is lowered after a long fast. Thus, final instar *Aeshna* larvae will attack full-grown larvae of the water-beetle, *Dytiscus marginalis* L., if they are very hungry, whereas otherwise they may let them pass unmolested. Both the size of the dragonfly larva and the degree of activity of the prey also seem to influence this threshold.

In captivity, larvae will eat almost anything that conforms to the appropriate specifications of size and movement, even feeding on pieces of meat if these can be made to move. In some cases, they will even climb out of the water to get food if very hungry. Small larvae can be reared successfully on Protozoa, small Crustacea (*Cyclops* and *Daphnia*), Oligochaeta and small aquatic insects; then, as they become larger, they will eat earthworms, tadpoles and small fishes. Thus there need be no great difficulty about finding food for captive larvae. Some dragonfly larvae have "fads," but these are unusual. For instance, several species will seize scarlet water mites (Hydracarina) but always seem to release them immediately. Few larvae seem to like adult water beetles, although they will consume their larvae readily. And among the Aeshnidae, *Anax* larvae seem to be exceptional in their dislike of fly maggots.

There is one important aspect of feeding behaviour which we still have to deal with, namely cannibalism. It need not surprise us to learn that dragonflies are incorrigible cannibals. Not only will they eat other smaller species, but often younger individuals of their own species. Their habit of lying motionless in wait for prey probably does much to reduce the occurrence of cannibalism, on account of the important part that movement plays in stimulating feeding. Nevertheless, cannibalism does occur in nature, and presents some interesting ecological problems.

On account of a reluctance to tackle individuals of their own size, one might expect cannibalism to be less marked in populations where most larvae were of the same size. Such a condition is uncommon in nature, but it is clear that the smaller the size-range in a larval population, the less will be the occurrence of intra-specific predation. Of course, the converse is true in populations where the larval size-variation is very wide; so that cannibalism is likely to be most pronounced in species which have a larval duration of two years, such as *Anax*. For here, a newly-hatched larval population has to contend with a hungry age-group of larvae, a year old and already three-quarters grown.

Anax seems to have evolved an ingenious device to protect smaller larvae against members of the senior age-group. Anyone who has collected *Anax* larvae in late summer will have noticed that a proportion of larvae less than 20 millimetres long is transversely banded with black and white stripes. This banding is a juvenile coloration, and disappears with age (Fig. 18, p. 77). This appears at first to be rather surprising, until it is recalled that, up to a length of about 20 millimetres, that is during the first ten months of life, larvae are obliged to co-exist with a senior age-group. They have, of course, other enemies to contend with, but in a small pond, frequently supporting a large population, it is clear that older members of their own species must be formidable predators.

It now remains to be established that a coloration of black and white bands confers protection on its owner. A clue we have in this direction comes from the work of Breder on American fishes. Breder (1948) showed in a very convincing manner that light passing through wind-rippled water threw a pattern of dark and light bars upon a plain-coloured surface beneath. He did this by making a bottom-living fish, a ray, swim near the surface, and then photographing the pattern on its back. It is therefore likely that the general background among the leaves and stems of floating water plants, where newly-hatched larvae of *Anax* live, is a trellis-like pattern of light and shade. In such environment a banded pattern would almost certainly disrupt the outlines of small larvae, besides diffusing their outline and position during movement. A further observation supporting this interpretation is that young *Anax* larvae can modify the extent and nature of their black and white bands according to the background against which they find themselves. Thus, like Laban's cattle, they can become ringstraked if the occasion demands.

If this theory of the protective significance of striping is correct, it has interesting ecological implications. In *Anax,* with its two-year larval duration, we find that banding is lost after the first year, when it has been rendered unnecessary by the emergence of the senior age-group. This suggests that the size at which banding is lost bears a relation to the duration of the life-history. It may thus provide a useful guide to larval duration in cases where ordinary field analysis is difficult. The little information so far available suggests that this is

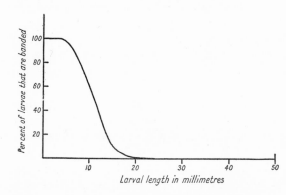

Fig. 18. The loss of the juvenile banded coloration in larvae of *A. imperator.* After they have reached a length of about 20 mm., at the end of their first year's growth, larvae are no longer obliged to co-exist with an age-group larger than themselves.

so. Several British species of *Aeshna* have larvae which are striped when young. Of these, *A. grandis* retains the banded coloration longest (until larvae are about 30 millimetres long), and there can be little doubt that this species has the greatest larval duration. An exception which may be regarded as supporting the rule is provided by *A. mixta.* Gardner (1950) has found that only the second instar larva shows a vestige of striping, and that this disappears at the next moult. *A. mixta,* however, differs from other British Aeshnids in having a larval duration of only about five months. Since all the larvae would be growing up together as members of a single age-group, there would thus be little need for a protective device against cannibalism.

This question of the protective value of banding in the early larval stages of weed-dwelling larvae may seem of only marginal importance, but it nevertheless has one very significant feature: its protective value can be assessed quantitatively. In *Anax* this could be done quite simply by analysing the food of larvae in the senior age-group. Then the proportion of striped larvae being eaten could be compared with the proportion actually existing in the junior age-group.

As we have already seen, it is possible that dragonfly larvae are their own worst enemies, especially in small, crowded pools. But nevertheless they are related, either as predators or prey, to a wide variety of other animals (see Chapter 13, p. 164).

Anisoptera larvae, especially Aeshnidae, have a very effective defence behaviour, which they employ if grasped by the head or thorax. This involves bending the abdomen forwards and stabbing the attacker with the sharp, terminal spines. Aeshnids may also use this to subdue a victim which is struggling violently. On certain occasions Zygoptera larvae also whisk the abdomen forwards in a similar fashion. *Agrion* larvae will do this if grasped by the anterior part of the body. Since, in Zygoptera, such an action cannot possibly hurt an attacker, it is difficult to imagine its function, unless perhaps it be one of aggressive display. This idea is supported to some extent by an incident I once witnessed on the bank of a Berkshire pond. A full-grown *Pyrrhosoma* larva, ready to emerge, had crawled out of the water on to the bank, and was searching among grass tussocks for a suitable place in which to transform. Suddenly, as it walked round a small obstacle, it came face to face with a spider. As quick as thought the larva flicked its caudal lamellae round towards the spider, and after a pause did so again. The spider, which was slightly larger than the larva, promptly withdrew. In the light of this observation, it may be advisable to keep in mind the possibility that distinctive patterns on the caudal lamellae may serve some function in aggressive display. But it is clear that much work needs to be done on larval behaviour before this can be stated with certainty. One particularly interesting and perhaps significant aspect of the little incident described above is that at the time the "larva" was morphologically an adult, since a few minutes later it emerged!

A defence behaviour of an opposite type is used by *Brachytron*. When handled, this larva will often fold the legs tightly against the body, and lie quite still for several minutes. If it is not molested any further, it will then unfold its legs and swim away. Since larvae of this species commonly live among sticks and dead roots, this habit can make it extremely difficult to find them in a net-load of débris. In fact the best way of dealing with them is to turn the contents of the net out on a tray or flat surface, and wait for them to unfold and walk away! A type of defence behaviour similar to this is encountered among larvae of the tropical genus *Gynacantha*.

An additional protective device possessed by many Zygoptera is the ability to detach an injured limb. This is usually effected in the region of the trochanter, and regeneration begins promptly with the next moult.

GROWTH AND DURATION OF LARVAL LIFE

The two environmental factors that are of greatest importance in determining rate of growth are temperature and food. Not only do these factors vary seasonally, however, but the responses of the larva towards them are also liable to change at different stages in the life-history. Therefore it will be realised that the rate of development is often far from being a simple resultant of these two factors.

From an ecological point of view, it seems that the duration of larval life is closely bound up with two major requirements:

1. the need for the winter to be passed in a stage which is resistant to cold, and
2. the need for emergence of adults to be synchronised, in order that the greatest numbers of the two sexes can be reproductively mature at the same time.

Little can be said about the first requirement until more is known of the temperature tolerance of different stages in the life-history. We do know that medium and large-sized larvae of several species (including *Aeshna* and *Anax*) can survive being frozen into blocks of ice, apparently without suffering any ill effects, for they swim away actively as soon as they have been thawed out. But it is unlikely that they have occasion to use this ability often in nature, because most overwintering larvae seem to retire to the deeper regions of a pond when the cold weather begins in autumn. Here, the winter temperatures show less variation, and since ice floats, the chances of being frozen are not so great. Younger larvae are probably far less tolerant of cold and, as we saw in Chapter 5, it seems likely that newly hatched larvae of the Aeshnidae are unable to withstand winter temperatures, and that their life-histories have become modified accordingly. Those species flying in spring lay eggs which hatch in summer, but those flying in summer lay diapause eggs which do not hatch until the following spring. Clearly any adaptation which involves a diapause stage will have a significant effect on the duration of the life-history, since it may prolong it by at least six months.

The second requirement concerns the need for individuals to emerge together at more or less the same season each year. This subject will be dealt with at greater length in the chapter on seasonal regulation. But we can obtain an idea of how important it is from the life-history of *Pyrrhosoma*. In this species, which emerges in spring, the larval stage usually lasts two years, yet the average life of reproductively-mature adults is no more than a week, and may be effectively reduced still further by loss of flying time due to bad weather. It is hardly necessary to say that seasonal regulation must be an efficient process in this species if enough fertile eggs are to be laid each year to secure its survival.

Several writers have given values for the duration of larval life in the Odonata, but very little careful field work has been done to substantiate these claims, and most of the statements made so far must be considered guesses rather than estimates. It is important to emphasise that the duration of larval life under artificial conditions of culture may be very different from that shown by wild populations and that, although rearing larvae in captivity can provide valuable information on many points, it is unwise to use it as a basis for estimating growth in the field.

One of the best ways to investigate the problem of larval growth-rate under natural conditions is to take well-known and easily-observable events, such as emergence and oviposition, and then to make collections of larvae at regular intervals between them. In Britain, and elsewhere in temperate latitudes, one is greatly assisted in this procedure by the knowledge that the duration of the life-history must be a whole number of years.

Recently, this technique has been used to estimate the larval

---

Plate 11. DRAGONFLIES (ANISOPTERA: AESHNIDAE AND CORDULEGASTERIDAE)

a. Aeshna isosceles, male. The following characters easily distinguish it from *A grandis:* Clear wings with yellow basal patch and dark membrane; yellow triangle on 2nd segment of uniformly brown abdomen; green eyes. The female is very similar.

b. Cordulegaster boltoni, male. Teneral and with wings only partly expanded, before maiden flight. The female is a similar black and golden ringed insect, but with a long, hard, shiny black ovipositor. (*John Markham*)

a

b

Plate 11.

Plate 12.

duration of several British species, and the results obtained have proved extremely interesting. One point which has emerged clearly from this work, and also from earlier studies made in East Germany by Münchberg (1931), is the necessity for continuing to collect samples right through the winter. On this matter Münchberg says, somewhat wistfully, that "in winter it was often necessary to break through several decimetres of solid ice with a hand-axe in order to obtain samples." It is with strong feelings that I endorse Münchberg's remarks!

Besides the weather, there is another factor which can make sampling difficult. This is the inaccessibility of certain species of larvae, which makes it impossible to obtain large numbers by conventional means. One way to tackle such elusive or rare species in the future may be for collectors to pool their information. If this were done, certain life-histories might be determined in far less time than would otherwise be required (see Appendix I, p. 191).

The results which have been obtained so far show that most of the British species probably require two or more years to complete their development in this latitude. In the following table, the British dragonflies have been arranged according to the estimated duration of the life-history. The species recorded in this table have been distinguished according to the strength of the evidence providing the basis for the estimate, and it is important to emphasise that for many species little or nothing is known of larval growth-rate from field observations, so that their position must be regarded as very provisional. In addition, we must remember that populations of a single species may vary to some extent in their developmental time from one habitat to another.

Bearing these qualifications in mind, it is nevertheless evident that most British dragonflies require two or more years in which to complete larval growth. This means that individuals of most species spend more than 95 per cent of their lives as eggs and larvae. One important consequence of this is that populations may take several years to recover from the temporary destruction of a habitat.

Plate 12. DRAGONFLY (ANISOPTERA: AESHNIDAE)

Aeshna cyanea, male. Immature colouring, which turns green and blue when mature. The distinguishing characters from *A. juncea* are: the black costa; two broad dorsal thoracic bands; the coloured spots on 9th and 10th abdominal segments entire.

LENGTH OF LIFE-HISTORY OF
DRAGONFLIES BREEDING IN BRITAIN

Duration	Species
ONE YEAR Invariably: (8) Usually: (9)	**A. mixta, S. danae,** *S. flaveolum,* *S. fonscolombei, S. sanguineum,* **S. striolatum** *L. dryas,* **L. sponsa** *(S. nigrescens), (C. armatum),* *C. hastulatum, C. puella, C. pulchellum,* *C. scitulum, E. cyathigerum, E. najas,* *I. elegans*
TWO YEARS Usually: (10)	*A. cyanea, A. isosceles,* **A. imperator,** *A. splendens,* **A. virgo, C. tenellum,** **C. mercuriale,** *(I. pumilio), P. pennipes,* **P. nymphula**
MORE THAN Usually: TWO YEARS (16)	*G. vulgatissimus, C. boltoni,* **B. pratense,** **A. grandis,** *A. juncea, A. caerulea,* *O. curtisi, C. aenea, (S. metallica),* *(S. arctica), L. depressa, L. quadrimaculata,* *L. fulva, L. dubia, O. coerulescens,* *O. cancellatum*

Notes. Bold type: Firm evidence from regular collections of larvae in the field. (Münchberg or Corbet).

Italic type: Slight evidence from various sources including small larval samples and information from larvae reared in captivity.

Species in parenthesis: No evidence. Assigned by guesswork on basis of mode of life and relatives.

Probably no species in Britain regularly requires more than five years to complete development, although there are indications that sometimes *Cordulegaster* and *A. grandis* may be exceptions. At the other end of the scale, it is interesting to note that those species which have life-histories lasting one year nearly always breed in still water. This fact may well be connected with the higher temperatures which prevail in such habitats, and the effect they must have on the growth-rate.

In Britain, nearly all larval growth is limited to the period between March and November. Some species, which are able to grow at relatively low temperatures, will of course have a longer season of growth than others. For instance, *Pyrrhosoma*, although it does not appear to grow so rapidly, begins earlier in the year and stops later than *Anax*.

Growth usually proceeds most rapidly in July and August, so that larvae hatching from eggs during these months may achieve spectacular

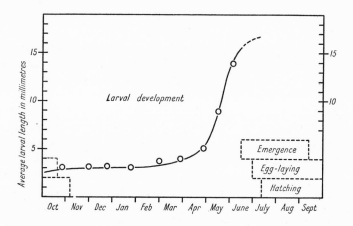

Fig. 19. The life-history and larval growth of *S. striolatum*. This diagram is based on records collected from a population in the New Forest.

rates of growth. *Anax* larvae, in the first three months of life, can show increases in body-length of 600 per cent, 50 per cent and 30 per cent respectively.

One of the most rapid growers among the British species is *L. sponsa*. This can complete the whole larval development in the re-markably short time of two months, thus vying with certain tropical dragonflies for speed. In *Lestes*, growth is too rapid for changes in rate to be detected clearly, but in *S. striolatum*, which grows more slowly, it is possible for this to be done. In Fig. 19, above, which is based on records from a population in the New Forest, we have a good illustration of the effect on growth-rate of the progressively-rising temperature in spring and summer. In fact, in nature, the growth-rate of a population is probably never the same from one month to the next.

METAMORPHOSIS

With the advent of metamorphosis, the larval existence enters its final stage. Several of the morphological changes associated with metamorphosis are clearly visible to the naked eye. Perhaps the best-known of these is the swelling of the larval wing-sheaths, which takes place as the adult organs develop in a concertina-like fashion inside. But there are other changes which, especially in the Anisoptera, can be used to follow the progress of metamorphosis with greater accuracy, and to predict when emergence is likely to occur.

In the Anisoptera, at an early stage in metamorphosis, the faceted areas of the compound eyes grow darker, and then begin to extend inwards over the top of the head, until finally (except of course in *Gomphus*) they meet in the centre. In *Anax*, at spring temperatures, the compound eyes show the first signs of extension about 45 days before emergence, and they meet for the first time about 20 days before. Later, changes can be observed in the condition of the labium: emergence generally occurs about 5 days after the tissues of the adult organ first begin to shrink towards the base of the prementum, and about 4 days after they first lie retracted completely within the post-entum.

By observing the occurrence of these stages in a larval population, one can predict with considerable accuracy when emergence may be expected to begin. I found this knowledge very useful in May, 1953 when making arrangements for Mr. S. Beaufoy to come and photograph emergence at a pond where I was studying *Anax*. On 14 May, from an inspection of 168 larvae, I estimated that emergence would begin on 26 May. Seven days later, I looked at 216 larvae and changed this estimate to 24 May, the date I mentioned to Mr. Beaufoy when I

Plate III. a. Anax imperator female ovipositing in *Potamogeton natans L.* Mid-morning, 13 July, 1951. (*P. S. Corbet*)

b. Anax imperator at the Fish Pond. Copulation. The male supports the pair; he has alighted on a sprig of heather about ten metres from the pond. Mid-morning, 13 July, 1951. (*P. S. Corbet*)

a

b

Plate III

a. *Anax imperator*. Successive stages of emergence. Stage Two. The resting stage. This lasts for about an hour in nature. (*S. Beaufoy*)

b. Stage Three. The adult is just withdrawing the abdomen from the exuvia, and the wings have just begun to expand; their costal margins are still corrugated. During expansion of the wings, which takes about thirty minutes, adults are very susceptible to physical damage. In 1953 about nine per cent of the emergence-group died due to injuries sustained in this stage. (*S. Beaufoy*)

Plate IV

telephoned him. Actually, emergence began on 25 May, by which time Mr. Beaufoy had already arrived, and he was therefore able to spend his limited time to great advantage.

A point worth noting is that metamorphosis always directly precedes emergence, never being separated from it by a diapause stage. Metamorphosis is therefore an important character to look for in the field since, whenever it is observed, emergence is certain to follow soon. Conversely, if final instar larvae without signs of metamorphosis are found consistently in summer, there is every reason to believe that they are in a condition of diapause.

Soon after metamorphosis begins, larval behaviour undergoes a marked change. For instance, mud-dwelling larvae become exceptionally easy to collect, on account of their habit of moving towards the shore and basking in the warm shallows. In May, 1951 (a rather 'late' year, biologically) I was able to obtain 98 Libellulid larvae in about two hours, from mud and leaf mould in the shallow water of a Berkshire lake. These larvae comprised 53 *O. cancellatum*, 28 *C. aenea*, 16 *L. quadrimaculata* and 1 *L. depressa*. All showed advanced signs of metamorphosis, except the *O. cancellatum* which were just beginning. Since the rate of completion of metamorphosis has a positive temperature coefficient, this habit doubtless reduces the duration of this vulnerable stage.

Just as mud-dwelling larvae commonly move to shallow regions at the time of metamorphosis, so do those living amongst weed come nearer to the surface. *Anax* larvae tend to colonise floating plants in the later stages of metamorphosis, about 10 days or less before emergence. This habit is perhaps known to certain natives of the East Indies, who, Dr. Lieftinck tells me, anchor floating mats of reeds in order to attract *Anax* larvae. Then, from time to time, they inspect the mats and consume the catch!

The movements of larvae during metamorphosis can be determined by marking them around the legs with rings of coloured wire or tin foil. Paint can also be used, but is less satisfactory, since the cuticle has to be dried first, and even then the paint will sometimes peel off. After individuals have been marked and released, they may then be recaptured either as larvae, or as cast skins after emergence of the adult. Amongst other information, results obtained in this way can provide estimates of survival-rate during metamorphosis. In a Berkshire pond in 1953, I found that only about 50 per cent of *Anax* larvae embarking on metamorphosis survived to emerge.

D—G

This chapter is the last to deal specifically with the aquatic stages. Some readers may perhaps consider that a disproportionate amount of space has been devoted to the eggs and larvae; but, if they do, I think it demonstrates how sadly these stages have been neglected by biologists in the past. Recent work has shown us that the more closely they are investigated, the more evident it becomes that the aquatic and aerial stages of a species should be considered together.

CHAPTER 7

EMERGENCE
(P.S.C.)

L'heure est critique pour l'insecte où il naît à la vie aérienne. Il se trouvera pendant quelques heures à la merci de tous les prédateurs. Les oiseaux surtout ne se priveront pas de gober les juteux imagos aux ailes impuissantes.

JEAN ROSTAND (1935). *La Vie des Libellules*

WHEN metamorphosis has been completed and a larva leaves the water for the last time, emergence can be said to have begun. The process of transformation which follows is one of the most beautiful and awe-inspiring sights that can be witnessed, and it has evoked some fine descriptive writing from naturalists in the past. Amongst them, few have written with greater artistry than Réaumur (1734-42), whose account, happily in French, should certainly be read by everyone interested in insect natural history.

The successive stages in the process of emergence have been described so often and so well that they need only be mentioned briefly here. In any case, the excellent photographs in Plate IV make a detailed account superfluous.

Emergence, as it occurs in nature, is perhaps known in greatest detail in *Anax,* and so it will be convenient to take this species as our example.

About two days before emergence, *Anax* larvae select the upright sticks or other supports which they will use when they climb out of the water. To do this, they seem to orientate so as to swim towards shaded regions of the shore. But although this process of orientation presumably takes place during daylight, most larvae do not swim towards the shore until after dark.

The logic involved in this discovery is quite entertaining, because it is open to criticism on the grounds of being Procrustean. This is due to the fact that one cannot usually watch aquatic animals at night without using some means of illumination, which itself might be causing the behaviour observed. Thus it is possible that larvae seen swimming towards the shore at night are simply showing a positive response to a localised light stimulus. This conclusion was actually drawn by one observer in America, who noticed that large numbers of dragonfly larvae came towards a light which had been placed near the shore of a pond for collecting moths. In fact the suggestion was made that this would provide a useful method for collecting larvae in the future! Actually it seems far more likely that the larvae observed in this instance were already in the process of selecting their emergence supports—the time of year was appropriate—and that they were illuminated while doing so. In my own observations, I was fortunate in having an independent check to my conclusions: I had previously marked about half the larval population with daubs of paint and metal rings, and this enabled me to ascertain whether any new individuals had arrived when my light had been extinguished. As it happened, new larvae were arriving all the time, and this showed which interpretation was the correct one.

The external factors to which larvae respond in order to find suitable emergence supports would make a very interesting study. Since different species emerge in different places, it is unlikely that all species respond to the same factors. For instance, small damselflies, which emerge near the shore in the morning, seem to select their supports immediately before emergence, in a rather impromptu fashion. These larvae may perhaps follow a rising temperature gradient in the surface water, which would lead them to the shore.

Several observers have remarked that the larvae of nocturnal emergers may leave the water and return again for several nights before emergence actually takes place. That this does happen sometimes is unquestionably so, but I am inclined to think that it is less frequent in nature than is generally believed. Although I watched carefully for any sign of this happening in *Anax*, on the three nights before emergence began in 1953 I never saw a larva with more than its head out of the water. Inevitably, most if not all records of these ineffectual nocturnal climbs refer to captive larvae, and I think that this may be significant.

In those species which emerge at night, it is often possible to induce a larva to return to the water by shining a strong light on it. A possible explanation for many of these recorded instances is that a larva which would otherwise have emerged without delay was forced to return to the water after having been subjected to the illumination necessary to

a. *Gomphus vulgatissimus*, male. Still only semi-mature and not yet green. Note the width between the eyes ; the dilated end to the abdomen ; the totally different shape to the principal wing - cells. Female similar.

b. *Cordulia aenea*, male. Mature. The thick yellow down is clearly seen on the thorax, this being almost entirely absent from the other three British Cordulines. These are all distinguished by the anal appendages. The females are all very similar.

Plate 13. DRAGONFLIES (ANISOPTERA : GOMPHIDAE AND CORDULIIDAE)

a. Orthetrum cancellatum, male. Teneral colouring. Note the black abdominal pattern and the entirely clear wings.

b. Orthetrum cancellatum, male. Fully mature. The blue pruinescence entirely obscures the black pattern, but the wings remain quite clear. Intermediate colour stages are found in semi-mature males.

Plate 14. DRAGONFLIES (ANISOPTERA : LIBELLULIDAE)

observe it. This matter is far from settled, however, and until more careful observations have been made, I think we should reserve judgement concerning the frequency of pre-emergence nocturnal excursions in nature.

The site chosen for emergence is nearly always close to the shore, but tends to vary according to the species, being related, amongst other things, to the posture adopted during emergence. Most Odonata prefer near-vertical supports but some, including certain Gomphidae and Zygoptera, can emerge successfully in a horizontal position. A comparative study of the posture adopted by dragonflies during emergence has been made by Straub (1943).

An accurate knowledge of the emergence habits of species likely to occur in a habitat is of great value if a census is being made, for one of the best ways of doing this is to make collections of the exuviae, or cast larval skins. These often remain *in situ* on emergence supports for several days (Plate V*b*, p. 116), and since they can usually be identified and sexed, regular collections can be very useful. One would, for instance, look for exuviae of *Gomphus* on horizontal banks amongst grass and stones by the sides of streams; those of *Anax* on robust, upright sticks or reeds in shaded regions near pond margins; and those of *Sympetrum* or *Pyrrhosoma* low down among grass or reeds near the bank.

The distance travelled by larvae before transforming is usually only a few inches, but there are occasional striking exceptions. Exuviae of *Cordulegaster* have been found in the position of emergence many yards from the parent stream, and larvae of *Anax* may climb to heights of fifteen feet or more above the water before emerging. The wandering behaviour of *Cordulegaster* may have a protective significance, as we shall see later on, but the habit of high-climbing in *Anax* is less easy to understand. It is not to be explained wholly by the necessity for a suitable position to be reached on an indifferent support, since on the same support certain larvae may emerge near the water and others high up. The impression I have gained is that during the emergence period there are "high" and "low" nights. Perhaps the degree of crowding below the surface before emergence has something to do with it.

An emerging larva climbs quickly and purposefully out of the water. Having reached a suitable position, it stops, and a few moments later wriggles the abdomen violently from side to side. This behaviour pattern is encountered in the Aeshnidae and most Zygoptera, but apparently not in the Libellulidae or in species which emerge on horizontal surfaces. It is perhaps concerned with the need to test the grip of the tarsal claws, and to ensure that ample space exists for expansion of the wings.

The larva then remains motionless for some time, about three-quarters of an hour in *Anax*, and it is during this period that the method of respiration seems to change from rectal to spiracular.

Eclosion begins with the appearance of a split in the mid-dorsal region of the thorax; this extends forwards in the shape of a T, following approximately the same line of weakness as that found in larval moults. Having extracted its head, thorax and legs from the larval skin, an emerging dragonfly enters the "resting stage," which is one of the most remarkable features of the whole process of trans-formation. During this stage most Anisoptera (again excluding those which emerge horizontally) hang head downwards, supported only by the abdomen which remains in the larval skin, this in its turn being held to the emergence support only by the empty tarsal claws. In the Zygoptera and some Gomphidae the anterior part of the body does not hang downwards, but remains parallel to the larval skin, facing forwards.

The function of the resting stage is obscure, but may be concerned with the hardening of the legs or the accumulation of blood pressure in the thorax. The former is of course particularly important before emergence can proceed further. At normal spring temperatures at night in Britain, the resting stage in *Anax* lasts about an hour. When it has been completed, the individual bends forwards with a quick movement and, grasping the exuvia with its legs, extracts the un-expanded abdomen.

After this things happen quickly. First the wings, and then the abdomen, reach their full size. The wings expand so rapidly that one can almost see them enlarging. In *Anax*, they may attain their full size in only twenty-six minutes, and the abdomen in an even shorter time. Expansion is achieved by blood being pumped into the organs under pressure and, if at this time the wings are punctured by any obstacle (such as the claws of another larva clambering over them), they are damaged irreparably. Very soon after the expansion is complete, the two outer layers of each wing stick together and then harden in preparation for flight. The glistening appearance characteris-tic of the wings of adults which have recently emerged is apparently caused by residual fluid which has not yet dried out between the two layers forming the wing. The general drying out which occurs at this

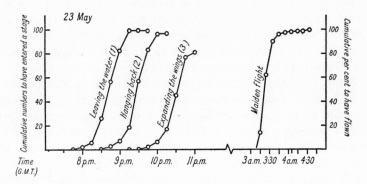

Fig. 20. Normal diurnal rhythm of emergence in *A. imperator*, illustrated by field counts of larvae. Stage 1 represents larvae which have left the water but not yet split the cuticle. Stages 2 and 3 are illustrated in Plate IV. Stage 2 begins when the cuticle splits, and stage 3 when the abdomen is withdrawn from the exuvia. The maiden flight at dawn is even more closely synchronised than the evening emergence.

time is considerable, and Schafer (1923) found that it may cause a loss in body-weight of as much as 50 per cent during the first day after emergence.

The defenceless immobility of dragonflies during emergence makes this stage a very vulnerable one in the life-history. In tropical regions, where night temperatures are high, it may be completed very quickly: sometimes only twenty minutes elapse between an individual leaving the water and being ready to fly. But the process is doubtless more hazardous in higher latitudes, where it may take much longer.

Susceptibility to attack by predators (mainly birds) varies with the mode of emergence. The most vulnerable species are large, conspicuous Aeshnids (especially if they exist at a high density and emerge all at the same time). Libellulids, which are cryptically coloured and which emerge low down among marginal rushes, are less exposed to attack, and most Zygoptera, on account of their size, least of all. It is not surprising, therefore, to find that most Aeshnids and some Libellulids (*Sympetrum* seems to be an example) usually emerge at night.

The normal emergence rhythm of *Anax* is shown in Fig. 20, above, in which the stages have been numbered to correspond to the photographs in Plates IV and V*a* on pages 85 and 116. It is very likely that most Aeshnidae in Britain show a similar rhythm. One striking feature about this daily rhythm is its close synchronisation. From what has been said, we can see that this has great advantages, since any larvae leaving the water after more advanced individuals have begun the resting stage, or worse still begun to expand the wings, are likely to damage the others by climbing over them.

It is not known to what environmental factors larvae respond in order to achieve this synchronisation, although certain observations can provide us with some useful clues. Firstly, it seems unlikely that they are responding merely to light of a given crepuscular intensity, since emergence does not occur at the corresponding time at dawn. Secondly, larvae which have already taken up their positions on emergence supports begin to show signs of pre-emergence activity in the late afternoon, several hours before dusk.

It is possible that the responses involved may work somewhat after this fashion: as light intensity begins to fall, larvae are stimulated into a state of "preparedness." During this period they jostle each other and seem to manoeuvre into suitable positions on emergence supports; some may even momentarily put their heads above water. But no larva actually leaves the water until the light intensity has fallen below a certain critical value. In this way a synchronised exodus would occur soon after dusk.

Not much is known about the emergence times of other British species in the field. A few stray observations have been made, but careful counts of large numbers are badly needed. Records suggest that, apart from Aeshnids, *Cordulegaster* and perhaps *Sympetrum*, which emerge at night, most British dragonflies emerge in the early part of the day. In view of the obvious selective advantage of emerging during the night, this is rather surprising, but an explanation is suggested by certain abnormal behaviour of *Anax*.

Sometimes one is treated to the remarkable sight of *Anax* emerging during the daytime (Plate VI*a*, p. 117). Such an emergence differs from an evening one in that the stages are not well-synchronised. Also, even though one may be making exuvia collections daily, there are nearly always numbers of empty larval skins, indicating that emergence occurred normally the previous evening. This suggests that the evening emergence group has somehow become divided, and closer investigation reveals that this is indeed the case.

When they are transforming, individuals of *Anax* are very sensitive to air temperature, and cold may greatly prolong the process. On account of the relatively high specific heat of water, larvae probably cannot discern low air temperatures until they actually leave the water. A divided emergence is probably caused by a fall in air temperature below a certain value (about 10°C) after larvae have left the water. Those larvae which have not already begun to moult return to the water, and emerge when temperatures rise the following morning. This point has been established by marking larvae which were returning to the water, and obtaining all the recaptures the next morning (Fig. 21).

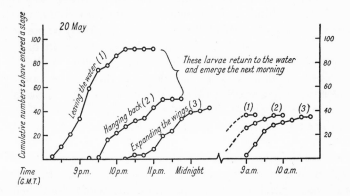

Fig. 21. Divided emergence in *A. imperator*, illustrated by field counts of larvae. This phenomenon occurs when low air temperatures disturb the normal emergence rhythm. Some of the larvae which have left the water in the evening return again and emerge early the following morning.

It might be expected that larvae would postpone emergence until the following evening, when they would be less vulnerable, and it is possible that some actually do this. But the main reason why emergence usually occurs so soon seems to be that most larvae have already changed over from aquatic to aerial respiration, and can therefore spend only a limited time under the water. This is indicated by the fact that, in the morning, most larvae are unable to swim to their emergence supports by jet propulsion.

The phenomenon of divided emergence in *Anax* provides an indication of why more British dragonflies do not emerge at night. In the tropics it is customary for nearly all Odonata to emerge at this time. It may be that, in higher latitudes, low night temperatures become the limiting factor making it necessary for emergence to take place in the daytime. This could well be an important circumstance limiting the northerly distribution of large and conspicuous Aeshnidae.

Because emergence is localised in space and time, it is sometimes possible to make a reliable estimate of the mortality which occurs during this vulnerable stage in the life-history. In a population of *Anax* I investigated in 1952 and 1953, the three main causes of mortality were (1) failure to moult completely, (2) failure to expand the wings without damage, and (3) predation by birds. The effects of the first two items could be assessed quite easily by counting the crippled individuals left behind after emergence. The third item, predation, was caused by a pair of Blackbirds (raising a brood) whose territory included the emergence site. Dragonflies were taken in one of two ways. A few were caught as larvae while they were clambering over surface débris on their way to the shore at dusk. The birds would hover over the water and lift them out with their feet. Probably very few larvae were caught in this way, since most of them did not swim towards the shore until after dusk, when the birds would be unable to see them.

Almost all the dragonflies were taken in the early morning, before they had flown from their supports. A Blackbird would take a teneral adult to a bare patch of ground, peck off the wings, and then either eat the body or take it to the nest. The number of adults killed in this way was calculated by counting the dismembered wings left behind on the Blackbirds' "anvils." The results, together with estimates of mortality due to incomplete ecdysis or expansion of the wings are given in the following table. It can be seen that, although mortality due to predation by birds was considerable, it was no greater than that caused by incomplete expansion of the wings.

The higher mortality in 1953 (especially marked for item 2) was probably connected with the lower temperatures prevailing during the period of peak emergence. Divided emergence was far more frequent as a result, and must have deprived individuals expanding their wings of the protection they would otherwise have enjoyed from synchronisation.

An interesting point to notice here is that, although the bird predation appears to have been greater in 1953, the actual numbers of dragonflies involved were almost the same in both years (133 in 1952 and 146 in 1953). This suggests that the Blackbirds (who defended their territory successfully) were reaching the upper limit of their capacity for this kind of food. Thus, in this respect, the extent of bird

MORTALITY OF THE EMPEROR DRAGONFLY
DURING EMERGENCE

Cause of death	Mortality (expressed as per cent of total numbers emerging per year)	
	1952	1953
1. Incomplete ecdysis	1·2	1·9
2. Incomplete expansion of the wings	4·3	8·9
3. Predation by birds	3·0	5·0
Total mortality	8·5	15·8

Total numbers emerging: 1952: 4,368
1953: 2,944

predation was largely independent of the numbers emerging. This finding is perhaps rather unexpected, but Lack (1954) has recorded similar examples, where birds tended to eat constant numbers of insects whose numbers fluctuated annually.

Mortality due to mechanical causes, on the other hand, is likely to be density-dependent. That is to say it will be affected less by the total numbers emerging during the year, than by the degree to which these

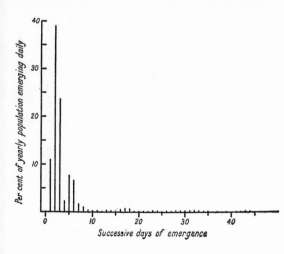

Fig. 22. Seasonal emergence in a population of *A. imperator*. Although emergence is spread over a period of about six weeks, more than 90 per cent of the adults emerge within the first ten days.

are concentrated on the peak nights. In 1953, synchronisation of emergence was unusually efficient, and about 30 per cent of the annual population emerged on the second night. One of the effects of such concentration is a severe competition for emergence supports (Plate Va, p. 116), which usually prevents all but the last arrivals from completing ecdysis. Some larvae show an obtuseness almost amounting to cruelty in the way in which, failing to recognise other individuals, they use them as emergence supports. Mortality of this kind must be regarded as a price which has to be paid for close synchronisation of annual emergence.

As a result of physical interference, newly-emerged adults some-times become dislodged and fall into the water. They do not sink, but remain struggling on the surface, and a few may manage to drag themselves out again, and dry the wings sufficiently to fly. At the Fish Pond (Plate Ia, p. 68), the habitat in Berkshire where I made a study of an *Anax* population, Great Crested Newts used to congregate underneath emergence supports at night, and would grab dragonflies which had fallen into the water. This fact was probably of greater biological significance to the newts than to the dragonflies, whose overall mortality was probably not altered to an appreciable extent. Most of the dragonflies eaten by newts would have died in any case.

Besides showing a diurnal rhythm, emergence also shows a seasonal rhythm, the study of which can reveal a great deal about a life-history. An investigation of this kind is made very much easier on account of the spatial and temporal localisation which occurs during emergence. Perhaps the best method to adopt, at any rate for large, vertically-emerging species, is that of making regular collections of exuviae. The diurnal rhythm, as we have seen, makes it a simple matter to separate collections into day groups.

Results obtained in this way can be very informative. For instance, an emergence curve of the *Anax* type (Fig. 22, p. 95) is usually a feature of a life-history in which a diapause is developed in the final larval instar. A similar curve is also found in *Pyrrhosoma* and in certain other species which emerge in spring. Dragonflies which emerge in summer often have a different life-history and lack a final instar dia-pause; they commonly have a more symmetrical emergence curve, with the greatest numbers occurring in the middle of the emergence period.

The collection of exuviae has other uses. It can provide exact information on the total numbers emerging throughout the year, and

a. Orthetrum cancellatum, female. Mature and closely resembling immature male. Clear wing-bases and black abdominal pattern, distinguish her from all Libellulas. Large size and no dorsal thoracic stripes, from *O. coerulescens* below.

b. Orthetrum coerulescens, female. Immature, and rather similar to a *Sympetrum* female. Wing bases always clear, and two cream dorsal stripes usually to be seen.

Plate 15. DRAGONFLIES (ANISOPTERA : LIBELLULIDAE)

a. Orthetrum coerulescens, male. Immature and very similar to female. Some young males, and females, have yellow along the costal edge of the wing.

b. Orthetrum coerulescens, male. Mature, but still with the dorsal cream thoracic stripes, which eventually are lost beneath the blue pruinescence. The wings are now entirely clear, but the pale pterostigma is a distinction to *O, cancellatum*.

Plate 16. DRAGONFLIES (ANISOPTERA : LIBELLULIDAE)

also on the sex ratio at the time of emergence, a question over which there has been much controversy in the past. In addition, it can be used to estimate mortality, if larvae have been marked in the final instar. It also provides a quick, all-weather method for determining what species are breeding in a given habitat. For this purpose, it is obviously more reliable than collections of either adults or larvae.

A detailed knowledge of the emergence habits of dragonflies can be of great value in field studies. Work on the movements and flight range of Anisoptera, subjects of the closest relevance to the vexed question of migration, is greatly hampered by the difficulty of catching and marking enough specimens to provide sufficient recaptures. But in *Anax,* as we have seen in this chapter, a very large proportion of the population is accessible, between midnight and dawn on peak emergence nights, around the margins of the larval habitat. At this time newly-emerged adults can be marked fairly easily (see Appendix IV, p. 236). This method has already been demonstrated to be practicable, and it is to be hoped that it may help to answer certain of the difficult problems of adult life which await solution. One of the more attractive features of this technique is that it enables the exact adult age of all recaptures to be known—a rare achievement in population studies.

CHAPTER 8

ADULT LIFE: MATURATION
AND LONGEVITY
(P.S.C.)

*Thus the Dragon-Fly enters upon a more noble life than that it had
hitherto led in the water, for in the latter it was obliged to live in
misery, creeping and swimming slowly, but now it wings the air.*

J. SWAMMERDAM (1758). *The Book of Nature*

IN THOSE dragonflies which emerge at night, the first flight usually
occurs at dawn the following morning.

I first witnessed the maiden flight of *Anax* at the Fish Pond, on a
June morning in 1951. At this time I was unaware of the emergence
rhythm in *Anax,* and I had risen before sunrise with the intention of
finding out when it took place. I arrived at the Fish Pond at about
2 a.m. (G.M.T.). It was then still dark, but by shining my torch I
could see that emergence had already occurred some time before, for
the branches and trunks of trees near the water's edge were thickly
festooned with motionless dragonflies, each with its glistening wings
folded together over its back. My first emotion was one of mild
disappointment at having once again failed to discover the time of
emergence, but the sight that I was about to witness more than com-
pensated for this.

The first sign of movement occurred when the dragonflies began to
open their wings. This happened about one hour before sunrise,
when I was first becoming aware of a subtle increase in light intensity.
Shortly afterwards, at about the time when the last bat disappeared,
the nightjars ceased their churring and it was becoming possible to
read without the aid of a torch, the first individual began to vibrate
its wings and, as the others followed suit, the air became filled with a
loud rustling sound.

It was about forty minutes before sunrise and the whirring of wings
had been continuing for about twenty minutes when the first adult

began to climb up its support, meanwhile increasing the frequency of its wing-beats, until finally it became airborne. Then it flew slowly upwards, weaving a tortuous course through the canopy of overhanging branches. In a few moments the air seemed filled with ghost-like dragonflies, rising up into the mist and flying away out of sight. Some were still so soft that the abdomen hung downwards from its own weight.

In what seemed a very short time, it was all over, and, apart from the first murmurings of the dawn chorus, the only sound to be heard was made by the fluttering wings of those unfortunates that had collided with branches and fallen into the water.

The first birds began feeding at the pond only about ten minutes after the maiden flight had ended. These included a pair of Blackbirds which I discovered later to be the chief predators of emerging Emperor Dragonflies at this pond.

The dawn flight, then, can be seen as an important protection against bird predation at the time of emergence.

It seems probable that the maiden flight does not occur simply when the light rises above a certain threshold intensity, but that it is actually stimulated by light of a certain crepuscular value. If for any reason (sometimes low temperature) flight is prevented at dawn, adults show little inclination to leave their supports during full daylight, and when conditions have again become favourable later, flights are sporadic and lack unison. Individuals which have emerged in captivity and have been prevented from flying at dawn tend to remain quiescent during the day, but show a renewed burst of activity at dusk. It is occasionally possible to evoke precocious maiden flight in dragonflies by shining a very bright light over the emergence area.

An adaptation which must necessarily be associated with a response to low light intensity in this case is the ability to fly at low air temperatures. For the maiden flights to be a success, *Anax* has to fly at air temperatures of 6 to 10°C. These are much lower than those at which ordinary adult flight takes place subsequently, and it seems likely that the long period of wing-whirring which precedes the first flight is causally related to this need. Sotavalta (1954) has recently shown experimentally that insects can raise the thoracic temperature above that of the surrounding air if they vibrate the wings beforehand. Wing-whirring before take-off is perhaps best known in hawk-moths. It can also be observed in roosting dragonflies disturbed on warm evenings, although in this instance it seldom lasts for more than a minute or two before flight takes place.

After taking-off, newly-emerged *Anax* adults rise to a height of about ten feet above any obstacles impeding the view, and then set off in fast level flight in a well-defined direction. They orientate so as to fly away from water, and in doing so they seem to respond to the position of a plane reflecting surface (see Chapter 10, p. 128). This observation strongly suggests that, like certain other arthropods studied recently, dragonflies may respond to a source of polarised light—a possibility which it would be very interesting to investigate experimentally. Once again we find the eyes playing a very important part in determining the dragonfly's responses. This orientation away from the aquatic habitat forms a very necessary part of the adult behaviour pattern for, as we shall see in the next chapter, delicate and teneral adults stand very little chance of withstanding the violent clashes associated with aggressive behaviour of mature dragonflies over water. It is therefore important that the early, vulnerable part of adult life be spent well away from water.

In *Anax,* the length of the maiden flight may vary from twenty yards to a distance greatly exceeding two hundred yards, and is probably determined to a considerable extent by fatigue, which in its turn will depend on air temperature. Adults have been seen to settle on trees from one to ten yards above the ground, or low down among clumps of heather. In such places their coloration makes them very difficult to see (Plate VI*b*, p. 117). If the weather is fine, they may leave these positions later the same day. We may suppose that air temperature and perhaps hunger (the dragonfly will not have fed for at least five days before emergence) are the principal factors stimulating the second flight. The maiden flight doubtless plays an important role in effecting dispersal of certain dragonflies.

The maiden flight probably follows the same general pattern in all nocturnal emergers. Species which emerge in the day-time fly much sooner after transformation, and do not exhibit such a well-marked synchronisation. This is to be expected since the air temperature is more favourable, and light is not a limiting factor. For instance, in *Pyrrhosoma,* which emerges at about 8.30 a.m. G.M.T., adults may fly at any time after about 9.30 a.m. Here the maiden flight is only about twenty feet, but is nevertheless directed away from water.

The first part of the adult life is spent away from water. The gonads of newly-emerged dragonflies are in an undeveloped state, and it can be assumed that during this period they attain sexual maturity. At this time both sexes feed actively and mingle without showing sexual behaviour. They also retain their negative response to water, and if during this period a dragonfly encounters a body of water, it will turn away and fly in another direction.

In *Anax, Pyrrhosoma* and *Lestes,* the only British species in which it has so far been estimated, this maturation period lasts for about two weeks (Fig. 23, below). Its duration may be reduced under conditions of fine weather, which suggests that maturation can be accelerated by

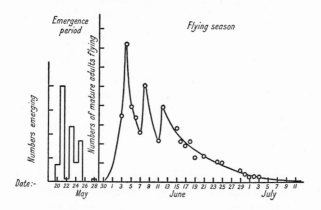

Fig. 23. The relationship between daily emergence and daily numbers of mature adults in a population of *P. nymphula*. The three emergence peaks are followed by three groups of adults arriving at the population by the pond. The interval of about fifteen days which separates corresponding peaks of emergence and adult arrival represents the maturation period and is spent away from water.

higher temperature or longer feeding time, but in Britain it is probably never less than a week. In the very warm spring of 1952, some *Pyrrhosoma* adults were mature only nine days after emergence, whereas two weeks is a more usual maturation period for this species. The maturation period can be said to have ended when sexually-mature dragonflies return to water.

The reproductive period represents the time when adults exhibit sexual behaviour over water. Because adult dragonflies are most often noticed when they are over water, this period is probably broadly equivalent to the much-used term "flying season." The latter may be usefully defined as the period elapsing between the arrival of the first mature adult at the aquatic habitat and the disappearance of the last.

D—H

One of the first indications of the return to water in the Emperor Dragonfly is provided by males making flights of a few minutes' duration over the pond. It is typical for such males to stray from their feeding beats nearby, to fly to and fro over the water for a minute or two, and then to return to their previous positions. This behaviour begins about a week after emergence, by which time males have assumed the mature coloration. It is not until nine to fourteen days after emergence that they begin to remain over water for any length of time. About two or three days after arrival of the first sexually-mature males, females return to the water to oviposit. This earlier return of the males is brought about by their more rapid maturation and not by their earlier emergence.

A subject which is discussed further in Chapter 10 is the significance of the maturation period as a dispersal stage, and in this connection it is interesting to note that a dragonfly ectoparasite, the water-mite *Arrenhurus,* has a larval stage which is carried from the water on emerging dragonflies, develops on them during the maturation period, and is then in a suitable condition to drop off again into the water when they begin the reproductive period. In the life-history of this water-mite (described by Münchberg in 1935) the maturation period of the dragonfly seems to have been utilised for achieving dispersal from one aquatic habitat to another. One such mite can often be found on immature adults of *Pyrrhosoma* in Britain (and also on other Coenagriidae), and some populations may show an eighty to a hundred per cent infestation. On account of the habit these mites have of dropping off as soon as adults return to the water, the presence or absence of mites on a freshly-caught dragonfly can be used to estimate its age. In a heavily-infested population, an adult without mites is very likely to be more than two weeks old, since it will already have completed the maturation period.

The length of the reproductive period is clearly of the greatest significance biologically, for this is the only time that mating and oviposition can take place. Nevertheless, surprisingly little is known about the length of life of adult dragonflies under natural conditions. Several writers have given values for longevity, but these have seldom been based on reliable evidence.

At present the only reliable way of obtaining an estimate of adult longevity is to mark members of a wild population with date-specific marks, and then release them to be recaught on subsequent occasions (see Appendix IV, p. 236). If used carefully, this technique can also

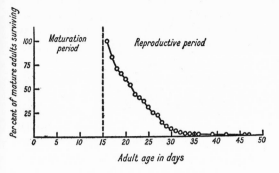

Fig. 24. Survival curve for mature adults of *P. nymphula*. Although certain individuals may live as long as forty-seven days after emergence, more than half the males have died within seven days of becoming sexually mature.

provide information on the total size of the population and on the emergence, death and movement of its members. The development of analytical methods whereby such information can be calculated is due largely to the work of Fisher, Ford and Jackson, whose papers should be consulted before studies of this kind are undertaken. To employ capture-recapture methods it is usually necessary that the population studied be closed and isolated, and that fairly large samples be obtained. This means that Anisoptera are not particularly amenable to study by such methods, and that most detailed information of this nature must necessarily be derived from species of Zygoptera. Apart from factors relating to dispersal and migration, however, it is unlikely that the two groups show differences of a significant nature in this respect.

So far only one species has been studied in detail in this way. This is the spring-emerging dragonfly, *Pyrrhosoma*. In this case, for various reasons, only mature adults were sampled, and therefore results applied only to those adults which had already survived the maturation period (Fig. 23, p. 101). Although the maximum life-span was quite high, being about seven weeks after emergence, the expectation of life was less than half this, and 50 per cent of adults which survived the maturation period had died within a week of becoming sexually mature (Fig. 24, above).

For 50 per cent of the annual reproduction to have to occur within a week, with a further possible reduction of flying time due to bad weather, seems to leave very little margin for error. But it must be remembered that *Pyrrhosoma* is one of those species which, like *Anax*, has an efficiently synchronised emergence resulting from a diapause in the final instar. It can now be seen that a short adult life and a synchronised emergence are probably associated ecological features.

In those species in which most individuals emerge at the beginning of the emergence period, it is clear that the maximum life-span will amount to a relatively high proportion of the flying season, most of the population being of the same age. Actually, in *Pyrrhosoma*, the ratio

$$\frac{\text{flying season}}{\text{post-maturation maximum life-span}}$$

is about 1·6. This ratio can be used to obtain a rough estimate of longevity in other dragonflies with a similar ecology, and for which the emergence curve and flying season are known. Substituting in *Anax*, we obtain values of eight and a half weeks for maximum life-span and four weeks for average expectation of life at emergence. These estimates include the maturation period, and apply only to adults surviving it. Making allowance for their size, and the time of year in which they fly, it is probable that most species with an emergence curve of the *Anax-Pyrrhosoma* type live for comparable periods.

Those species, on the other hand, which do not have a synchronised emergence may be expected to live longer. Emergence being temporarily dispersed, this will be necessary in order to realise the reproductive potentialities of the populations. The few observations that exist tend to support this idea, but much further work is needed before it can be considered proven. A male of *L. sponsa* has been caught at least sixty-nine days after emergence, which suggests a long maximum life-span when compared with the values of forty-six and fifty days obtained at the same habitat for *Pyrrhosoma*.

In the past, the flying season for a single species has sometimes been used to give a direct estimate of its longevity. On two counts alone, this practice is unjustified. Firstly, values given for flying seasons commonly include several populations which may be emerging at different times. Secondly, as we have just seen, the degree to which emergence is synchronised varies, and this can be expected to have a marked effect on longevity. However, it seems generally true that species with a well-synchronised emergence have a shorter flying season than other dragonflies, and also a shorter life-span. Thus, there appears to be a correlation between length of flying season and length of life. But we must remember that the relationship is far from being a direct one.

We cannot leave the subject of longevity without mentioning a small species of Zygoptera, *Sympecma fusca* (Van der Lind.), studied by

a. Libellula quadrimaculata, Male. Mature, and a very heavily marked specimen. Often there is less colour at the wing-tips and along the costa, but the black on the lower wing-base is always present. Female very similar.

b. Libellula depressa, male. Mature and already the abdomen covered with blue pruinescence. The yellow spots laterally along the abdomen, are the last to become obscured. The black bases to all four wings are always present, and they are a distinguishing character from *O. cancellatum*.

Plate 17. DRAGONFLIES (ANISOPTERA : LIBELLULIDAE)

a. Libellula fulva, male. Immature and similar to the female. The males usually have clear wing-tips, but sometimes they are smoky-brown, as in the female. The dark wing-bases are always present. The bright fulvous colour is distinct from the slate-brown *L. quadrimaculata*, and the black dorsally on the lower abdomen, is distinct from *L. depressa*.

b. Libellula fulva, male. Fully mature and blue, but still showing black on the abdomen tip.

Plate 18. DRAGONFLIES (ANISOPTERA : LIBELLULIDAE)

Geijskes in Holland. In *Sympecma fusca*, which is a close relative of *Lestes*, the adult is the diapause stage and overwinters. Adults become active in spring, and it is only then that the reproductive period begins. The eggs are laid shortly afterwards and then the rest of the life-history proceeds without interruption. Then, when the adults emerge in late summer, they embark upon diapause, and spend the winter amongst vegetation near the ground. Thus, in *Sympecma,* although the reproductive period is probably quite short, the total adult life must extend for at least six months.

To sum up, it may be said that most dragonflies spend the first two weeks of adult life away from water attaining sexual maturity. Those surviving the maturation period return to water, after which Zygoptera may expect to live a further one or two weeks and Anisoptera a further two or three weeks, although the maximum life-spans of the two groups are probably about eight and ten weeks at least. Whatever the exact periods may be, the adult life represents only a very short part of the total life-history in most British dragonflies.

Having discussed the framework of the adult life, we can now pass on to a consideration of the most significant part of it—sexual behaviour.

CHAPTER 9

THE BEHAVIOUR OF
THE ADULT DRAGONFLY
(N.W.M.)

At first sight fighting may seem to be exactly the opposite of co-operation; it is antagonism. Yet, as I hope to show, fighting between animals of the same species, although not of use to the individuals, is highly useful to the species, however paradoxical this may sound.

N. TINBERGEN (1953) *Social Behaviour in Animals*

DAILY LIFE

THE STUDY of behaviour resembles the study of anatomy. Whether a part be a bone or an instinctive action, we cannot understand it unless we take the whole animal into account.

In this chapter we will consider all that an adult dragonfly does and then describe how and why it does some of these things. Reproduction is the main theme of a dragonfly's adult life, but we shall see that only a small fraction of this time is actually spent in mating or laying eggs.

Let us take one individual dragonfly and describe how it spent its day and then discuss to what extent it is typical. The insect was a male *Libellula quadrimaculata*—a large brown darter dragonfly with splashes of dark colour on its wings (see Plate 17, p. 104). It was late in the afternoon of 29 June 1952, that I first saw it. It was perched on a water plant by the edge of a little river in the Somerset moors—fens they would be called in East Anglia. (See Plate VIIa, p. 132). Earlier in the day I had watched many of its species perching and beating up and down the stream, but now most had disappeared and so had most of the *Brachytron* and *Anax* and *O. cancellatum* which also occurred on the stream. Occasionally it flew at a passing fly which it did not always succeed in catching. Most of the time it perched motionless half way down the plant. It held on with its second and third legs. The front ones were flexed and held just behind the eyes. Suddenly at twenty one minutes past ⸴ 'G.M.T.) it flew rapidly away and perched on a tuft of rushes in the water meadow which bordered the stream. Then it got up again and perched on another rush, this time 130 yards from the water. It held on to the head of the rush which bent slightly under its weight. It was about 2 feet from the ground but only about 12 inches from the surrounding grass. The fore-wings were held slightly forward and the hind-wings were depressed. The axis of its body was at right angles to the sun. Some minutes later a small beetle climbed up the rush and disturbed the dragonfly, which changed its position so that its back was towards the sun. About an hour later it returned to its original position and remained there until 9.20 p.m. (G.M.T.). As it appeared to have gone to sleep at 9.20, I decided to follow suit in my sleeping bag a few yards away. I woke up at 4.45 the following morning. In the dim light I could see the dragonfly. It had moved to another rush in the night. It had probably been disturbed by the cattle which had also spent the night in the field—I found a cow's hoof print near the dragonfly.

During the day the abdomen of a *L. quadrimaculata* is held at an angle to the vertical but now it hung vertically like that of a perching *Aeshna*. I saw no movements until 7.47 when it moved its head. At 8.26 it cleaned its eyes and antennae with its fore-legs. Nearly half an hour later it flew and caught a fly. It made many sorties after that, each time returning to its perch. At 9.35 it bent its abdomen downwards and forwards and sperm was transferred to the accessory genitalia near the base of the abdomen. At 10.20 it flew back to the stream to a spot near where I had first seen it in the evening. Other males of its species were already at their positions on the river, and since I had not marked the one I had been watching I lost him. I have watched many of his kind during the day and from these observations can describe what would have happened later: on his arrival at the water he flies low over it and dips the tip of his abdomen on its surface. The function of this act is not known but it may be a method of testing by which the sight of water is confirmed by another sense organ. Soon he is pursued by another male of his own or of another species which has already arrived. In his turn he chases other males. During the morning much of his time is spent in flight chasing males, females, and prey, in fact anything that he sees move near him—even thistledown blown by the wind and cabbage white butterflies. Sometimes he is disturbed by a cow coming to drink at the stream but soon returns to a perch, often the same one again and again. While perched he is not motionless. His head is moved to look at a Yellow Wagtail flying over him. His enormous eyes are cleaned frequently. Sometimes one eye is cleaned by the leg on its own side and then the other eye by the other leg. But sometimes both eyes are cleaned simultaneously, the head either remaining fixed or moving against the leg. These movements always remind me of a cat washing herself. Occasionally the antennae are cleaned by moving them through the crook made between the tarsal and tibial parts of the fore-legs, and sometimes the frons is cleaned too.

The food of *L. quadrimaculata* mainly consists of small insects (gnats, small beetles, etc.). They are usually eaten in flight but often part of the prey is eaten while the dragonfly is perched. Then one can hear the mandibles crunching the chitinous exoskeleton of the prey and see it being turned round by the mouth parts and the wings floating down to the stream discarded.

Most of the warmer part of the day is spent perching and feeding and chasing males by the stream, but occasionally a female appears. At once a male flies at her, with extraordinary precision he grasps the back of her head with his anal appendages, and the mating position is assumed in flight. In about 3 seconds the whole process is over—the female laying her eggs and the male hovering over her. He makes no further attempt to mate while she is laying eggs, but pursues other dragonflies which approach him. However, as soon as she begins to fly away from the river, he makes pursuit of her and attempts to mate again, but usually does not succeed.

His encounters with male dragonflies are far more frequent; generally these are no more than confused chases—first one and then the other in pursuit—but sometimes they result in noisy clashes; occasionally both insects tumble into the water. Severe injuries may result from these clashes (See Plate VIII*b*, p. 133). Sometimes the male is seen to attempt to mate with the other male.

During the afternoon fewer and fewer flights are made and most of these are after food, not dragonflies. Then some time during the late afternoon the male flies away from water, sometimes straight to roost but often to feed in a sheltered place still warmed by the sinking sun.

In fine weather this pattern of behaviour is repeated day after day—that is the warm part of the day is spent feeding and in sexual activity by water, the rest of the 24 hours resting or feeding away from water (see Fig. 25, p. 109). But bad weather completely changes this daily rhythm. If it is cold and wet, the male *L. quadrimaculata* does not fly at all—it remains suspended on a plant. The only visible

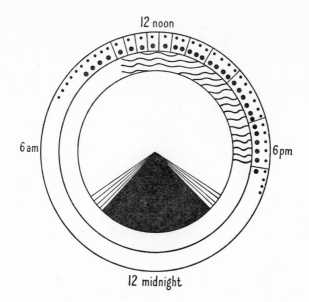

Fig. 25. The pattern of activity of a male *L. quadrimaculata* during a fine midsummer day. This pattern is typical of the males of most other British species.
Inner ring: day—white, night—black.
Middle ring: time spent away from water—white, time spent by water—wavy lines.
Outer ring: time spent perched and motionless—white.

        slight activity while perched (cleaning eyes, etc.)—small dots.
        Hunting—large dots.
        Reproductive behaviour (mating, territorial fighting, etc.)—black lines.

movements are respiratory movements in the abdomen and sometimes when a raindrop falls on the head it is removed by the fore-legs. Shortly after the sun comes out (unless it is late in the day) the dragonfly flies to water as in the morning of a fine day. It must be warmth rather than sunlight alone which determines whether a male dragonfly goes to water or not; because on fine days when the wind is cold, dragonflies seek out the warm sheltered places in the lee of hedges and wood and feed there but do not fly to water.

The main difference between the daily behaviour of the female and the male *L. quadrimaculata* is that even when it is fine the female spends a very small part of the day by water—only a few minutes. She practically never feeds by the water. As soon as she appears a male seizes her, mating occurs, and then she lays her eggs by hovering over

Fig. 26. Female *A. imperator* not ready to mate.
"Oviposition" posture adopted in flight when pursued
by male. It usually prevents male seizing female.

the water and dipping the tip of her abdomen into the water and so
washing away the eggs. The male with whom she has mated usually
hovers over her and dashes at other males which approach. When she
flies away the original mate or another male often attempts to mate with
her. Occasionally she allows another mating but usually she escapes
by flying from the pond. Sometimes dragonflies indicate an unwilling-
ness to mate by bending the end part of the abdomen downwards as if
laying eggs. I have only once seen this performed by a female of *L.
quadrimaculata*. Similar behaviour in *Anax* can often be observed
(see Fig. 26, above). By marking individual dragonflies one can
show that females, like males, may mate several times in one day.
M. E. Jacobs has recorded that a marked male of the American
species *Perithemis tenera* (Say) mated 127 times in six days. Not all
oviposition takes place immediately after mating. Often a female
appears unobtrusively at the stream's edge and lays her eggs alone. If
a male does see her he rarely attempts to mate with her while she hovers
but will do so once she flies on.

Sometimes the female arrives at a pond at which no male is present.
She then advertises her presence by flying over the water. In some
species the method of flight is unlike the usual direct flight; the
S. striolatum females fly up and down in a dipping manner. This
certainly makes them more conspicuous to the human observer
and probably does so to the male dragonfly. Female invitations to mate
are rarely seen under normal circumstances because any female
approaching the water is usually seized at once by the nearest male.
It can be induced at small ponds by catching all the males present.
No special female courtship flight has been observed in *L. quadrimaculata*.

Most of the day of a female dragonfly is spent resting and feeding away from water. But whereas each male usually patrols one small area of water, often not more than 10 yards of stream, the female ranges over a much wider area of country.

How typical is the daily behaviour of *L. quadrimaculata*? All the other British Libellulines behave in much the same way. But there are minor differences. The two *Orthetrum* species spend much more time perched on the ground than does *L. quadrimaculata* and so to a slightly lesser extent do the *Sympetrum* species. The mating time of *L. quadrimaculata* is exceptionally short; in *O. cancellatum* it may last up to 5 minutes. In *S. striolatum* (see Fig. 2, p. 9) the period is several minutes but on one occasion it took 24. In this species the pair perches while mating. In the *Sympetrum* species the males often participate in egg-laying. The *Sympetrum* male does not release the female's head after mating but flies with the female in tandem to a suitable oviposition site. The male hovers above the water and the end of the abdomen of the female dips again and again on to the surface thereby releasing eggs. It is not obvious whether the female moves her own abdomen downwards or remains still while the male swings her up and down. The problem has been solved experimentally: if a dead female is attached to a cotton thread tied to a stick (like a bait on a fishing line) and is moved about near a male, the male will usually attempt to hold the dead female in the tandem position. Then it will attempt to mate. Having failed to do so it will usually release its hold of the dead female and fly away, but occasionally it will take her to an oviposition site, and the normal motions of egg laying will then be made. It is clear therefore, since the female is dead, that it is the movements of the male which make the female's abdomen dip up and down. However at other times a female may return to the water and lay eggs unaccompanied by the male: on these occasions the oviposition movements are her own. So both sexes make oviposition movements but under different circumstances. Incidentally, the experiment referred to above shows that since oviposition movements of the male can occur without being preceded by mating, the whole behaviour mechanism is not a rigid chain reaction.

The daily life of *Anax*, *Brachytron* and *Cordulia* is not unlike that of the Libellulines. But the males of the genus *Aeshna* often leave the water during the warm part of the day and hunt in the surrounding country. All the Aeshnines spend much less time perched and may remain airborne for very long stretches of time. Mating takes much longer—and the insects perch the while away from water. Egg-laying may take a long time too. I watched one female *A. cyanea* in Somerset lay eggs for 48 consecutive minutes. Unlike the Libelluline the female *Aeshna* perches while laying her eggs and either inserts the eggs into aquatic plants, floating wood etc., or as in the case of *A. cyanea* lays on soil and moss on the banks of streams and ponds.

In some species of Anisoptera the male spends very little time by water. *Gomphus* is in this category. In others, for example the American Corduline *Macromia magnifica* McLachlan, the visits to water do not occur in the hottest part of the day. In this species the males are by water from 7 to 10 a.m.

The salient features of the behaviour of most British Anisoptera are the pronounced daily migration to and from water and an apparent absence of male courtship behaviour before mating. I say "apparent" because the movement may exist but be too quick to see with the naked eye. This problem could be solved fairly easily by taking ciné-photographs. (Dragonflies are ideal subjects for photography and much else could be learned by filming them.) Courtship behaviour does occur in many foreign species. One of my most treasured memories of a short visit paid to West Africa some years ago is of the dance of the males of the little Libelluline *Palpopleura lucia* (Drury). They were over a stream which flowed through the forest by the edge of the River Gambia. They fluttered in and out of an intricate pattern of brilliant light and deep shade. Spots of sun on golden brown water and on the dark blue wing markings of the dragonflies made regular patterns which varied continually like chips of glass in a kaleidoscope. Male courtship dances are not confined to the dragonflies with coloured wings. Also in the Gambia, I watched a male and female of the sombrely coloured *Olpogastra lugubris* Karsch flying in a continuous figure of eight low over a shaded creek. Suddenly they shot vertically upwards and disappeared into the sky.

The daily behaviour of damselflies (Zygoptera) is similar to that of the larger dragonflies (Anisoptera), but as is to be expected everything is on a smaller scale. The migration to and from water can usually be measured in inches rather than yards—from the rushes and grass near the shore to the rushes growing submerged on the edge of the open water. Although female damselflies spend less time by water than do males, they are more frequently to be seen feeding and resting by the water's edge than are the females of the larger dragonflies.

Compared to most Anisoptera the Zygoptera are weak flyers and

a. *Libellula fulva,* female. Mature, and the typically coloured wing-tips, clearly seen.

b. *Libellula depressa,* female. Fully mature, and browner than the young female. The yellow laterally, on the abdomen, and the dark wing-bases, with otherwise clear wings, are always present. Note the great width of the abdomen in comparison with *L. fulva* above.

Plate 19. DRAGONFLIES (ANISOPTERA : LIBELLULIDAE)

a. *Leucorrhinia dubia*, female. Mature, and orange-spotted. In young specimens the spots are yellow. The black and yellow wing-bases are pronounced. Young males are like the female.

b. *Leucorrhinia dubia*, male. Mature, and spots and thoracic stripes are crimson-red. The white face, and the very square pterostigma, can be clearly seen. Distinct from *Symp-etrum danae* by the black wing-bases, and yellow or red spotting on the abdomen.

Plate 20. DRAGONFLIES (ANISOPTERA : LIBELLULIDAE)

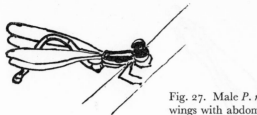

Fig. 27. Male *P. nymphula* "cleaning" wings with abdomen.

spend much more time perched. Perhaps because of this their toilet is more complicated and more frequently performed. Not only do they clean their eyes and face with their fore-legs, but they also rub their fore-legs together afterwards as does a housefly. They also clean the end of the abdomen with their hind-legs (Aeshnines also do this), and afterwards rub the hind-legs against each other. C. Buchholtz has watched a female *Agrion splendens* clean her ovipositor on a blade of grass. Whereas an Anisopteran cannot clean its wings, those of a damselfly fold together above its back and so can be reached by the long flexible abdomen. Damselflies can often be seen lifting the abdomen upwards and dividing the wings from each other (see Fig. 27). By this means damselflies probably prevent their wings— which as we have seen act separately—from becoming stuck together by gossamer.

The reproductive behaviour of the British species of damselflies appears to follow the same general plan in all species. The male takes the female either in flight (as in *Platycnemis* and as we have seen in most Anisoptera) or perched (as in *Agrion*): he then grasps the top of the first thoracic segment (not the head as in Anisoptera) with his anal claspers. After a short flight in tandem the male perches; then he fills his accessory genitalia with sperm (this action has been observed by Wesenburg-Lund to occur in some Anisoptera at the same juncture— again cine-films would show how often this action takes place at this moment). Then the male repeatedly touches the female's head with his accessory genitalia, and then both male and female bend their abdomens and adopt the mating position. After copulation, which is aided by vigorous bending movements of the abdomens of male and female and which lasts several minutes, the pair fly in tandem to the egg-laying site. In the family Coenagriidae to which most of the British species belong, the female inserts eggs into the water plants with

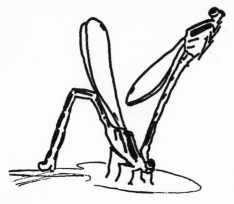

Fig. 28. Pair of *C. puella* ovipositing in tandem. Male on the right.

her ovipositor; the male usually remains attached but inert; his legs are held close to the body and are not in contact with the ground. (See Fig. 28, above). At other times (see chapter 5, p. 57), when underwater oviposition occurs, the male holds on to the waterplant. Females also lay eggs unattended by males.

In all Coenagriidae studied, both male and female have a threat display: the wings are slightly opened and then closed again (see Fig. 29, p. 115). This apparently indicates that the individual is not in mating condition; though in males of some species it may also be an invitation to mate, as it is in *Agrion* (see below). Males of *Agrion* often attack other males.

Both *Agrion* species and *Platycnemis* have courtship displays. In *A. splendens* the male reacts to the presence of a passing female by bending the abdomen upwards and spreading his wings; the female lands near him and then the male performs an aerial fluttering dance backwards and forwards in front and behind this female—he faces her throughout. Then suddenly he lands on the female and the procedure is as described above. The female does not lay her eggs in tandem. Sometimes the eggs are laid on the surface, at other times the female goes under the water to lay her eggs. In *Platycnemis* the prominent white legs of the male are dangled before the female in display.

EXPERIMENTAL STUDIES

So far we have been dealing mainly with what can be discovered by simple observation. Now we shall consider mechanism; this can only be analysed by experiment. Considering the immense complexity

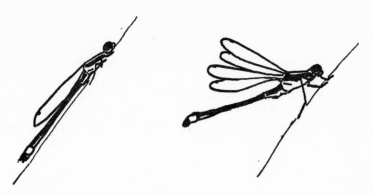

Fig. 29. "Threat display" of *I. elegans* (see p. 114). Insect on left in resting position. Insect on right showing threat display when approached by another male. The conspicuous bright blue abdominal segment (8th) is raised and the wings half opened.

of the brains of insects and other higher animals, it is amazing that so much can be learned about their behaviour by simple analytical experiments. Recent advances in this field are largely due to the ideas and experiments of K. Lorenz and N. Tinbergen and their followers. Of course in no single instance can we yet describe the whole process: that stimulus A stimulates sense organ B, messages are sent down nerve C to part D of the brain where E etc. occurs—messages are sent down nerves F etc. to muscles G, with the result that the animal performs action H. Very little is known about any animal brain. It is as if we were confronted with a motor car for the first time and by many experiments and observations we had discovered and recorded what happened when the ignition key was turned, the brake taken off, and the air let out of the tyres, but had no conception of the working of the internal combustion engine. By following the pipes from petrol tank to carburettor and some of the wires from battery to distributor, we had seen that petrol and electrical currents were essential parts of the process, but until we had mastered the theory of the petrol engine, the exact functions of the parts we had studied would remain obscure.

One of the most important ethological questions is—is the action instinctive?—in other words, is it inherited by all members of the species in the same way that characteristics of body shape and colour and development are inherited, or is it learned by the individual during the course of its life-time? In man so much is learned and so little is instinctive that one of the most dangerous forms of anthropomorphism is to assume that animals do things the same way. They do not. One of the main lessons derived from modern ethological work is that no assumptions can be made about any reaction: some birds learn their song; in others the song is as much inherited as their plumage. One animal may learn to recognise its mate, another may react instinctively to one feature of its mate, and if these are obscured will not react to its mate as if it were its mate. Whether an action is instinctive or learned can only be answered for absolute certainty by rearing the animal in isolation and watching its reactions to the stimulus when it meets it for the first time. But repeated observations can often provide the information for making a very good guess.

There is of course an innate element in all learning processes. What an animal can learn, the stage of development when it can learn it, and the speed with which it learns, are all more or less decided by the structure of the nervous system. The relationship between learning and instinct is one of the most interesting in the realm of behaviour.

As a first step to understanding the mechanism of an instinct we must ask: what is the exact nature of the stimulus which produces the response? In some instances the stimulus is extremely simple, for example, N. Tinbergen (1951) has shown that the red belly and zig-zag movement of the male Stickleback in spring, are the only, or much the most important stimuli which produce fighting in other male sticklebacks. In others it is more complicated—the sexual pursuit of the Grayling Butterfly results in a stimulus with 3 main elements—darkness+fluttering flight+nearness. As far as this reaction was concerned colour, scent etc. were ignored, that is did not act as a stimulus. In many species of animals signals have been evolved to which other members of the species react instinctively, *e.g.* the red belly of the male Stickleback. These sign stimuli are called *Releasers*. The nature of releasers is investigated by making models and recording the reactions of the animal to them. By elimination of inessential features a model is designed which contains only those which are essential to produce the normal response.

Dragonflies provide wonderful opportunities for experimental behaviour studies but so little has been done that practically all of it can be mentioned in the following paragraphs. Christiane Buchholtz has investigated the releasers which evoke the reproductive behaviour of *Agrion splendens* and the closely related species occurring in Asia Minor, and of *Platycnemis pennipes*. D. St. Quentin, M. E. Jacobs, and the writer have investigated the aggressive and sexual behaviour of

a. Larvae of *Anax Imperator* clustered on an emergence support soon after leaving the water at the Fish Pond, at about 2200 B.S.T., on 26 May, 1953. The first larva to climb the support has itself been used as a support by the next one, and so on. Only the outside larva shown here will be able to complete emergence satisfactorily. Between one and two per cent of the total population emerging died at the Fish Pond in 1952 and 1953 due to overcrowding of this sort. (*S. Beaufoy*)

b. Final instar exuvia on grass stems after emergence. When slender supports such as *Glyceria* are used, often several stems are drawn together and used as one. (*S. Beaufoy*)

Plate V

various Anisoptera species, and H. Steiner the sign stimuli of oviposition in *Leucorrhinia dubia*.

C. Buchholtz (1951) presented various dummies of different shapes
and colours to males of *A. splendens* in order to discover what stimuli
evoked the courtship dance. She found four simultaneous stimuli were
necessary to produce the response: movement, size, colour and wing
transparency. Motionless females or dummies were ignored. So were
objects whose dimensions were more or less than 3·9 × 1·8 cm. and
2·3 × 0·9 cm. respectively. Objects of the right size were not courted
unless they were yellow green or greenish blue and were so transparent
that 60–80 per cent of the light penetrated them. She found that the
shape of the wing made no difference—males courted a wide variety
of shapes so long as they were the right size, colour, transparency and
showed movement. Only one "wing" was necessary, and models with
red and yellow wings—so long as one wing had the right characters—
were courted.

C. Buchholtz (1956) has also investigated the behaviour of *P.
pennipes*. In this species the releasers which cause courtship by the
male are:—

1. To and fro movement.
2. Greenish brown or greenish yellow colour.
3. Form and size of head.
4. Alternating dark and light green stripes on the thorax.

Models consisting of head, thorax, and one wing only were sufficient to
produce a response of the male. The grasping movement of the male by
which he holds the female's prothorax is released by the pattern on the
prothorax. Work of this kind not only makes sense of the behaviour of
dragonflies but it also shows the significance of some of those curious
colour patterns found on their bodies and wings. Where these differ
in closely related species, there is a strong likelihood that they act as

---

Plate VI. a. Left. Anax imperator at the Fish Pond. Divided emergence in progress on
an oak tree, 9–10 a.m. G.M.T., 8 June, 1951. Note the lack of synchronisation of the
emergence stages and also the presence of untenanted exuviae left by individuals
which had emerged the previous night. (*P. S. Corbet*)

b. Right. Immature adult *Anax imperator*, fifteen hours old, in position of first rest after
the maiden flight; this is about a hundred metres from the pond. 30 May, 1953.
(*P. S. Corbet*)

D—I

releasers. In the higher animals striking colour patterns of fur, plumage or cuticle are rarely fortuitous.

Many dragonfly species are confined to special habitats. This must mean that either the larvae are unable to live in other habitats because of physiological limitations, or because of competition, or because the suitable habitat is actively sought out by the egg laying female or because of a combination of these factors. H. Steiner (1948) has investigated this problem in *Leucorrhinia dubia,* a dragonfly of acid moorland as we have seen. By placing out artificial ponds of black paper surrounded by white paper, he attracted females of *Leucorrhinia* which flew by. When they arrived they dropped down to the surface of the "pond" and then flew away. He interpreted their behaviour in this way. Dark areas surrounded by a light area are perceived visually and act as a directing stimulus towards them. If on arrival they receive the necessary olfactory stimulus from their antennae, they oviposit in the dark area. The pools in which *Leucorrhinia* breeds are black peaty pools, these are usually surrounded by Sphagnum moss which in the summer dies out and bleaches in the sun. Steiner found that *Leucorrhinia* larvae could thrive in an aquarium if provided with less acid water; in this species distribution probably results from habitat selection plus competition.

TERRITORIAL BEHAVIOUR

Anyone who has sat by a river or a pond on a fine day in summer and watched the dragonflies by it, must have been struck by the way the males return again and again to the same place. Whether they spend most of the time perched or go beating up and down the water, their activities mostly occur within a stretch of a few yards. The number of fights between males also appears to be very great. An ornithologist may spend hours watching a male bird without seeing it fight another male of its own species, and an even longer time before he sees a fight between males of different species; but the dragonfly watcher will be very unlucky if he does not see a dragonfly fight another dragonfly within a few minutes of his arrival at a pond.

Many mammals, birds, reptiles and some fish, are known to be territorial. That is the male, and sometimes the female, defends some particular area which is important to it. Sometimes it is a small area round the nest, sometimes a large tract of country in which it feeds. It is often extremely difficult to be sure what is the function of territorial behaviour, but in many cases it almost certainly prevents disturbance of reproductive activities, and in others ensures a private food supply; in most it causes dispersal. Several arthropods—fiddler crabs and some beetles for example—have been shown to have territories. It certainly looks as if dragonflies have them too.

Territorial behaviour is very interesting to the ecologist as well as the behaviourist, for, as a result of localised fighting the population becomes dispersed: in other words a low population density may not indicate that the species is rare and could be commoner, but merely that a behaviour mechanism prevents it from being more abundant.

It was territorial behaviour that inspired a naturalist to carry out some of the first field experiments on dragonflies. In 1931, D. St. Quentin (1934) began his observations on dragonfly territory in the Carpathians. He noted that male dragonflies of many species were found in limited areas by water and these chased and fought with males of their own and other species of Anisoptera. Most species do not fight when they are away from water. But St. Quentin observed that males of *Somatochlora flavomaculata* (Van der Lind.) and *Aeshna grandis* were exceptional in that they defended their beats (or "territories") away from water.

In order to discover if the same dragonfly returned each day to the same territory St. Quentin marked 30 *Somatochlora metallica* and *Aeshna cyanea*. In only one case did he find an insect returning to the same place three days running. He never saw the other 29 again. He marked his insects by attaching a small bit of white cotton to the insect and by cutting out a small bit of the middle of the wing with scissors. His lack of recoveries may have been due to his methods. He also made the experiment of catching every *A. cyanea* that appeared at a small pond for 11 days. By the afternoon of most days a new male had appeared and begun patrolling the pond. When he let go a captured dragonfly by the pond the "owner" always drove out the introduced insect. He then recorded the reactions of males to dead dragonflies suspended on a fine thread tied to a stick, and moved about in their territories and noticed that they always flew up to the dead insects and sometimes attacked them.

St. Quentin assumed that dragonfly territory was a hunting territory; that it had feeding not reproductive significance.

A. grandis, one of the most impressive insects found in Britain, is a common species. It would repay a much closer study than it has so far received. Unlike most species the male spends much less time

by water than does the female. On 28 July 1947 I was walking beside
a ditch near Oulton Broad late in the evening and was amazed to see
seven *A. grandis* flying up and down the ditch one behind the other.
The behaviour appeared to be social but I observed no clue of its
significance, nor have I seen it since.

In 1948 I received a grant from Trinity College, Cambridge, to
study dragonflies in the Gambia. The Gambian dragonfly fauna is
richer in species than the British and the variety of behaviour patterns
found in it is much greater. The males of the Libelluline *Tholymis
tillarga* (Fabricius) were strikingly territorial. They beat up and
down a narrow stretch of flood water and vigorously attacked other
males that appeared near them. The curious white spot on the wing
appeared to be used for threat display, like the red breast of a Robin.
Observations on them convinced me of the particular interest of
dragonfly territorial behaviour and I became determined to study
territory in dragonflies on my return to Britain, and accordingly the
next year I started a study of the dragonflies of a little stream (see
Plate VIIa, p. 132.) and a small pond near Bristol, where I was then
working (Moore, 1952, 1953).

When I began my study I believed that all British dragonflies
like *Tholymis tillarga* were territorial; my aims were to study the
exact nature of their territorial behaviour and to measure its ecological
effects. During the years 1949-1952, experimental areas were visited
at different times of the day and at different times of the year and in
different weathers. First I discovered that male dragonflies of the
species I studied (*Brachytron, Anax, L. quadrimaculata, L. depressa, O.
cancellatum,* and *S. striolatum*) were most abundant by water at noon
on fine days. The records showed that, except on one occasion,
there were never more than 91 males on the half mile stretch of water
I was investigating; usually there were less than 70. On the pond
(circumference *c.* 320 yards) there were never more than 22 males.
I divided the stream's length into seven approximately equal parts.
The highest steady density of dragonfly males recorded in each part
was remarkably similar: expressed as male dragonflies per 100 yards
the figures were 14·9, 14·6, 13·0, 11·1, 10·0, 12·3, 11·0. Hundreds
of large larvae could be taken from this stretch of river, and large
numbers of teneral adults haunted the neighbouring water meadows,
hedges, and scrub. Food was super-abundant. It was clear that but
for the behaviour of the insects themselves, many more could have fed
and rested by the stream. Territorial behaviour not only caused

dispersal and prevented a large total population, but caused a remarkably even distribution along the stream.

Clashes occurred throughout the day but there were more clashes between males in the morning than in the afternoon. Frequently no changes in position resulted from the clashes. But it was obvious at other times that some insects avoided the scene of encounter. In some cases the beats were seen to be modified by the clashes. A remarkable instance of this occurred on 20 July 1951. 1951 had a late spring and as a result the flying period of the spring species was later than usual and coincided with those of the summer ones. (Fig. 37, p. 169). On this date I made my first count at 10.29 a.m. and recorded the exceptionally high figure of 91. On one stretch of stream density was 17·9 males over 100 yards of stream. This was easily the highest record ever obtained on the river. In all there were:—

> 5 *Anax imperator*
> 21 *Orthetrum cancellatum*
> 29 *Libellula quadrimaculata*
> 36 *Sympetrum striolatum*

At 12.09 I made the count again. The figures then were:—

> 7 *Anax imperator*
> 28 *Orthetrum cancellatum*
> 30 *Libellula quadrimaculata*
> 14 *Sympetrum striolatum*

The numbers of the larger species had all increased. But *S. striolatum* had been reduced to less than 40 per cent of their original number. There could be little doubt that many of the much smaller *S. striolatum* had been ousted by their larger and more powerful relations. These studies showed that there was both intraspecific and interspecific competition for space.

More recently I have investigated the problem experimentally in the small Zygopteran *Ceriagrion*. I made an artificial pond by sinking an enamel dish into the mud at the bottom of an old bomb crater (C on Plate VIIIa, p. 133) on one of the Dorset heaths. Each day I caught a varying number of males from a nearby bog pool and marked them distinctively with cellulose paint. I then released them by the pond. The following day I recorded the dragonflies present and added a further batch. The results observed are given on next page:—

Date	Number on first visit	Number added after first visit	Notes
7.7.55	0	5	Hot and water in pool
8.7.55	2	5	unless otherwise stated
9.7.55	4	5	
10.7.55	4 or 5	5	
11.7.55	4	5	
12.7.55	0	5	Water very low
13.7.55		No observations	
14.7.55		5	
15.7.55	5	5	
16.7.55	4	5	
17.7.55	2	10	
18.7.55		No observations	
19.7.55	4	4	Cloudy
20.7.55	7–8	10	Much cloud.　Cooler
21.7.55	12	5	Dull
22.7.55	4	3+5 Pyrrhosoma nymphula +10 Ischnura elegans	
23.7.55	2 (+1 Ischnura elegans)	5	
24.7.55		No observations	
25.7.55	3	11	
26.7.55	3	10	
27.7.55	5		
28.7.55	2	5	
29.7.55	1		

Those figures in the second column suggest that 4 or 5 was the maximum number of males which this pond, *i.e.* about 9 sq. ft. of water, surrounded by 3 clumps of rushes, could hold. It will be seen that abnormally high populations were found on 20th and 21st. The reason for this is almost certainly that the 19th and 20th were both cloudy days. As a result both the established insects and the ones which I released remained perched on the rush stems: in other words the bad weather prevented territorial behaviour and hence a consequent reduction of the number present by the pond. An analysis of the data and observations made after the introductions of males, showed, as St. Quentin had observed, that on the whole the established insects remained and the introduced ones left the water. But this may well have been due to my technique: however careful one is, an insect that has just been captured and marked is probably more likely to fare worse in an encounter with another male which has not been subjected to the same shocks. In nature the new arrivals are probably more successful. This was in fact shown to be the case in Philip Corbet's population study on the more robust species *Pyrrhosoma* (which he describes on page 103). The experiments on *Ceriagrion* described above were repeated in 1958 with the same results. Similar experiments and observations (also unpublished) on other species in Dorset have shown that each species has its own normal maximum density, which is not much affected by the presence of other species unless they are of similar size and appearance. Thus the pond figured on Plate VII*b* has been shown by observation and experiment to be able to support among other species, an adult male population of 1 *Anax*, 2 *L. quadrimaculata*, 6–11 *P. nymphula*, and 20–36 *Ceriagrion*. If densities of other ponds were compared they showed a similar ratio between species. In general the smaller the species the greater is its normal maximum density but it was interesting to note that species confined to acid water (*S. danae* and *Ceriagrion*) both showed consistently higher densities than other species of their size.

The behaviour which led to dispersal from the experimental pond was often observed. An established male would rush at the newcomer. Generally the attacked insect flew away but sometimes there was a struggle. In a number of instances the attacking male was seen to attempt to mate with the newcomer. This brings us to the difficult and not fully solved problem of what is the exact nature of the territorial behaviour of dragonflies.

In my studies on the Anisoptera in Somerset, I frequently observed males attempting to mate with other males of their own and other species, and also with females of other species. Sometimes the attempts resulted in the male achieving the tandem position. On two occasions I observed a male *S. striolatum* achieve the tandem position with a male which itself was in tandem with a female. I caught a male *Brachytron* in tandem with a female *L. quadrimaculata* and watched a male *A. cyanea* attempt coition with a female *S. striolatum*. By using St. Quentin's fishing line technique, I presented free male dragonflies with other dragonflies attached to cotton threads and recorded the results. I presented females and males of their own, and females and males of other species. As was to be expected males presented with a female of their own species attempted to mate with her in most cases. When males were presented the Aeshnines (*Brachytron*, *A. cyanea*, and *Anax*) immediately attempted to mate with them if they came in contact with them.   With the Libellulines (*L. quad-rimaculata, O. cancellatum, S. striolatum,* and *S. sanguineum*) one of two things occurred, either there was a confused clash or the male attempted to mate with the male on the string.   Clashes occurred about twice as often as attempts to mate.   Too few experiments with female insects of other species were done to produce significant results.   When male insects of other species were presented they were usually approached and then ignored, but when the insects came into contact there did appear to be a tendency for Aeshnines to attempt to mate and for Libellulines to clash.

At the time I thought that the clashes were abortive attempts to mate, and that males of the dragonfly species I had been studying attempted to mate with any other dragonfly, and therefore that the basis of territorial behaviour was sex rather than aggression. That is that the initial attack was an attempt to mate and fighting only occurred when the attacked male attempted to free itself. This being so dragonflies were not strictly territorial since they did not defend an area.

Further experimental studies on territory have been made by M. E. Jacobs in the two American Libellulines *Plathemis lydia* (Drury) and *Perithemis tenera* (Say) (Jacobs 1955). The results of his experiments show clearly that both these species (like *A. splendens*) are truly territorial.   The upper surface of the abdomen of *P. lydia* is blue brown or bluish white.   When one male sees another male it flies at it and facing it displays its abdomen by raising it upwards.   The white abdomen is only used for threat display to other males, when chasing females the abdomen is lowered.   When females whose abdomens had been painted white were offered to males, the males usually attempted to mate with them, in other words, the releaser of sexual behaviour was not the colour of the abdomen but some other character or characters and was stronger than the threat sign-stimulus.   When Jacobs collected out all the males from an experimental area, he noticed that females attacked other females arriving at the water.

The threat sign stimulus of *P. tenera* was its amber coloured wings which are displayed as the insects "dance" over the water.   In this species the male has a courtship display as well: he "dashes towards her and follows her while swaying from side to side. He then turns and flies slowly to the site while the female follows, or if she does not follow flies after her again. Upon reaching the site, the male hovers intensely on it while fluttering his wings and sometimes bending up his abdomen." The releaser again appears to consist partly of movement and partly of wing colour.

Thus some dragonflies of both the Anisoptera and the Zygoptera —notably those with a courtship display—show true territorial behaviour. They defend an area, however temporary the area may be. But, there appears to be rather fundamental differences in behaviour between males of *Brachytron, Anax, A. cyanea, A. juncea, L. quadrimaculata, L. depressa, S. striolatum, O. cancellatum,* on the one hand; and on the other, of that of the *Plathemis* and *Perithemis,* and *Agrion,* and probably *Tholymis.* In the American (or African) species and in *Agrion* the males show a definite aggressive display easily distinguishable from sexual behaviour.

The reaction of the males of the British Anisopteran species to other males is either an attempt to mate or a clash which appears to be an abortive attempt to mate but may be interpreted as aggression.

After many hours of observation, a few instances of probable aggression were recorded in British Anisoptera: in these cases the males flew at the undersides of the new arrivals—these could not be sexual movements since in sexual behaviour the male always seizes the female from the back.

The following hypothesis is put forward to account for the behaviour of the British Anisoptera.

All dragonflies possess both sexual and aggressive instincts. Under normal conditions a male reacts to a female sexually and a male aggressively. The dragonflies are essentially a tropical group, and the abnormal behaviour in Britain is correlated with the prevailing climate. Bad weather by preventing sexual activity causes an increase in the tendency to act sexually and so males react to stimuli which are suboptimal. Sex overcomes aggression in these circumstances. As a result male dragonflies often or usually act sexually to other male dragonflies, although they possess aggressive instincts which under better conditions would overcome the sexual instincts when confronted with a male. Attempts to mate with all and sundry might have selective advantages; it is conceivable that in Britain selective pressure is at work substituting sexual behaviour for aggressive. It is most interesting that in her recent work on very closely related species of *Agrion,* C. Buchholtz found that the intensity of several behaviour patterns of these species is correlated with climate. Also that within this group there exist 3 forms—those where the male remains in one territory, those in which the male changes territories, and those which show no territorial behaviour at all.

The immense complexity of the accessory genitalia of dragonflies suggests that for many millions of years the behaviour mechanisms which prevent interspecific crossing have been insufficient and so an anatomical barrier has been evolved as well. Far more work, particularly field work with a cine-camera will have to be done before this problem is finally resolved. It is hoped that this discussion will encourage others to study the sexual behaviour of dragonflies in the field.

Finally, we may speculate on the function of territorial behaviour in dragonflies. St. Quentin thought that dragonflies defended hunting territories. M. E. Jacobs believes that territorial behaviour prevents disturbance of courtship and egg laying. I have emphasised the dispersal value of territory.

If it is fine enough for male dragonflies to be present at water, hundreds of other insects—potential prey, are also present; it is unlikely that maintenance of an adequate food supply is the main function of dragonfly territories. On the other hand, their behaviour undoubtedly results in dispersal, particularly of the younger and older members of the population; also it probably does prevent disturbance of mating and oviposition in some species. (In others these problems are solved by mating occurring away from water and by the females laying eggs late in the day or in dull weather when few or no males are about).

Evolution, unlike a scientist, is not analytical. It is possible, even probable, that territorial behaviour has several functions, in other words that it has evolved as the result of several different biological pressures.

CHAPTER 10

DISPERSAL
(N.W.M.)

When we are studying any particular animal or community of animals, we are brought up, sooner or later, against questions connected with dispersal: with the movements of animals in search of food, of shelter, or of their mates. This movement, on a large or small scale, is characteristic of animal communities, as compared with plant communities, and it forms a very important part of the lives of wild animals.

C. ELTON (1927) *Animal Ecology*

EACH SPECIES of animal is adapted to a particular range of habitats. These are continually changing as a result of changes in climate, local catastrophes, or natural development. Therefore, if a species is to survive it must continually push outwards and colonise new breeding places before the old ones have become unsuitable. Dispersal is almost as necessary for animals as reproduction. It is particularly important for fresh water animals, since these—especially those that live in pools and lakes—live in a habitat which changes rapidly: pools and lakes become quickly silted up, open water changes to marsh and then to dry land. The question of overcrowding is of course intimately connected with dispersal. Overcrowding may result in starvation, epidemics of disease, and interference with reproduction. The biological advantage of not being overcrowded may be as important as the biological advantage of colonising new areas.

Eventually it may be possible to say what are the exact functions of dispersal behaviour in some animals, which is a shorthand way of saying—how did the dispersal behaviour of the animals arise in the course of evolution? We are very far from that stage with most animals, certainly with all dragonflies. The most useful approach is to try and answer simple questions about what happens: what causes an animal to disperse?, what decides its route once started?, what causes it to settle in a new area?, and how far does it travel? These questions all have both ecological and behaviour aspects: the subjects are of course inseparable. The mechanisms, by which dispersal is achieved, vary from the passive drifting on ocean currents by planktonic larvae to the purposive colonisations of man. The mechanism which is used will depend largely on the size of the animal and therefore is to some extent correlated with the stage in the life history in which it occurs. In some animals (*e.g.* most marine invertebrates) dispersal takes place in the immature or larval stage. Generally this means that the animal is very small and so its movements are passive. These animals can only control direction by waiting for favourable currents. In others, notably in the birds and insects, dispersal occurs mainly in the adult stage: flight is essentially an adaptation of dispersal in adult animals. But even in these animals the initiation and direction of dispersal movements is also partly decided by outside factors.

In dragonflies dispersal could theoretically occur at any stage in the life-history. As we have seen, the eggs of many species are dropped into the water or on floating vegetation. It is quite possible that a certain amount of passive dispersal in the egg stage occurs in rivers. Similarly larvae may also be swept downstream at times of spate. Adult dragonflies of some tropical species have been observed by F. C. Fraser and M. A. Lieftinck to migrate upstream. This habit must help to counteract any passive drift downstream, which if continued too far might take eggs or larvae into unsuitable habitats. When the larvae of *Anax* hatch they disperse from the oviposition site. It is possible that small scale dispersal movements of this kind are made by the larvae of many other species. The search for food and shelter must also cause some dispersal. Before emergence the larvae of *Cordulegaster* sometimes walk far from water—this habit may have adaptive value in reducing predation.

But as we have emphasised before the adult is the main dispersal stage; in fact dispersal is the first action of the recently emerged adult. The exact nature of the stimuli involved is not known, but since dragonflies on their maiden flight turn back when they come across water, they probably avoid water instinctively and the stimulus is probably visual. The distances travelled during the maiden flight vary from a few feet to at least hundreds of yards. There is great variation in one species. Much depends on the strength of the convection currents existing at the time of the maiden flight. When these are strong the fluttering insects rise quickly in the windless hollow or valley in which the lake or river lies. Then suddenly they reach the wind and are blown away before it.

As we have seen in Chapter 7 dragonflies are particularly vulnerable at emergence: not only do they fly slowly at this stage, but their abundance makes them very conspicuous. As a result predators are attracted to them and can kill a relatively higher number than they would if their prey were able to fly faster and were dispersed. But for the maiden flight, casualties would be far worse than they are.

The life of the immature adults is spent away from water. Undoubtedly they wander at this stage but whether the direction is decided by an instinctive mechanism or whether it results from a series of accidental factors is not known. Time of day and changes in the direction of wind make first one place and then another suitable feeding places for the dragonfly away from water. Its reactions to food and temperature must often cause considerable movement away from the spot where it settled at the end of its maiden flight.

As the sexual organs mature, dragonflies begin to seek water. We do not know whether they ever attempt to return to the area in which they spent their larval life. At a later stage males of some species show they have good topographical memories; for each day they fly direct to their beat on water from distant roosting places. It is conceivable that the dragonfly remembers the route of its maiden flight and sometimes retraces it when it becomes mature. In isolated habitats the ability to home after the maturation period would have considerable survival value.

In 1955 I carried out some experiments in Dorset in order to discover if mature dragonflies showed any tendency to home if taken outside their normal roosting area. I chose two bomb crater ponds separated by about 150 yards of heath (A and B on Plate VII*b* and Plate VIII*a*). Each day I caught all the dragonflies at both ponds and marked them distinctively. I then released the population of pond A at B and B's at A. 119 dragonflies (mostly *Ceriagrion tenellum* and *Ischnura elegans*) were caught, marked, and transferred. 43 were caught again where released, two were found elsewhere, none had returned to the pond where they had been caught originally.

At maturity another dispersal mechanism comes into play—that of territory. Clashes between males both sexual or aggressive cause dispersal. I have demonstrated this experimentally in *Ceriagrion* (the little red damselfly whose headquarters in Britain are the bogs

of the Tertiary heaths of southern England). I have described in
Chapter 9 how, by introducing varying numbers of males from neighbouring ponds and letting them go at the experimental pond, the
population had always adjusted itself by the following day to a constant
level. In other words some of the insects remained and others left.
By surrounding the experimental pond with other experimental
ponds, *i.e.* large flat dishes filled with water and Sphagnum, I was
able to record whether the clashes observed did cause the new artificial
habitats to be colonised. On several occasions these new ponds were
colonised by marked individuals from the main experimental pond.
This demonstrated that territorial behaviour both reduces population
density of males at the home water and causes local dispersal; but
whether it initiates long range dispersal or migration is not known.

Sexual chases of females by males may result in dispersal of females
in the way that Geyr von Schweppenburg and Lorenz have shown that
Mallard ducks are dispersed by the sexual chases of Mallard drakes
(Tinbergen, 1957). But so far there is rather little evidence for this
in dragonflies. We do not know what causes females to disperse.
Do they rely on the maiden flight and wandering in the immature
stage, on fortuitous wandering in search of food in the adult stage,
or do they have any more systematic mechanism of dispersal? Once
they have discovered a breeding place they frequently return to it—
this suggests that like males they make use of topographical memory.

Apart from the pioneer work of Steiner on *Leucorrhinia dubia* (see
p. 118) practically nothing is known about habitat selection in dragonflies. In other words we do not know what stimuli cause a dragonfly,
male or female, to stop flying and settle by the new found breeding
area. Some species are found in an immense variety of habitats and
will even attempt to colonise most unsuitable breeding areas. I have
seen Libellulines ovipositing on a tarmac road in the Gambia and an
A. cyanea laying eggs by the edge of a stony lane in Dorset. I have
also seen *L. dryas* and *Enallagma* laying eggs in a shaded water-filled
iron-pit in a Sussex wood, a habitat in which no dragonfly larva could
survive, and males of several species setting up their territories round
a pool (D in Plate VIII*a* p. 133) in *Spartina* marsh—crabs scuttled
about on the mud and at the next spring tide the pool was indis-
tinguishable from the rest of Poole Harbour!—others like *Leucorrhinia*
and *Erythromma* are found in very restricted habitats. Therefore
there must be great variation in the degree of habitat discrimination.
I suspect that there are also differences between the sexes: some

male *Ceriagrion* released by an unsuitable habitat—a bomb hole
a few yards from Poole Harbour full of slightly brackish water of
pH 6·5—remained there for several days, but females flew away
and did not return.

Some species of dragonfly are migrants. That is they make seasonal
dispersal movements whose direction is at least partly controlled by the
instincts of the dragonflies. In Britain the student of dragonflies is
rarely lucky enough to see a migration of dragonflies in progress. I
have only seen one migration—it was an awe-inspiring sight. On 9th
September, 1948, I was just about to leave the Gambia and was
studying the wading birds in the mangrove swamps that surround
the port of Bathurst. I was interested in the large numbers of non-
breeding waders from the Arctic and the North—Greenshank, Curlew,
Turnstone, etc., which were feeding rather incongruously along with
the Pelicans, Darters and Egrets. I had my 12-bore with me as I
wanted to collect some specimens for dissection. Night began to fall
and so I extricated myself from the maze of channels and made for a
track nearer the mouth of the great river. When I reached firmer land
a large Libelluline dragonfly flew by me quite low over the ground—it
went eastwards. Then I saw another—then another. They were all
going east, some skimming the ground, others at about 30–40 feet up.
Hundreds flew by me in the dark, all flying eastwards. I tried very
hard to get a specimen. I had no net as I did not expect to find dragonflies in the mangrove swamps. Up river I had found that a shotgun
loaded with dust shot was useful in collecting Gomphines and other
species which flew tantalisingly out of reach among the great
mahoganies and baobabs: I had no dust shot so I tried 6's. It was so
dark that I could not see far and so had to fire at close range. I blazed
away ineffectively until I had no more cartridges and no dragonflies
either. And so I failed to identify the migrants. Some Africans had
stopped and looked on with friendly but enquiring faces—Gambians
are among the kindest of people. The truth would not have been very
enlightening, so we just grinned and I returned to Bathurst. The
cicadas seemed to jeer at me in the dark.

In Britain we have five species (*A. mixta, L. quadrimaculata, L. depressa,
S. striolatum, S. sanguineum*) which are frequent migrants and which
breed here regularly. They include some of our commonest species
and, with the exception of *A. mixta*, do not appear to be dependent
on continuous migration from abroad. They are in the same position
as the Small Tortoiseshell Butterfly (*Aglais urticae*). In addition our

populations of *A. grandis* and *A. cyanea* and probably other species are also sometimes reinforced by migrants.

Besides these, there are two species which, like the Clouded Yellow Butterfly (*Colias croceus* Fourc.) pay frequent but irregular visits, but cannot establish themselves for more than a year or two. These are *Sympetrum flaveolum* (the species with the conspicuous yellow wing patches) and *S. fonscolombei*. These species are not very uncommon: during the last 20 years I myself have come across *S. flaveolum* on six occasions and *S. fonscolombei* on two. In addition, two migrant species occasionally visit our shores as vagrants. They are *Sympetrum vulgatum* and *S. meridionale*. Very little is known about dragonfly migration in Britain. We do not even know if they are migrants in the strict sense, that is that there is a coming and going with the seasons as occurs in most migratory birds and the Monarch Butterfly in North America. Or are they mere emigrants, neither they nor their descendants destined to return?—like the westward moving hordes of Lemming and Springbok?

Spectacular migrations have been reported since 1673 from all parts of Europe, but it is only in recent years that there has been any evidence to show that a return migration takes place. On 13 October, 1950, D. and E. Lack (1951) recorded a return migration for the first time. They watched *S. striolatum* flying W.S.W. through the narrow Port de Gavarnie in the High Pyrenees. They estimated that the dragonflies were passing at the rate of several thousand an hour. The insects flew close to the ground. Migrating with these dragonflies were hundreds of birds (mainly Chaffinches, Goldfinches, Linnets and Wood-Pigeons) and butterflies (mainly Clouded Yellows and Red Admirals) and very large numbers of Hover flies (*Episyrphus balteatus* Degeer). An autumnal return migration may well occur in Britain, but so far it has not been observed.

Generally we do not know where our migrants come from. Some-

Plate VII. a. Above. Portbury Stream, North Somerset. The total population density of male dragonflies (Anisoptera) along this stream very rarely exceeded thirteen dragonflies per hundred yards of stream during period of study, 1949-1952. Dragonflies roosted in water meadow on right and among trees on skyline. (*N. W. Moore*)

b. Below. Water filled bomb hole, Arne Heath, Dorset. (Pond B on Aerial Photograph *Plate VIII.*) The population of this pond rarely exceeded three male Anisoptera with forty male Zygoptera during period 1954-57. The pond was used for homing experiments. (See p. 129.) (*A. P. Tuck*)

Plate VII

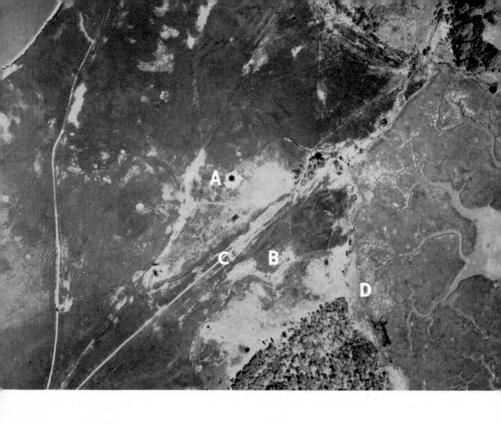

Plate VIII

times it is possible to make a guess. During September 1947 one of us
(C.L.) was lucky enough to see part of an immense migration of
S. striolatum on the southern shores of Ireland. The insects arrived
at scattered parts along the whole coast and were seen travelling
inland. They penetrated as far north as Co. Clare and Co. Kildare.
The movement—which probably involved over a million insects—
lasted at least six weeks. All the dragonflies were mature and in one
locality they were flying in tandem. Over the sea they flew in narrow
columns, each insect about a foot from the next. When they reached
land they tended to spread out. They flew with the wind behind them.
But quite low hills appeared to have acted as barriers and to have
determined the direction of their movements once they reached the
land. All the individuals captured were the dark form of this species and
so must have come from the west of Europe rather than the east. As
Cynthia Longfield (1948) points out in her paper on this remarkable
event, this shows that they must have travelled at night for at least
part of their journey.

The most spectacular dragonfly migrations in Europe are those
made by *L. quadrimaculata*. This species breeds in enormous numbers
in the lakes of Scandinavia and Eastern Europe. Occasionally vast
emigrations spread outwards from this area. They seem to be
correlated with a situation when barometric pressure is high, temperatures are high and there is little cloud and winds are light. There is
great variation in direction but sometimes they fly westward in vast
numbers—the greatest migration, that of 19 May 1862, was observed
in Germany; it was estimated to have consisted of about 2,400,000,000
insects. On 5 June 1900 the air over Antwerp "appeared black" with
them. Some of this flight reached Margate on 10 June, Berwick on
17 June and Huddersfield on 2 July.

So far I have only mentioned migrations to Britain. There is some
evidence of local migrations within the British Isles. Some of these may
represent return migrations to the continent. Some migrations
apparently originate from the British Isles: on 6 and 11 September

---

Plate VIII. a. Above. Experimental area: Aerial photograph of Arne Heath, Dorset,
showing bomb holes used for experiments on homing and population density.
Scale approximately twelve inches to one mile. (*Crown copyright reserved. Royal Air
Force photograph*)

b. Below. An old male *Orthetrum cancellatum* showing injuries due to territorial fighting.
Note wear in cellulose paint identification mark. (*K. Wood*)

D—K

1954, hundreds of *S. danae* were observed flying north-west over Tory Island, Co. Donegal. It seems likely that this flight originated in Ireland. If the present climatic trend continues it is by movements such as these that the extensive marshes and lakes of Iceland will be colonised. But since there are relatively few extensive marshes in the British Isles, large scale migrations are more likely to end in these islands than to start from them.

Our ignorance about migration in dragonflies extends to every aspect of the problem. We do not know what conditions stimulate migration nor what directs the flight. F. C. Fraser (1945) has shown that dragonflies migrate both as mature and teneral insects. From his observations in France P. Grassé (1932) points out that dragonflies often fly along the coast and against the wind, but as we have seen this is not always the case elsewhere. Grassé noted that individual dragonflies were attracted by the migrants and joined them. These observations suggest affinities with locust migrations. It is likely that migration follows overcrowding, which is often due to the seasonal drying out of lakes: the drier parts of Europe and North Africa are probably the best places in which to study dragonfly migration. But much work could be done in Britain. Regular migrations should be looked for and the behaviour of migrants recorded with the meteorological conditions prevailing at the time. Massed migrations seem to be rare in Britain but movements on a broad front with individuals spaced far apart or flying in small groups may be much commoner than is supposed. This is well illustrated by *S. flaveolum* and *S. fonscolombei*. Most records of these species must refer to migrants since the climate rarely allows breeding to occur in the British Isles. Yet in nearly every case the insects were found established by a pond— usually in quite small numbers—when they were first seen. It is very rare that anyone sees them migrating.

Many extremely useful records on dragonfly migration have already been collected. If naturalists kept an eye open for dragonflies, particularly in late summer on the south coasts, I am sure many more records could be obtained. Whether or not something is seen depends so much on whether it is looked for—so far very few people have looked for migrating dragonflies. Records should be sent to Mr. R. A. French of the Rothamsted Experimental Station, Harpenden, Herts. Whenever possible use should be made of the standard card, which can be supplied from Rothamsted.

How far do the dispersal movements of dragonflies take them?

Direct observation can, of course, only tell us about very short flights, for example some maiden flights. To get information about the larger distances we must mark them. So far most marking experiments on dragonflies have been undertaken in order to study territory or changes in population. However some incidental information on dispersal has been acquired in the process. The American entomologist Borror (1934) was the first to mark large numbers of dragonflies. He marked 830 old and teneral individuals of the damselfly *Argia moesta* (Hagen). He saw 178 of these insects again; none was more than 300 yards from where he marked it. In his population study of *Pyrrhosoma*, P. Corbet marked 421 insects and got 233 recoveries (55 per cent). He never found a marked insect at the nearest pond which was less than a mile away. In the course of working on the territory of dragonflies in Somerset, I marked 110 *Anisoptera*. I saw 30 of these again. A female and a male *O. cancellatum* were later seen 500 and 240 yards respectively from the places where they had been marked.

During 1954 I started some investigations on the extent of movements of dragonflies on the Arne peninsula in Dorset. During the war many bombs were dropped on the heaths of the northern end of the peninsula. The bomb holes have filled with water and become ideal breeding places for many species of dragonfly (see Plates VII*b* and VIII*a*, pp. 132, 133). Each pond is easily accessible and because it is small (the average diameter is about 8 yards) it is possible to catch almost all the dragonflies present at each pond. During 1954 and 1955, I marked 491 individuals and recorded their movements. I saw 121 again but of these 114 were at their own ponds. There were only 7 recoveries at other ponds. The largest distance travelled by a male was 230 yards, and by a female 300 yards. Most of the insects marked were mature. These experiments suggest that either the amount of dispersal in the mature stage is rather limited or that the insects dispersed to places outside the Arne peninsula.

Some indication of the distances travelled and the effectiveness of dispersal mechanisms can be obtained simply by looking for dragonflies in areas where there are very few breeding places and immigration from outside is limited. Some isolated groups of islands, such as the Isles of Scilly, are suitable for this type of study. Only two species of dragonfly occur in the Isle of Scilly, *S. striolatum* and *I. elegans*. There are only about half a dozen breeding places on the islands; all are in the islands of St. Mary's, Tresco, and St. Agnes. During a stay in the summer of 1952 I searched all the inhabited islands for

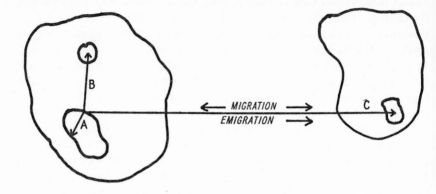

Fig. 30. Diagram showing three types of dispersal found in dragonflies. A, short range. B, medium range. C, long range.

dragonflies. I found many near the fresh water pools, and at least 35 over 1,000 yards from the nearest breeding place. Most of these insects were immature *S. striolatum*. All except one *I. elegans*, were less than 200 yards from water—the one exception was 400 yards away.

Another approach is to study the rate at which new reservoirs and ponds are colonised by the species found in the neighbourhood. The new Hastings Reservoir near Robertbridge in E. Sussex was colonised by *L. quadrimaculata* and *O. cancellatum* within two years of its filling. The nearest breeding place of these species is *c.* 7,000 yards away.

The sudden appearance of a species outside its normal range can also give some indication of the minimum distance travelled by the insect. During the hot summer of 1949 a male *O. coerulescens* suddenly appeared by the stream I was studying in N. Somerset. Its nearest known breeding place was 40 miles away on the Black Down Hills.

To conclude it may be useful to those who may wish to study the problems of dispersal to classify the dispersal behaviour of dragonflies. The following categories cover all the known types of behaviour by which adult dragonflies leave their breeding places:—

1. *Maiden Flight* of newly emerged adults away from water.
2. *Flights in search of food, shelter, etc.*—Other behaviour which results incidentally in dispersal.

3. *Territorial Behaviour*—Behaviour in which males defend an area and drive out other males from it.

4. *Pseudo-territorial Behaviour*—Behaviour in which males attempt to mate with other males and females of their own or other species, which results, as in true territorial behaviour, in males driving out other males (and sometimes females) from their breeding area.

5. *Migration*—Seasonal movements by which individuals bred in one area, disperse to breed in another, and then they or their progeny return to the original area.

6. *Emigration*—Long range movements in which neither the insects nor their progeny return seasonally to their breeding area.

It looks as if a useful distinction can be made between short, middle, and long range dispersal (see Fig. 30, p. 136). The first consists of dispersal throughout a suitable breeding area, for example round the shores of a lake, or up and down a river. This is mainly caused by territorial and pseudo-territorial behaviour. Short range dispersal ensures that full use is made of all suitable parts of any one body of water. Middle range dispersal ensures colonisation of new breeding areas within the geographical barriers which enclose the original breeding place. It is caused by all "mechanisms" listed above except migration and emigration. Long range dispersal consists of migration and emigration and is probably the principal method by which temporary bodies of water are colonised. Colonisation of new areas which are isolated from the original breeding area by large stretches of sea or desert is achieved by emigration. In recent times the spread of species must have been helped by man, whose ships, aeroplanes and cars, sometimes give lifts to dragonflies as well as smaller insects.

Enough has been said to show how very little we know about any of these mechanisms of dispersal and their exact functions. There is here an enormous and almost untouched field for future research, both for the professional and the amateur, for individuals and for teams of observers.

Two techniques have already proved most useful with dragonflies—making "models" to discover the nature of stimuli and marking insects to discover the movements of individuals and populations (see Appendix IV, p. 236). They could be greatly extended to investigate all the problems raised in this chapter.

CHAPTER 11

SEASONAL REGULATION
(P.S.C.)

. . . the matter of food is a great regulator of the actions and proceedings of the brute creation: there is but one that can be set in competition with it, and that is love.

GILBERT WHITE (1789). *Natural History of Selborne*

THE ANNUAL fluctuation in temperature, which is so characteristic a feature of higher latitudes, has a profound effect on the cold-blooded animals that live there. It will be sufficient to consider a single example. In Britain, the lower threshold temperature for flight (and therefore reproduction) is such as to restrict the adult stage of dragonflies to a period of less than six months each year. Within this period, which extends from April to October, we find that the various species tend to fly at restricted and regular times. This seasonal restriction of emergence fulfils two important needs: firstly, it ensures that each year adults fly in the season for which they are best adapted; and secondly, it guarantees that the most economic use will be made of the potentialities of the short-lived reproductive stage.

In a given population, the date upon which emergence begins in any year is probably determined largely by the heat budget to date, that is to say the accumulated temperature which a given habitat has received so far that year. It is well-known to naturalists that there are "early" and "late" years, in which insects and also plants of unrelated groups show a tendency to deviate in the same direction from the average dates of emergence and flowering. Since cumulative variations in temperature become smaller as the season progresses, we usually find that first dates of emergence of spring species show a far wider variation than those of species emerging later in the year.

Quite another matter is the way in which the emergence of individual members of a population is distributed during the emergence period. As we saw in the chapters on emergence and adult life, it has important ecological consequences whether most of a population emerges at the beginning or in the middle of the emergence period. Thus, the shape of the emergence curve (see Fig. 22, p. 95) will determine indirectly the time at which most of the eggs will be laid, and is probably correlated also with the length of adult life. Furthermore, as we shall see, it can also be used to provide information about larval ecology.

British dragonflies are variably efficient in the extent to which they achieve seasonal regulation, and it is possible to recognise two fairly distinct types. Dragonflies of the first type, which includes *Anax* and *Pyrrhosoma*, have been called "spring" species. These fly early in the year and have a well-synchronised emergence with an early peak.

The second type is represented by species which emerge later in the year and do not show a close synchronisation. Such dragonflies have been called "summer" species, and include *S. striolatum* and *L. sponsa*.

Both the time of emergence and the degree to which it is synchronised are governed by the bionomics of the larval stage. The way in which larval responses interplay with the environment to bring about a regulated emergence is best understood in *Anax*, and it will be as well to follow the salient features of its life-history to see how regulation in a spring species can be achieved (Fig. 31, p. 140).

Adults of *Anax* emerge between mid-May and mid-July, and egg-laying usually lasts from late June to early September. The eggs hatch in about twenty-four days and the larvae, which grow extremely rapidly, are approximately half-grown by October. After this, low temperatures prevent further growth until the following April. Then growth is resumed and most larvae enter the final instar in August, about a year after hatching of the eggs. By this time variation in size among larvae of the same age is considerable, the final instar being entered in any month of the second year between May and September. This gives one a good idea of the extent of the variation in growth-rates which can accumulate during a year, and which, somehow, must be reduced before emergence takes place.

Anax reduces this temporal variation in an effective and ingenious fashion, during the nine months which remain at its disposal before emergence occurs the following spring. Those larvae which enter the final instar in August do not metamorphose and emerge, despite the favourable environmental conditions, which are actually more suitable at this time than in May and June, the time of greatest emergence.

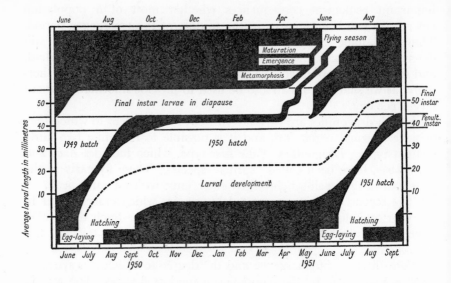

Fig. 31. The life-history of *A. imperator*. The dotted line indicates the average larval size, and the white areas the extent of variation encountered in a population in nature. There are two emergence groups: the first consists of larvae two years old, and the second of larvae one year old. This diagram emphasises the very short season of larval growth, between May and October.

This is because, in *Anax,* the final larval instar is a resting, or diapause stage, similar in some respects to the overwintering egg of *L. sponsa* (see Chapter 5). Like the egg of *L. sponsa,* the final larval instar of *Anax* undergoes the first part of its development more rapidly at autumn temperatures than at summer ones. One result of this is that larvae entering the final instar in summer are obliged to develop very slowly indeed until autumn. Then, when temperatures fall to within a suitable range, all those larvae in the final instar complete diapause development quickly, so that when spring comes all are capable of responding together to factors stimulating metamorphosis.

The diapause in *Anax* acts very much as do traffic-lights on a stream of cars. During summer, when temperatures are high, the red light shows, obliging cars to stop and accumulate behind the white line. Autumn, with its intermediate temperatures, represents the amber light which enables the necessary preparations to be made for moving off promptly. These preparations correspond to the completion of diapause development. Finally, the green light, which allows all cars to move away simultaneously, represents the rising spring temperatures stimulating synchronised metamorphosis. In this way metamorphosis, and therefore emergence, are synchronised and postponed until spring. Thus, the precocious individuals lose the temporal advantage they had gained over their fellows, and similarly the laggards are enabled to catch up.

This interpretation can be checked in several ways. For instance, if final instar larvae are removed from their pond in February, and subjected to spring conditions of food and temperature, they will metamorphose and emerge without delay, even when experiencing a six-hour day (that is, an eighteen-hour night); this shows that diapause development has already been completed in nature, and that the age-group is in a position to respond simultaneously when conditions become favourable.

This is not quite the whole story in *Anax*. If it were, larvae entering the final instar in May (at the time when individuals a year older than themselves are emerging) would be obliged to postpone emergence for a further year. This would undoubtedly reduce their chances of survival to the adult stage. It therefore comes as a relief to learn that larvae managing to enter the final instar before the beginning of June do not pass through a diapause stage, but can metamorphose and emerge immediately. What is so remarkable about this arrangement is that a larva seems to be able to tell the date immediately after its moult to the final instar. The available evidence indicates that it does so by assessing the changes in successive daylengths, and that, until daily increases fall below a value of about two minutes, it is able to forgo diapause.

In Britain, it is probable that about 90 per cent of *Anax* adults emerging each year are two-year-old individuals which have spent their second winter in diapause. The remaining 10 per cent consist of precocious one-year-olds which have managed to reach the final instar before June in their first spring (Fig. 32, p. 142). Thus we can see that the larval responses of *Anax* are adapted towards the maintenance of a two-year life-history, but that they are sufficiently plastic to offer dispensation to quick growers, these being permitted to emerge after only one year. In Britain, *Anax* is near the northernmost limit of its geographical range, so that we may expect the proportion of one-year-olds to increase as we go southwards.

The life-history of *Anax* has been described in some detail because

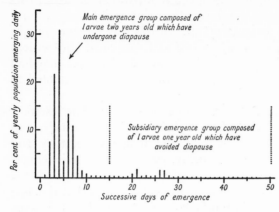

Per cent of yearly population emerging daily

Main emergence group composed of
larvae two years old which have
undergone diapause

Subsidiary emergence group composed
of larvae one year old which have
avoided diapause

Successive days of emergence

Fig. 32. Seasonal emergence in a population of *A. imperator*. This graph shows the separation of the emergence curve into its two components. The lack of synchronisation amongst non-diapause individuals is very apparent.

it is valuable as a model against which to compare other life-histories which are less well-known. In *Anax*, the synchronisation of emergence can be seen as a direct consequence of the diapause in the final instar. It is therefore useful to select this final instar diapause as the criterion separating the two ecological types of dragonfly.

Thus, spring species possess a diapause in the final larval instar, whereas summer species do not. This does not mean that summer species are always without a diapause stage. On the contrary, we have already seen that one exists in the egg of *L. sponsa*. But if diapause is present in a summer species, then it is never located in the final instar.

This classification may seem at first to place undue emphasis on the final instar as a diapause stage. But not only is its effect on emergence unique in this position, but, as we shall see later, diapause probably performs a different ecological function if located elsewhere.

One consequence of the diapause in spring species is that final instar larvae can be found in a resting condition in late summer or autumn, after the flying season each year. In summer species, the final instar is usually entered shortly before emergence, and thus final instar larvae are rarely found after the flying season in any year. Using this as a basis for diagnosis in the field, we can make a provisional classification of the British dragonflies into spring and summer species, as in the table opposite. Future observations may alter the status of a few doubtful species in this scheme, but the main classification is probably fairly accurate.

AN ECOLOGICAL CLASSIFICATION OF THE
BRITISH DRAGONFLIES

Spring species (21)	Summer species (22)
G. *vulgatissimus*	1. Univoltine (15)
C. *boltoni*	A. *mixta* (M)
B. *pratense*	S. *striolatum*
A. *caerulea?*	S. *danae*
A. *isosceles?*	S. *sanguineum* (G)
A. *imperator*	S. *nigrescens?*
O. *curtisi?*	S. *flaveolum* (L)
C. *aenea*	S. *fonscolombei* (L)
S. *metallica?*	L. *sponsa*
S. *arctica?*	L. *dryas* (G)
L. *depressa*	C. *puella*
L. *quadrimaculata*	C. *pulchellum*
L. *fulva?*	C. *hastulatum* (G)
L. *dubia*	C. *scitulum* (G)
O. *coerulescens*	I. *elegans*
O. *cancellatum*	E. *cyathigerum*
A. *virgo*	2. Not univoltine (7)
A. *splendens?*	A. *cyanea*
P. *pennipes*	A. *juncea*
P. *nymphula*	A. *grandis*
E. *najas*	C. *mercuriale*
	C. *armatum?*
	C. *tenellum*
	I. *pumilio?*

Notes. These species have been classified on the basis of the author's own observations unless indicated otherwise:

  (G) Inferred from rearing work carried out by Gardner

  (L) Inferred from observations by Longfield.

  (M) Field observations by Münchberg

  ? No reliable evidence available; assigned by guesswork

In this table the summer species have been subdivided further, according to whether or not the life-history has to be completed in one year. There is a good reason for this. Although summer species cannot (by definition) use a diapause to synchronise emergence, there are indications that they have available some other device which can reduce temporal variation before emergence. It seems probable that this comprises a series of rising temperature thresholds for successive developmental stages. Such a system would operate rather like diapause in reverse, and would be restricted to spring and early summer, instead of autumn. The principle involved is extremely simple and may be explained as follows.

Let us consider a population resuming growth in spring, and comprising larvae in the three last instars (as is the case, for instance, in *Coenagrion mercuriale*). Now if the temperature at which the penultimate instar can be entered is below that allowing ecdysis to the final instar, an accumulation of larvae may occur in the penultimate instar until the appropriate temperature for ecdysis is reached. Then there will be a mass entry to the final instar. Similarly, if the lower temperature threshold for metamorphosis is higher still, and that for emergence yet higher, there will be a considerable reduction of temporal variation before emergence.

Now such a mechanism cannot function effectively if the successive developmental stages are close together in time, for this will provide little opportunity for accumulation in any one stage. Therefore species which grow very rapidly (such as *L. sponsa*) will not have access to such a mechanism. Accordingly, univoltine species have been separated from the rest, since they probably have the most widely-dispersed emergence of all. With regard to synchronisation of emergence (and therefore probably shortness of adult life) the groups of dragonflies fall into the following order: (1) spring species; (2) semivoltine summer species; (3) univoltine summer species.

If it is present, the position of the diapause stage in summer species may provide an interesting clue to their past history. In most of the known cases, it is developed in the egg. Here we encounter another important function of diapause: to ensure that the whole population overwinters in a resistant stage. As we saw in Chapter 5, p. 64, there are good grounds for assuming the egg to be best fitted for surviving the winter. In spring species, this is not even a secondary function of diapause, since most of the larval instars, including the final one, are able to overwinter.

Two good examples of the need for a diapause egg are provided by *Lestes sponsa* and *Aeshna mixta*. In these species, the eggs hatch in spring, and the whole larval development is completed in two to five months; then the adults emerge in summer to lay diapause eggs. Such an arrangement not only maintains a univoltine life-cycle, it also ensures that the larvae (with their very high temperature coefficient for growth) are never subjected to winter temperatures. To confirm this line of reasoning, it would be very interesting to find out whether the late larval instars of these species are capable of surviving winter temperatures. This seems unlikely, since they are persistently uni-voltine and keep the same flying season. Münchberg (1931) has sug-gested that an important factor limiting the northerly distribution of *Aeshna mixta* will be the ability of larvae to complete development before autumn; this will depend on the heat budget of the habitat. Such a restriction may well be important in other univoltine summer species.

However, not all our dragonflies are as intolerant of winter tem-peratures as *A. mixta*, and it is instructive to enquire how they may have come to develop the tolerance which has enabled them to colonise high latitudes. In the case of *A. mixta*, one of the first con-sequences of extending its distribution northwards will be that the final instar larva will be overtaken by the winter before it can meta-morphose. Therefore an early development which is needed in this process is a final instar larva which can survive winter temperatures. As this tolerance extends to earlier instars, the species will be able to move farther north. Examples of dragonflies in which this trend seems to have advanced a considerable way are *Aeshna grandis*, *A. juncea* and *A. cyanea*; and, when we have discovered more about its biology, we may well find that *A. caerulea* is the best example of all. Here, at the expense of lengthening the life-history, temperature tolerance has extended down to a fairly early larval stage. The diapause eggs still ensure that newly-hatched larvae will experience April temperatures, and will have a good opportunity to reach a fair size before their first winter. An inspection of these life-histories indicates that, of all the stages, newly-hatched larvae seem to be the least resistant to cold. This fact may be connected with their high temperature coefficient for growth. The seasonal ecology of the most northerly Aeshnids, such as *Aeshna subarctica* Walker and some Canadian species, might throw a valuable light on these ideas.

It savours of the obvious to say that temperate regions have been colonised from lower latitudes. The periodic glaciations, which have been such a dramatic feature of recent geological time, have made many regions temporarily unsuited for habitation, and their retreat will have permitted re-colonisation only from warmer climes. Therefore, it is to sub-tropical and tropical regions that we must look if we are to find the models from which the British life-histories have evolved.

In tropical regions, the absence of major annual fluctuations of temperature seems to result in the production among dragonflies of a continuous succession of generations throughout the year. Rain is probably the most important seasonally-variable factor in such an environment, and this has resulted in many species having a high thermal growth coefficient and a short larval life, necessary attributes for survival in temporary pools. The adult life seems to be relatively long, perhaps on account of the need for dispersal and the discovery of new habitats. (In parenthesis, we may note that the best-known migrants, such as *Pantala* and *Trapezostigma*, are inhabitants of temporary pools, and it may well have been under such conditions of enforced nomadism that the migratory habit in dragonflies first became established.)

One of the first ways in which such a life-history must be modified for existence in higher latitudes is for the adult stage to be restricted to the warmer season and the resistant stage to the colder one. As we have seen, a diapause in the egg fulfils both these requirements. Synchronisation of emergence is liable to be poor, but since the adult life is primarily long, this is not a serious consideration. Thus, the life-history of our univoltine summer species is probably very similar to the first stage in the colonisation of temperate regions (Fig. 33, p. 147).

This is not to say that all the British species in this category are necessarily recent arrivals, or that they are ill-adapted for existence at northern temperatures. A glance at the distribution of either *S. striolatum* or *L. sponsa* should be sufficient to demonstrate this. What is suggested is that the univoltine life-history, particularly that of *L. sponsa* which features a diapause egg, represents a basic type. The fact that the univoltine type of life-history persists in several successful northern species may perhaps be the result of their having developed adaptations in other directions.

However, in many species, univoltinism is no longer possible in more northerly populations. It seems likely, for instance, that *Anax* completes its life-history in one year in southern Europe, but usually requires two years in Britain. The survival of such European species as *C. puella*, *C. hastulatum*, *I. elegans* and *E. cyathigerum* in northerly regions may be due to their ability to become semivoltine under conditions of low temperature, but this must remain hypothetical until some information can be obtained on growth-rates in Scottish populations.

When univoltinism is no longer possible on account of the shortened season for growth, tolerance of low temperatures may be expected to begin in the final instar (the first that is likely to be overtaken by the winter) and then to extend to earlier larval stages. At this point we have a life-history of the semivoltine summer species type. Such species seem to have achieved success in their northerly movement by throwing off the yoke of obligatory univoltinism. Such an evolutionary

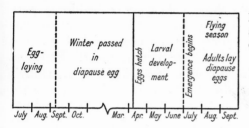

Fig. 33. The life-history of *L. sponsa,* a univoltine summer species of dragonfly.

step extends the larval life, which is already becoming very much longer than that of the adult, and also creates a need for synchronisation of emergence. The latter, as we have seen, can now be achieved by a series of rising temperature thresholds, since the larvae are growing relatively slowly.

Spring species seem to represent the final stage that has been reached in the process of northerly extension. Except, perhaps, for the eggs and newly-hatched larvae, all the larval stages seem to be able to tolerate winter temperatures, and a resistant stage no longer seems to dictate the need for regulation. The whole emphasis is now laid on the synchronisation of emergence. The temperature tolerance of the adult has become greater and it can now fly in spring. Efficient synchronisation allows the adult life to be very short.

In following the progressive colonisation of northerly latitudes, as shown by these types of life-history, certain consistent trends can be discerned. One of the most striking is that the relative durations of the larval and adult stages have become reversed. Thus in the tropics, we find a long-lived adult which must survive the dry season and be adapted to covering large distances in search of water, and a larva which must complete its growth as quickly as possible before its habitat dries up. At the other extreme, in high latitudes, larval life is greatly protracted by slow growth and by the necessity for a diapause stage in the final instar in order to synchronise the emergence of the very short-lived adult. Another trend which can be observed is the general increase of tolerance towards low temperature, which extends last of all to the reproductive stage. In addition, there is the evolution of various devices which help to maintain an annual cycle and to reduce temporal variation. Thus, from a simple obligatory diapause in the egg of *Lestes sponsa*, we come by degrees to such a complex arrangement as the facultative final instar diapause of *Anax*, controlled by a critical response to changing length of day.

Although it is likely that the three main types of life-history were evolved in the order given above, it is clear that independent adaptations have taken place in a variety of directions, and that many ecological factors besides the few that have been mentioned determine the present distribution of the British species. Thus, a dragonfly's distribution cannot be inferred directly from its life-history, and we must look to other causes to explain why *L. sponsa*, a univoltine summer species, extends farther north than *A. imperator*, a spring species. It is possible that the limiting factors in some cases may be extremely complex, perhaps involving subtle relationships between the temperature thresholds permitting metamorphosis, emergence and adult flight. From the little information we have available concerning emergence mortality in *A. imperator*, it is not difficult to imagine this becoming a severe selective factor under circumstances where the spring nights are consistently cold.

The ecological classification which has been proposed on the basis of life-histories answers certain questions while at the same time posing others. It simply represents a new way of looking at an old problem.

a. Sympetrum striolatum, male. Fully mature and red. When young and sandy-yellow, it is very like *O. coerulescens*. Distinct by the dark pterostigma, and the black marks dorsally on last abdominal segments. The venation is also quite distinct from *Orthetrum*.

b. Sympetrum striolatum, female. Very immature and almost showing cream bands on the thorax. These fade into the darker sandy-yellow of the mature female. The yellow at the wing-bases is less than in most other British *Sympetrum* females. The structure of the vulvar scale is the only sure identification.

Plate 21. DRAGONFLIES (ANISOPTERA : LIBELLULIDAE)

a. Sympetrum sanguineum, male. Fully mature, with clubbed abdomen and nearly all-black legs. The red is more crimson than in *S. striolatum*, but the black abdominal markings are similar. The young male can only be distinguished by the secondary genitalia.

b. Sympetrum danae, male. Fully mature and black all over. Easy to distinguish, except from *L. dubia*. Young males resemble the female, and all stages towards the black are found. The thoracic dorsal black triangle is always distinctive.

Plate 22. DRAGONFLIES (ANISOPTERA : LIBELLULIDAE)

CHAPTER 12

FOSSIL HISTORY
(P.S.C.)

Over the streams and pools, through the oppressive greenish light, with a clittering of glassy wings, twist gigantic dragonflies, the largest insects the earth will ever know.

JACQUETTA HAWKES (1951). *A Land*

WHETHER or not an animal is fossilised depends to a large extent on its structure and habits, and on the environment in which it dies. Bottom-living marine animals, especially those with a calcareous exoskeleton, tend to be preserved in very good condition. Consequently our knowledge of the evolutionary history of oysters and sea urchins is unusually wide when compared with that of most other animals. With the possible exception of the Mollusca, whose shells resist decomposition for a long time, the fossil record of freshwater animals is relatively poor.

One reason for this may be that deposition of sediment usually occurs at a far slower rate in freshwater than in the sea, and that consequently most dead creatures decompose before becoming properly buried. But, in the case of aquatic insects, another reason is that the chitin forming the exoskeleton dissolves slowly in water. Thus it is generally only in cases where sedimentation has been exceptionally rapid, or where deposits have become impregnated with water rich in mineral salts, that aquatic insects are preserved as fossils.

In spite of this, the fossil record of dragonflies is a long and relatively good one. It is better than that of any other aquatic insect group, and, among the insects as a whole, stands second only to that of the cockroaches. I therefore feel that no excuse is needed for devoting a chapter to fossil dragonflies in a book about their natural history.

In a fossil state, dragonflies exist chiefly as impressions of wings. From the point of view of tracing their affinities, this is singularly fortunate, because long before the discovery of most of the fossils known to us to-day, Selys had based his classification of the Odonata on the wing venation.

There are, of course, many tantalising gaps in the geological record of dragonflies, and this subject still provides an arena for energetic debate and speculation. On several finer points of affinity, and on certain major ones, there remains disagreement between authorities, and this controversy cannot be reviewed in a worthwhile manner save by producing a lengthy dissertation, tedious to the general reader, and delving deeply into the technicalities of venation. Such a review would, I am sure, be out of place in this chapter. Some of the principal theories which have been put forward, however, are explained briefly in Appendix II. But, despite existing differences of opinion, certain evolutionary trends seem to emerge fairly distinctly from the geological record, and it is to these that we shall pay most attention here.

In following the fossil history of the Odonata, I will try to show how their past ecological background could have moulded them into the creatures we know as dragonflies to-day. It must be remembered, however, that much of what is said on this subject is inevitably speculative, and that deductions about the ecology of extinct species are bound to be more hypothetical even than inferences concerning their morphology.

The oldest fossil dragonflies which are known to us come from the coal measures at Commentry, near St. Etienne in France. These deposits lie right at the top of the Carboniferous series there and, from the plant remains that they contain, are perhaps more correctly regarded as a transition series to the Permian era. In any case, they are probably about 220 million years old. Insects belonging to several major groups are preserved in the Commentry beds, most of them being much larger than their present-day relatives.

The Commentry dragonflies are recognisable as possible ancestors of recent forms on the basis of their body-form and wing-shape, but their lack of a nodus, pterostigma and triangle, as well as their four-jointed tarsus and dense wing-reticulation, would deny them access to the Order Odonata as we now know it. These creatures have been assigned to the Protodonata, and it is probably from this Order that present-day Odonata are descended.

The earliest known fossil cockroaches and mayflies also come from Commentry, but the origin of these groups from a more generalised type of insect must have taken place long before this—perhaps in the

Middle or Lower Palaeozoic eras—because they are already clearly differentiated when we first encounter them. The rocks which contain the clue to the origin of insects have not yet been found, and perhaps never will be. It may be that the agents of erosion have, through countless ages, worn away and dispersed the only fragments of evidence which could ever have provided the answer to this question.

The scene at Commentry must have been one of great luxuriance and grandeur. In dense stands around the shores of a shallow, muddy lake grew Giant Mare's Tails, *Calamites,* and several species of fern-like cycads; and amongst the thick foliage of these plants flew giant dragonflies. The size of these creatures almost defeats the imagination. One of the best-known species, *Meganeura monyi* Brongniart, had a wingspan of twenty-seven inches. This makes it almost exactly four times as large as the biggest dragonflies living today, yet even some of these have been mistaken for birds when in flight! Although so enormous, it is unlikely that these early dragonflies were as agile as their present-day counterparts: the absence of a nodus and other strengthening features must have made the wings far less powerful.

Mention of their flight raises the question of what they ate. To-day, the feeding habits of adult dragonflies immediately bring to mind those of bats and swallows. All three groups have, by virtue of their aerial agility, succeeded in utilising the vast assemblage of small, weakly-flying insects which comprise the "plankton" of the air. Nowadays this plankton is made up very largely of adult Diptera, among which the Chironomidae play an important part as food of dragonflies. The Diptera, however, like the Hymenoptera and Lepidoptera, have evolved relatively recently, and probably originated in the Jurassic period, at least 50 million years too late for the giant dragonflies of Commentry to use them for food. Indeed, it seems unlikely that any insects of such a small size existed at the time, and we may well suppose that the dragonflies fed on larger insects—perhaps primitive mayflies and stoneflies—some of which they probably caught in flight, but others of which they may have taken from leaves and branches, or even from the ground. Dragonflies are, in fact, known to catch quite large insects to-day, and there are several records of Aeshnids consuming species of *Sympetrum.* As for the other method of feeding, I have seen *Enallagma* hovering over a bush and removing beetle larvae from the leaves with its legs.

The present-day habit of feeding efficiently on small insects in the air has probably evolved gradually from crude beginnings, and has doubtless depended for its progress upon corresponding developments in the size of the compound eyes, the skewness of the thorax, the disposition of the legs and, in the Anisoptera, the breadth of the hind-wing. The habit may have developed since Jurassic times, when the arrival of the Diptera and Hymenoptera provided a rich and unexploited source of food.

One interesting feature of the remains at Commentry is that they include no larvae. This invites speculation, although we must beware of attaching undue importance to it. It is likely on several counts that conditions at Commentry may not have favoured the preservation of larvae. Apart from the fact that chitin decomposes in water, we must remember that the fate of a larva is to become an adult, whereas the fate of an adult is to die and perhaps be fossilised. Thus the larvae which escaped being eaten by fishes or other predators would normally only have left fragile exuviae as indications of their presence and form. Nevertheless, dragonfly larvae are known occasionally as fossils in later strata (the first is encountered in the Jurassic period), so that we may perhaps be excused the indulgence of some speculation as to why none have been found at Commentry.

One of the most attractive explanations for their absence has been put forward by Tillyard. He suggested that perhaps at that time the larvae of dragonflies, mayflies and stoneflies had not yet become aquatic. There is considerable evidence in support of this theory, for the closed tracheal system of most freshwater insect larvae shows clearly that they are only secondarily aquatic, and originally must have breathed air. In the case of dragonflies, all we know from the fossil record is that larvae have been aquatic since the Jurassic period, about 150 million years ago.

Tillyard suggested that the larvae at Commentry may have lived in damp earth, and that the amphibious, swamp-like conditions pertaining there may have laid the foundation for their subsequent adoption of a completely aquatic life. Indeed, there is a dragonfly living to-day whose larva lives very much as these Carboniferous forms may have done. This is *Uropetala carovei* (White), a member of the primitive family Petaluridae, which is found in New Zealand. Wolfe (1953), who made a study of its life-history, found that the larvae inhabit flooded burrows and clamber about amongst damp grass and moss, feeding on spiders, beetles and other terrestrial animals. It may well be that the larvae of Protodonata led a similar sort of existence.

Wherever these larvae may have dwelt, they must certainly have been formidable creatures! A full-grown larva of *Meganeura,* for instance, must have been about 12 inches long! One is reminded of some of the creatures described by H. G. Wells in *The Food of the Gods.*

If the Protodonata larvae were indeed terrestrial, or at any rate amphibious, it is possible that the drier conditions of the Permian period, which would have had the effect of localising existing fresh-water into lakes and pools, may have provided the selective force necessary to make them become aquatic. Perhaps, in such an environment, it was only by becoming complete aquatics that larvae were able to maintain a low enough transpiration rate, and also to obtain sufficient food.

The precise circumstances in which larvae became aquatic may always remain a mystery to us, but nevertheless we should keep in mind the possibility that in Carboniferous times dragonfly larvae still led a terrestrial existence.

The next period, the Permian, is the last in the Palaeozoic era. In it we still find Meganeurids, but also some exceptionally interesting Zygoptera. Those of the Lower Permian, *Kennedya* and *Permolestes,* have been classified as Protozygoptera, whereas *Permagrion,* from the Upper Permian, is without doubt a true Zygopteran. Despite such valuable links as these in the evolutionary chain, fossils from this period are relatively scarce. It is particularly unfortunate that the geological record is not more complete at a time when such rapid and significant changes must have been taking place. In the Triassic period, which introduces the Mesozoic era, we already encounter some dragonflies very similar to certain species living to-day. Notable among these are the Heterophlebiidae. This family has been assigned to the sub-order Anisozygoptera, the members of which possess characters known to us from each of the two main recent sub-orders. About a dozen species of fossil Anisozygoptera are known to us from the Lower and Upper Lias in England, where they have been found in Gloucestershire, Warwickshire and Worcestershire.

Although the Anisozygoptera are known principally from their Mesozoic representatives, one species, *Epiophlebia superstes* (Selys), has survived to the present day in Japan. Both the larva and adult of this fascinating creature have lately received detailed morphological attention from Asahina (1954). It is possible that a second species of *Epiophlebia* exists in the Himalayan region, but so far this is known only from the larva, which is very similar to that of *E. superstes.* From his study, Asahina concluded that there is strong justification for assigning

Epiophlebia to the Anisozygoptera and thus for regarding it as one of the most primitive living dragonflies. Asahina (1954) and Fraser (1954) regard the Anisozygoptera as representing a condition in evolution near the origin of the Anisoptera.

The direction of the trends which make the Triassic a transitional stage in dragonfly evolution has become fairly clear by the Jurassic period. This great series of rocks, laid down between 170 and 140 million years ago, contains some of the most beautifully-preserved fossils that have so far been found.

The principal insect-bearing beds are the lithographic slates of Solnhofen, in what was formerly Bavaria. These sedimentary rocks were laid down in the sea, but nevertheless contain a considerable number of freshwater animals which were probably carried there by streams and rivers. The fine grain of these slates has been responsible for the preservation of some very accurate impressions of wings. Although in both quantity and variety the Solnhofen fossils surpass Odonata material from all other deposits, these strata are not actually rich in fossils. The wealth of material which has been obtained can be attributed to the assiduity of collectors: the fossils themselves are quite scarce, but the rewards offered to labourers working in the quarries have ensured that very few specimens have been lost or over-looked.

At Solnhofen, representatives of recent families of Zygoptera are encountered for the first time, together with close relatives of certain present-day Gomphids, Cordulegasterids and Petalurids. As the first larva—an Agrionid with three short caudal lamellae—had already been found in the Jurassic Dogger deposits in Siberia, we can see that the dragonfly fauna at Solnhofen was probably similar in most important respects to that of to-day.

This gives us a stirring reminder of the relative antiquity of the Odonata, when we remember that it was in the quarries at Solnhofen that the famous reptile-bird fossil, *Archaeopteryx*, was found. Thus, even a group as widespread and important as the birds was absent from the earth at a time when dragonflies were already millions of years old, and had already become established in more or less their present form. We may also note that at this time there were still no mammals on the earth.

After the valuable information left to us at Solnhofen, the fossil record is sparse and fragmentary until the Miocene period, towards the end of the Tertiary era, and about 30 to 25 million years ago.

Perhaps the most significant event occurring during this period is the appearance of the first Corduline, *Stenogomphus,* in the Oligocene of Colorado.

The Miocene period, in which much of our present-day scenery was produced, has provided two dragonfly-bearing strata of the utmost importance: the first at Florissant in Colorado, and the second at Öhningen in Germany.

The Florissant beds represent high-altitude lacustrine deposits, and have been assigned to the Lower Miocene. These beds now lie about 8,000 feet above sea-level, but they were probably fairly high up at the time when deposition was taking place. The dragonfly fauna, which apparently comprised only Coenagriidae and Aeshnidae, is roughly what one would expect to find colonising a high-level lake nowadays. The fossils include a Coenagriid larva with caudal lamellae.

The Florissant lake seems to have been long and narrow, and to have supported a warm-temperate flora on its shores. Insects belonging to the Hymenoptera, Coleoptera and Diptera were common there, so that the feeding habits of the dragonflies were doubtless much the same as they are to-day. In the lake there were also fishes and larvae of stoneflies and midges (Chironomidae). Had there been freshwater biologists in Miocene times, their work and general conclusions would probably have been much as they are now.

An interesting comparison with the Florissant fossils is provided by those at Öhningen, where there are low-altitude lacustrine deposits. The Öhningen beds consist of a thick series of marls, sandstones and limestones, both marine and freshwater, which were laid down in Upper Miocene times, some 25 million years ago. The uppermost strata, known as the Upper Freshwater Molasse, have yielded Crustacea, Mollusca, insects and fishes, besides many well-preserved plants. Here, the sediments probably accumulated slowly in water impregnated with lime, a circumstance which may well have assisted the preservation of freshwater animals.

As at Florissant, the dragonfly fauna is virtually the same as would inhabit a low-level lake to-day. The Libellulidae are well-represented, the Coenagriidae and Aeshnidae are present but not abundant, and there are perhaps a few Agrionids. The Öhningen fauna was in fact closely allied to the Holarctic fauna of to-day.

A particularly interesting feature of these deposits is that they contain large numbers of Libellulid larvae, but only relatively few adults. In this we may see the results of the water being rich in calcium carbonate. The larvae are reported as being jumbled together "in all stages of growth," some with the labium extended as if they had been killed "in the very act of catching their prey." I am a little doubtful about this interpretation of the condition of the labium, for, while in use, this organ is usually only extended for a fraction of a second. On the other hand, it is by no means uncommon to find the labium extended *post mortem* in larvae which have been killed by heat, or which have been allowed to decompose under warm conditions. It seems that the expansion of body fluids in the haemocoele is liable to extend the labium after death much as it does during life. Nevertheless, it seems likely, as Tillyard has pointed out, that a catastrophe of some kind overtook the inhabitants of this lake, perhaps early in the season, before many of the Libellulids had emerged.

If, in fact, these larvae were "in all stages of growth," then it seems probable either that they required several years to complete development, or else that their life-history was of the summer species type. Unfortunately, the fossils are not so well preserved that species can be distinguished easily, and therefore much of the size variation may be the result of the confusion of different species. Some larvae, at least, appear to be in the final instar, and these may well have been undergoing metamorphosis in warm, muddy shallows when they met their death.

This mention of the Öhningen beds brings us to the end of our brief survey of the outstanding episodes in the fossil history of dragonflies. One of the most valuable is undoubtedly the first, the saga of the giant insects of Commentry, for after this dragonflies quite quickly adopted many of the characteristics with which we associate them to-day. Some of the principal changes which have taken place since Carboniferous times are: reduction in the dense reticulation of the wing veins; evolution of the nodus, pterostigma and triangle; reduction of the tarsal segments from four to three; development of the skew thorax, and the corresponding raptorial disposition of the legs; and, in the Anisoptera, broadening of the hind-wing and extension of the area occupied by the compound eyes.

In addition to these modifications, we must remember two very important ones which happened at unknown times in dragonfly evolution, namely, the adoption of an aquatic larval life, and the evolution of the remarkable copulatory apparatus. The former, which physiologically may well have represented the greatest change of all, we have already discussed. The latter presents some baffling

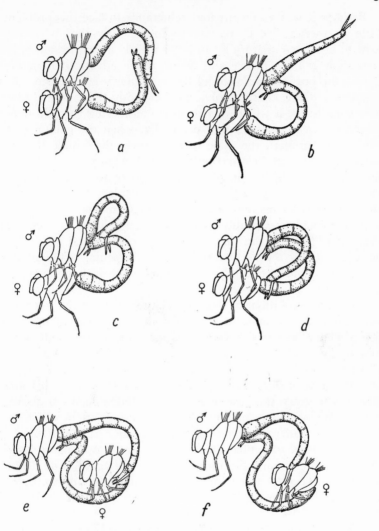

Fig. 34. Diagrams to illustrate the possible intermediate stages in the evolution of the present-day copulatory process. (After Fraser.)

problems, for it is indeed difficult to imagine a series of effectual intermediate stages which could have bridged the immense morphological and ethological gap which exists between the original condition where the genitalia were terminal, and the position obtaining to-day.

Perhaps it was a subconscious reluctance to face this problem that made Burmeister (1836) remark so ingenuously that what we now know to be the copulatory attitude "is merely an expression of mutual inclination"! Both Fraser and Moore have advanced hypotheses to explain the possible evolution of this copulatory mechanism. As their viewpoints differ considerably, and as both theories include some interesting ideas, it will be worthwhile considering them in detail.

Fraser (1939) assumes that originally, when the genitalia of both sexes were terminal, the male used to grasp the female thorax from above, with his legs, before copulation (Fig. 34,a, p. 157). He suggests that the female, in the process of curling her abdomen upwards and forwards to meet that of the male, came to place her genitalia on the ventral surface of his anterior abdominal segments (Fig. 34,b). The male, who had presumably been groping for her abdomen with his own, then "found" it in the region of his own second abdominal segment (Fig. 34,c). Fraser then postulates a deepening of the intertergital fossa in this region, resulting from the action of the combined genitalia there.

The next evolutionary step may have been for the male to have transferred his sperm from the tip of his abdomen to the recently-formed genital sac, under the second segment, before copulation, as he does to-day. The development of an intromittent organ connected with the genital fossa would doubtless have come later.

Next, Fraser suggests that the male tended to use his anal appendages to grasp the base of the female abdomen, from above, after copulation, for that would have been the position in which tandem flight could most easily have taken place (Fig. 34,d). If the tandem position had been adopted for oviposition, as it is in many Zygoptera nowadays, the female, if wishing to copulate again, would not have achieved success by curling her abdomen dorsally, and so, by chance, she might have brought it into apposition with the male genitalia (Fig. 34,c).

This stage having been reached, it would only remain for the male to grasp the female on her head, behind the eyes, instead of at the base of her abdomen, and so do this at the first copulation instead of the second, for the present-day posture to be achieved (Fig. 34,f).

A second hypothesis, as yet unpublished, has been proposed by Moore. Moore argues that, since fossil evidence for the evolution of the accessory genitalia is lacking, only studies on behaviour can at present throw light on the problem. Therefore he approaches the question from the point of view of a behaviourist, his theory being based in particular upon these facts:

1. In many predatory invertebrates the female is prevented from eating the male before copulation by a display which renders her harmless, usually because she is in a cataleptic state.

2. Copulation by means of accessory genitalia outside the Odonata occurs in animals with predatory habits, and in those which have elaborate precopulation displays (*e.g.* cuttlefish and spiders).

3. Courtship display is commonest in the most primitive family of the Odonata (Agriidae).

4. The elements of the reproductive behaviour are to some extent autonomous. That is to say, each movement in the sequence comprising the mating behaviour is not necessarily dependent on the one that normally precedes it.

The hypothesis is then developed as follows: It is probable that the rapacity of the female dragonfly was originally overcome by a male display—as is the case in spiders. This display caused a state of catalepsy in the female, and the male then placed packets of sperm (spermatophores) into the female reproductive opening. Perhaps because of the inactivity of the female some anterior part of the male was used to help push the sperm into the female. Later the anterior parts (sternites of second and third segments of the abdomen) combined to form the main organ of intromission and eventually the movements of base and end of abdomen became separated, so that the old copulation movements turned into the preliminary filling of the accessory genitalia. In the Anisoptera this became further dissociated from the rest of the sexual behaviour.

A set of intermediate stages between normal insect copulation and the situation found in the Odonata today is given in Fig. 35, on p.160. The male displays to the female, and this causes her to raise her abdomen (a). The male then seizes her by the abdomen (b) and flies off (c). The male lands and since the tarsi of the female do not touch the ground she remains immobile (d). The male then inserts the sperm into the female's genital opening, being aided by the second and third abdominal segments and their respiratory movements (e). When the male straightens his abdomen the tarsi of the female are touched, and the reflex clutching movements evoked (f). This causes the male to bend the tip of his abdomen round the head of the female. When he flies the female is carried in the fore-runner of the tandem position (g). (These last movements are suggested because leaving the female on her

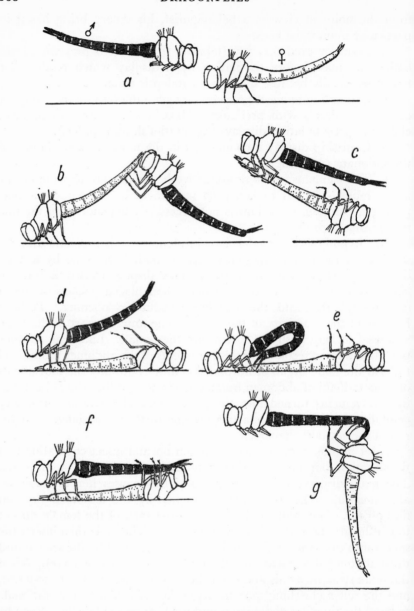

Fig. 35. Diagrams to illustrate the possible intermediate stages in the evolution of the present-day copulatory process. Male with black abdomen. (After Moore.)

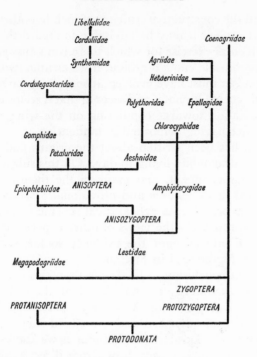

Fig. 36. Genealogical tree showing the descent of recent families of Odonata from the Protodonata stock. (After Fraser.)

back away from the water would clearly be biologically disadvantageous.)

Later the perfected tandem hold may have occurred at the stage represented by (g) in Fig. 35. Mating was attempted in this position; the end of the abdomen remained attached to the female's head or thorax and introduction of sperm (left on the abdomen by a previous copulation) into the female's genital opening occurred by means of the movements of the base of the abdomen alone. This method was perfected by the original mating movement turning into the filling of the accessory genitalia which henceforth always preceded the new mating movement.

I have given a brief account of these theories, not only because they seem to be the only ones available, but also because they give one a good idea of the complications involved in the evolution of this mechanism. The almost complete lack of evidence makes both the formulation and the constructive criticism of such hypotheses extremely difficult, and at present it may be advisable to regard this problem as an interesting mental exercise for which there is no answer. However, we are probably on safe enough ground if we assume two things: first, that this mechanism must have evolved at some very early stage, since it is found in all recent Odonata, and second, that it seems to be a highly specialised adaptation towards copulating on the wing, and perhaps mating again after having oviposited in tandem.

A great deal has been written about the origins and relationships of the families of dragonflies living to-day. On this subject, also, there is considerable disagreement, and many of the theories put forward must be regarded as speculative and provisional. Recently, however, Fraser (1954) has produced a genealogical scheme of affinities which seems to give expression to the views of other experts besides himself, and also to take into account the evidence so far available. This scheme has been reproduced in Fig. 36.

One important conclusion to be drawn from this genealogical tree is that the Anisozygoptera are not placed at the point of original divergence of the Zygoptera and Anisoptera. Instead, it is considered that they represent an advanced and specialised stage of Zygopteran evolution which finally led to the Anisoptera as we know them to-day. Another conclusion which Fraser draws from direct fossil evidence is that the Zygoptera, in particular the Coenagriidae, have the most primitive origin of all present-day dragonflies. The dramatic part played by the Carboniferous Meganeuridae, whose size gave them a superficial resemblance to the Anisoptera, is liable to give the false impression that Anisopterous dragonflies are the most primitive.

Their fossil record shows the Odonata to be one of the most primitive of insect groups, and an Order which has retained a recognisable individuality for at least 200 million years, longer than any other insects except perhaps the Orthoptera. The ability of dragonflies to exist as a successful and cosmopolitan group after having survived vast periods of time without undergoing appreciable change must make them one of the finest living vindications of evolutionary conservatism. Indeed, we may well ask how such morphological stability has been achieved.

I believe that part of the explanation lies in the fact that the ecological niche the adults occupy, apart from placing a premium on aerial agility and visual acuity (surely features that would always be of selective value), has not encouraged specialisation of feeding. Thus, retaining generalised feeding habits, and living in an element where overcrowding and competition for prey are virtually impossible, they have avoided two of the most severe selective forces with which other animals have to contend. Probably their major problem, at least since Jurassic times, has been to achieve survival for the larval stage, committed to a limited food supply in a habitat liable to severe restrictions in space and time. Certainly it is among the larvae that we encounter the greatest diversity of form and habit.

Whatever hazards they may have had to face, we may observe thankfully that they have overcome them with consummate success. If geological history repeats itself, then long after many of the animal groups we know to-day have disappeared from the earth, dragonflies will still be here, feeding impartially but well, on whatever small creatures swim or fly into their ken.

CHAPTER 13

DRAGONFLIES AND OTHER ANIMALS
(N.W.M.)

This ought to convince us of our ignorance of the mutual relations of all organic beings; a conviction as necessary as it is difficult to acquire.

C. DARWIN (1859). *The Origin of Species*

EACH ANIMAL is linked to every other animal by some sort of connection. Not only is each animal actually related genetically to every other animal, but at any one time there exists an immense pattern of ecological relationships—between prey and predator, host and parasite, and between competitors. Some of the ecological links are so tenuous that they can be ignored, others are vital. It is the job of the ecologist, the biologist who studies the relationships between plants and animals and the physical environment, to assess which ones are important and which unimportant. In this chapter I shall attempt to show what place the dragonflies have in the environments in which they occur in Britain.

Before deciding on whether dragonflies are ecologically important members of our fauna, we must define what we mean by important. By an important animal, I mean one which if it becomes extinct or much more abundant than it was before causes a revolution in the environment so that the numbers of other species are changed: the old balance is destroyed and a new one takes its place. The Lemming is an important animal—C. Elton and others have shown how it occupies a central position in the Arctic: the Lemming's numbers fluctuate and so as a result do those of the Arctic Fox and the other animals that prey upon it. Tsetse flies are important animals: their presence or absence determines whether a whole host of mammals, including man himself, can live in vast areas of Africa.

In Britain, man is much the most important animal—every species of animal and plant has been enormously affected by the great population increase of man which has occurred since the Ice Age. But other

a. Sympetrum sanguineum, female. Mature in colour. Black legs, black collar across neck, and rather strong yellow wing-bases, distinguish her from *S. striolatum* female.

b. Sympetrum danae, female. Semimature,. and very like the immature male, but with rather more black on the abdomen. Much brighter yellow laterally on the thorax, and distinct black dorsal triangle, distinguishes her from other *Sympetrum* females.

Plate 23. DRAGONFLIES (ANISOPTERA : LIBELLULIDAE)

a. *Sympetrum flaveolum,* male. Mature and unmistakable by the extent of the yellow colour on the wings. Female similar. In both sexes the black line across the frons is pronounced.

b. *Sympetrum fonscolombei,* female. Teneral, and very similar to *S. striolatum,* but more orange, than sandy, in colour, and with red veins, which develop quickly. Mature male is very red. The structure of the genitalia in both sexes, is quite distinctive.

Plate 24. DRAGONFLIES (ANISOPTERA : LIBELLULIDAE)

creatures are very important too. The Rabbit—a species introduced by man—which only in 1954 was one of the key animals of the British environment, is now (1958) quite rare in much of the country as a result of the depredations of the *Myxoma* virus, introduced by man into Western Europe. The changes of plant and animal life that we are now experiencing prove that the Rabbit was an important animal.

In our present state of ignorance it is much more difficult to say what animals are unimportant, but most very rare species must have very limited ecological importance.

Dragonflies are predators, but like Warblers, Seals, Perch and many other predators, they are also prey for larger animals. They are also hosts for a number of parasites. A parasite is of course a special form of predator. No dragonflies are parasites themselves. From the ecological point of view therefore we must think of dragonflies as providing food for other animals, including parasites, and as taking their share of the food available and therefore as potential competitors with other species.

First, we must consider what animals dragonflies affect in these ways and then try to assess what the effects are.

Dragonflies provide a source of food for other animals at all stages. Their eggs are parasitised by minute wasps. For example the eggs of *Anagrus incarnatus* (Haliday) are laid in them. The wasp's larva feeds on the eggs and after pupation inside them it emerges by swimming to the surface of the water with its minute oar-like wings.

The larvae are eaten by many of the other predators which live in fresh water. They are eaten by the larvae and adults of water beetles, which tear them to pieces with powerful jaws, and by aquatic bugs (*e.g. Naucoris* and *Notonecta*) which pierce them with their beak-like mouthparts and suck out their internal fluids by means of hydraulic pumps in their heads. Fish, both young and old, eat many dragonfly larvae, and so do newts. All these predators live with the dragonfly larvae in the water: other predators are terrestrial creatures which take some or all of their food from the water. Herons and ducks (especially diving ducks), Coots, and Water Rails eat many of the larger dragonfly larvae. Water Shrews also prey on them.

The larvae of dragonflies harbour many parasites, including Trematode worms, part of whose life-history is spent in a dragonfly and a later stage in a bird. For the parasite to survive the dragonfly containing the parasite must be eaten by a bird.

As soon as the adult dragonfly crawls out of the water still clad in

D—M

the skin of the last larval instar it meets a whole range of new predators. While emerging and on its emergence flight it is particularly vulnerable (see p. 91). Blackbirds, House Sparrows, Wagtails, Flycatchers, Swallows, Hobbies and Black-headed Gulls feed ravenously on teneral dragonflies. Many individuals drift into the webs of spiders and hunting spiders seek them out and devour them. Frogs, toads, Slow-worms and lizards, also feed on them. Occasionally small damselflies become entangled on the sticky leaves of Sundew and are absorbed by these plants.

Not only at emergence are dragonflies very vulnerable; egg laying is a dangerous time for many species. The fish, newts and predaceous insects which pursued them as larvae in the water also come up and take the females of those species which insert their eggs into water plants.

One of the best known parasites of adult dragonflies is the water mite *Arrenhurus* which is often to be found clustering upon the underside of the thorax. Its behaviour has already been mentioned by Philip Corbet in Chapter 8, p. 102. A minute parasitic fly (*Pterobosca paludis* Macfie) is sometimes found on the wings of dragonflies. It lives by sucking blood from the veins of the wing. Like the mite it becomes dispersed by the dispersal movements of the dragonfly.

This brief account shows that there are many predators of dragon-flies; similarly they themselves feed on a large range of other animals. As we have seen in a previous chapter both larva and adult attempt to eat almost any small object that is moving above a certain speed. Therefore almost any small animal that swims or flies past a dragonfly is taken. Dragonfly larvae feed on the larvae of mayflies, stoneflies, water-beetles and bugs, on fish fry, and terrestrial animals, such as earthworms which drop into the water and wriggle as they sink to the bottom. Only water-snails seem exempt—they move too slowly, but if one moves a water-snail held in a pair of forceps quickly in front of a dragonfly larva it will take it too. The adult dragonfly will eat many species of insect—mainly small flies and beetles but also bees, wasps, butterflies, moths, bugs, even caterpillars if these are swinging on threads from a tree. The indiscriminate method of feeding shown by dragonflies often results in their taking unpalatable and sometimes inedible objects and rejecting them later. They therefore kill more than they need. Nevertheless some individuals do show distinct food preferences: I have seen an *L. depressa* fly at hive bees, but repeatedly fly away from them after close inspection.

We have seen that dragonflies affect individuals of many other species. To what extent do they affect whole populations of other animals? Are any other species dependent upon them for food and are dragonflies dependent upon any species of prey? Do they compete with other species and cause them to occur in smaller numbers than would be the case if the dragonflies were not present? These are very difficult questions to answer.

Here we are dealing only with direct effects, but some indirect ones may be much more important. For example, a predator species P. may feed on two prey species, F.1. and F.2. Normally it controls F.1's population but not F.2's. F.1. and F.2. have no direct ecological connection between them—they may live in quite different habitats. If F.2. becomes much commoner, P. may switch most of its attention to it and so cease to control the population of F.1. In this case direct large scale predation by P. on F.2. may have no controlling effect on F.2's population, but F.1. may be greatly affected indirectly by F.2. with which it has no direct ecological link.

As among all invertebrates there is an enormous difference in numbers between larvae and adults. I once collected out all the large larvae I could find in a small pond in Somerset. I caught 61—mainly *A. cyanea*. Observations before and after showed that there were never more than 3 adult dragonflies at the pond at one time. This ratio is probably not unusual. That between adults and larvae of all sizes is of course enormously greater. We should therefore expect dragonfly larvae to be very much more important ecologically than adults. Not only are they much commoner but they are more concentrated in space. The painstaking research of C. H. Kennedy (1950) and others show what eats what, but can only give hints about the effects of different predator/prey relationships. However, they suggest that dragonfly larvae are an important food of some species of fish and some ducks, that dragonfly larvae can be an important predator of fish fry and that adult dragonflies may be important predators of bees. The economic significance of this is discussed in the next chapter. Most of the work on the food relationships of dragonflies has been done in the United States where dragonflies are more abundant than in Britain. The adults are almost certainly not important predators. Apart from parasites dependent upon them, only one species of animal in Britain seems to be affected by the distribution of dragonflies and for it they are probably only a minor factor affecting its distribution. The species is the Hobby. Owing to persecution this beautiful falcon is rare but those who are lucky enough to live where it is found will note how frequently it settles near ponds and is often to be seen hunting over them. It seizes emerging dragonflies with its feet and transfers them to its beak—the dragonfly wings can sometimes be seen fluttering slowly down to the water.

Perhaps the most striking type of ecological relationship shown by dragonflies is that between different species of the group. Dragonfly larvae eat each other and the adults eat each other and compete with each other for space above their breeding places. In previous chapters we have seen that there are explanations for these phenomena: dragonfly larvae feed on fast moving prey; larvae, especially younger ones or larvae belonging to smaller species, frequently provide the necessary sign stimuli to make the attacker feed on them. The interspecific relationship of adult dragonflies is particularly noticeable. On several occasions I have seen adult Anisoptera eat Zygoptera, and occasionally other Anisoptera. On one occasion I watched an *A. grandis* eat an *A. mixta,* a slightly smaller species of the same genus, by the edge of the moat of Michelham Priory in Sussex. Although Zygoptera are much larger than most of the insects taken by Anisoptera, they must usually provide food stimuli rather than mate stimuli. In the case of Anisoptera eating other Anisoptera, the attacking insect probably starts by fighting or attempting to mate with the prey insect but in the course of the struggle, its mouthparts come in contact with it and what was seized as a rival or mate is eaten, as it were, by accident.

The amount of interspecific fighting to be observed on almost any pond or stream far exceeds the amount of similar fighting between birds—as we have seen this is probably due to dragonflies frequently being in a physiological state in which they react to sub-optimal stimuli. The results of interspecific fighting can sometimes be directly observed. For example on 3 October 1949 I watched a male *A. juncea* flying up and down a stretch of a stream. Its beat was about 67 yards long. A male *A. cyanea* soon appeared in the middle of the *A. juncea*'s beat and established its own beat of about 17 yards there, thereby restricting the beat of the *A. juncea* to about 40 yards of the lower part of its original one. Whenever the insects met there was a vigorous chase—usually the *A. cyanea* chased the *A. juncea* over the adjoining field. After about 10 minutes the *A. cyanea* left—visits to water are often short in this species—the *A. juncea* resumed its original beat of *c.* 67 yards.

On page 121 I mentioned how a population of *S. striolatum*

appeared to be greatly reduced during a morning by clashes with larger species which were present by the same stream.

Recent observations and experiments of the kind mentioned on p. 124, show that interspecific fighting between adults varies between species: the greatest amount occurs between those which look rather similar, *e.g. Anax, A. juncea* and *A. cyanea.*

The amount of interspecific interaction may partly depend on the

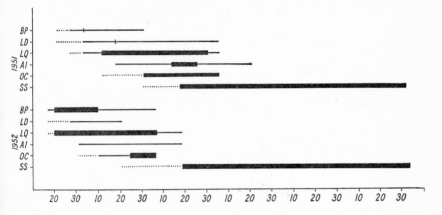

Fig. 37. The coincidence of seasons of the different species of dragonfly by a Somerset stream, 1951-52. (Half mile stretch.) BP, *Brachytron pratense;* LD, *Libellula depressa;* LQ, *Libellula quadrimaculata;* OC, *Orthetrum cancellatum;* SS, *Sympetrum striolatum;* AI, *Anax imperator.* Occasions of first record of immature insect and first record of adult insect are joined by dots. Lengths of observed adult seasons are indicated by lines, narrow when less than four, broad when more than three mature males were present. Figs.=days of months from May to October.

genetic constitution and the physiological state of the insects. But it also depends on physical factors. In 1951, the year when the *Sympetrum* referred to above were ousted, the spring was a very late one—and so the flying season of *S. striolatum* coincided with that of the spring species *Anax, L. quadrimaculata, L. depressa* and *O. cancellatum,* with the results that we have seen. Next year the spring was not late and by the time *S. striolatum* were mature the spring species had largely disappeared from the river (see Fig. 37, above). Roughly the same coincidence of season occurs each year; so we can say that, as far as adults are concerned, an early spring species like *Brachytron* never competes with a summer species like *A. cyanea.* It may well be that interspecific competition between dragonflies has caused the annual pattern which is so familiar to the student of dragonflies in Britain. The Aeshnine niche is first filled by *Brachytron*, then by *Anax* (and *A. isosceles*) then by *A. cyanea* (and the other Aeshnas). The Libelluline niche is first filled by the species of the genus *Libellula*, then a little later but overlapping with them come the species of the genus *Orthetrum* and then *Sympetrum*.

We must conclude this chapter by saying that in the British Isles there is very little evidence to suggest that dragonflies are ecologically important. There appear to be two reasons for this; comparatively speaking they are not at all numerous, and secondly they are generalised feeders. As such they can rarely control their prey because they begin to eat another prey species when the members of the original prey species begin to become uncommon. They appear to be nearly as isolated ecologically as they are systematically. If they were all to disappear to-morrow—many individuals of many species of many kinds of animals would be affected, but no great revolutions or re-adjustments of populations would result. But this is merely a guess . . .

CHAPTER 14

DRAGONFLIES AND MAN
(N.W.M.)

It is good to drink tea in the spring breeze,
At sunset on this flat terrace,
Inking my pen on the slanting stone balustrade,
I sit down to write a poem on the wu-tung leaf,
Here is a kingfisher singing on a bamboo clothes rack,
There is a dragonfly clinging to a fishing line,
Now that I know what quiet enjoyment is,
I shall come here again and again.

TU FU, *8th Century* A.D.

IN THIS final chapter we shall discuss the impact of dragonflies on man and man on dragonflies.

The question "are they useful?" is frequently asked by the non-naturalist. The layman who asks it is generally not ecologically minded so he tends to think of species as separate entities rather than members of the community in which they live. He thinks that if they eat something valuable to man they are "bad" and if they eat a pest they are "good." This is by no means always the case; predators may benefit their prey by preventing over-population. Therefore a predator can live principally on animals which are useful to man and by so doing can enable those animals to flourish and so man to benefit. And the converse can also happen—a predator may live entirely on some noxious pest and by so doing may be beneficial to the pest species. Or, again, if it does not eat a sufficient number of the pest, it may have no controlling effect upon it whatever. The question of usefulness is a most difficult one to answer. In our present state of ignorance about dragonflies and their prey and competitors, we can only give a qualified "do not know."

As we have seen dragonflies affect other species by being potential prey, by eating them, by providing parasites with a host, and by competition. As we have also seen, they are generalised feeders eating anything within a certain size range which moves quickly enough across their field of vision, and so are less likely to control their prey than species with more specialised feeding habits. Even so there is evidence that in some circumstances dragonflies have an economic effect; in some instances it has been sufficient to stimulate man to control their numbers.

Dragonfly larvae, since they are far more numerous, are much more likely to be of ecological and therefore of economic importance than adults. The work of a number of American biologists suggests that dragonfly larvae are an important food of fishes of economic importance, and perhaps of some diving ducks. For example, C. B. Wilson (1918) found that dragonfly larvae made up 62-70 per cent of the total food of the 290 Largemouth Black Bass of over 90 mm length, which were dissected, and C. Cottam (1939) found that in October dragonfly larvae made up 14 per cent of food taken by 18 Ring-necked Ducks (a close relation of our Tufted Duck).

In several places in the tropics dragonflies are directly useful to man: they are eaten. Carveth Wells (in Needham and Heywood 1929) describes how they were caught in Malaya with the aid of long sticks, smeared with a kind of bird lime. At the end of the day the dragon-flies were eaten having been fried in oil and garnished with onions and shrimps: (why is it respectable for us to eat shrimps but not dragonflies?).

On the debit side there is good evidence that the larvae of some of the larger species (*Anax, Aeshna, Cordulegaster,* etc.) can have a serious effect on fish fry in fish ponds. O. R. Kingsbury (1937) estimated that *Anax* larvae were capable of halving the number of fish reared in a rearing pond.

As we have seen, dragonflies both larvae and adult, harbour the intermediate stages of many parasites. Some of these are economically important, for example the fluke *Prosthogonimus macrorchis* Macy which affects the oviducts of hens and can cause a 90 per cent loss in egg production. Libellulines provide the intermediate host of this trematode. The larvae (cercariae) of this parasite emerge from a freshwater snail and are sucked into the rectum of a Libelluline larvae by its respiratory movements. Later the cercariae make their way into the muscles and encyst in the blood spaces—there they may remain until the dragonfly has emerged as an adult. The trematode can only become an adult if the larval or adult dragonfly in which it is encysted, is eaten by a bird, its final host. Chickens should be kept away from ponds so that they cannot eat larvae and emerging adults and thereby infect themselves.

Larval and adult dragonflies eat large quantities of larval and adult mosquitoes and other noxious insects. E. H. Hinman (1934) records that seven larvae of the large Libelluline *Pantala flavescens* in an aquarium tank ate 1,200 mosquito larvae in one day. These facts have been used for pro-dragonfly propaganda. For example dragonflies have been described as "particular friends of mankind" on this account. So struck was Dr. R. H. Lamborn with the possibility of controlling mosquitoes by increasing the number of dragonflies that he offered prizes for essays on the subject. Even R. J. Tillyard suggested that colonies of dragonflies should be "planted" in ornamental parks and gardens in order to keep down gnats. When we consider the immense abundance of mosquitoes and the comparative rarity of dragonflies, and that their population density is further decreased by territorial behaviour, it is extremely unlikely that dragonflies ever control or could control mosquitoes. But it should be emphasised that there is no experimental evidence one way or the other. Individual services to mankind are another matter: over 700 years ago a dragonfly pounced on a gadfly that had stung the arm of the Japanese Emperor. So grateful was the Emperor that he asked his poets to write a poem to commemorate the occasion. Not surprisingly perhaps they did not respond very quickly to his request and so he composed one himself:

> *Even a creeping insect*
> *Waits upon the Great Lord*
> *Thy form it will bear*
> *O Yamato, land of the dragonfly*

The adults of two large American species *Anax junius* (Drury) and *Coryphaeshna ingens* (Rambur) are serious predators of hive bees in the south-eastern United States. In this area they do so much damage that queen-rearing is impractical. M. Wright (1946) recorded that when no dragonflies were present 75–85 per cent of the queens returned to the apiary after their nuptial flights but when dragonflies were plentiful only 5 per cent returned. So many workers were taken that the colonies "were severely weakened." In Britain dragonflies have been recorded as taking bees but they do not appear to be a serious pest.

We can summarise the economic effect of dragonflies by saying that the larvae are an important prey of some fish and duck which are important to sportsmen, but that under certain conditions, they are also an important predator of fish fry; the adults, except for local depredations on bees are unimportant either as a pest or an ally of man. But again we must emphasize that we do not know for certain—in the intricate pattern of cause and effect, involving the whole web of life, dragonflies may be found to affect man in ways he has never expected.

It is not in the field of economics that dragonflies can be claimed to be important. Their value to man is scientific and aesthetic. We hope that this book has at least suggested some of the ways in which dragonflies are interesting and that the opportunities they provide for study far exceed their ecological or economic importance. To the student of ecology and behaviour they are extremely valuable creatures.

It is customary to mention the aesthetic side of a study at the beginning of a book not at its end, but there is some point in saving up what is most important to the end (the reason, admitted or not, that the naturalist or scientist is studying animals is generally aesthetic). Animals (especially dragonflies!) are valuable because they are beautiful.

Considering the obvious beauty of dragonflies and that it can be seen clearly with the naked eye, it is surprising that they have not entered more into the consciousness of man. In Britain many mammals, birds and butterflies have been known by English names for hundreds of years, indicating an affectionate familiarity, but no dragonfly to-day has a real English name. In fact the opposite to affection is implied in most of the names given by the English to the Odonata: Horse-adders, Horse-stingers, Devils Darning-needles, Snake-doctors, even Dragonfly itself. All these names are uncomplimentary, if not libellous: no dragonfly has a sting nor can it hurt man or horse. But they are large, and look as if they could sting, and they are often attracted by the swarms of flies which collect round man or beast in the field: it is not surprising that they are held in awe. The Norwegians go even further: A. Tjønneland writes (1951) that in the south of Norway they are called Oyestikker ("eye-stingers") and further north they are called Orsnell ("ear snail") and are believed to creep into the ear as the English—surely with rather more justification—believe that earwigs do.

Only one species of British dragonfly has acquired a naturalist's name. It is *Agrion virgo* which is sometimes called King George—

presumably a flattering but delightfully unsuitable allusion to George III. The French name Demoiselle has largely replaced King George in recent times, and also the other vernacular name of "Kingfisher" mentioned by Harris in 1782. In some parts of the world no distinction is made between dragonflies and other insects, for example in parts of West Africa the same word is used for both dragonfly and butterfly.

The Japanese are the honourable exception to the general obtuseness of man to dragonfly. Tombo (the dragonfly) is one of the Empire's emblems. Japan is often referred to as Akitsushima (the Dragonfly Island). This is a good biological description—since the Japanese dragonfly fauna is outstanding, but the historical reason given for this description is that when the first emperor Jimmu Tenno gazed at his domain from a mountain he thought that it looked like "a dragonfly licking its tail" (cleaning its ovipositor or transferring sperm to the accessory genitalia?).

Thirty-two species of Japanese dragonflies have common names. To the Japanese the dragonfly is a playful irresponsible creature. To be called a dragonfly in Japan is like being called a butterfly in Britain. But one dragonfly at least is held in high regard, the Shoryo tombo, the Dragonfly of the Dead, for it is this species which carries the august spirits of the Ancestors to their families on their annual visit during the Bon festival.

Not only are dragonflies often mentioned in the writings of the Japanese, they are depicted with delicate appreciation by their artists. In the British Museum there is a beautiful Hokusai print showing a male Libelluline (Print B.178). A small part of one wing is damaged— Hokusai had clearly observed the territorial fighting of dragonflies and its physical effects. The picture is the visual complement to the lines of the poet Yayu—

> *Lonesomely clings the dragonfly to the*
> *underside of the leaf*
> *Ah! the Autumn rain.*

The Chinese are not as dragonfly conscious as the Japanese; nevertheless the most beautiful dragonfly paintings in the world come from China. "The Insect Scroll" by the thirteenth century artist Ch'ien Hsüan is particularly fine. Parts are reproduced in William Cohn's *Chinese Painting* (Phaidon Press): a Libelluline with coloured wings is poised for flight and a horde of gnats is under attack from three great Aeshnines—three little frogs watch the proceedings. Chinese poets too have noticed them, witness the lines by Tu Fu at the beginning of this chapter.

The physical impact of man on dragonflies has been far greater than the impact of dragonflies on man. He has drained marshes and lakes, polluted rivers and changed their rate of flow with weirs and locks. On the other hand he has made countless ponds and reservoirs, artificial lakes and ditches, and in Western Europe has connected all the main river systems with canals. The distribution of most of our species must have changed enormously during the last few hundred years as a result of human activities.

For many species man has probably been a help rather than a hindrance. Take for example an area in the Sussex Weald, the land within a 4 miles radius of Battle. In the Dark Ages this consisted mainly of thick forest divided by brackish marshes and shallow arms of the sea. The little streams can only have been suitable (as they are to-day) for *A. virgo*, *Pyrrhosoma* and *I. elegans*, and the less saline parts of the marshes for *L. sponsa* and *dryas*, *I. elegans*, *S. striolatum* and *S. sanguineum*. There can have been little suitable habitat for Aeshnines, Cordulines or the large Libellulines. Today in this small area there are two reservoirs, eight large artificial ponds (old hammer ponds and ornamental lakes) many small artificial ponds (cattle ponds and water-filled iron-pits) and many yards of drainage ditches. At least 21 species of dragonfly breed in this small area: one reservoir has been colonised by 15 species, the other by 10, *Anax*, *A. cyanea*, *A. grandis*, and *S. striolatum*, are common throughout the area. *Cordulia* breeds in at least 6 man-made localities *O. cancellatum* in 4, *L. dryas* in 2. There can be little doubt that the present day dragonfly fauna is much richer than it was a thousand years ago.

While the commoner species probably benefited throughout Britain from man's activities, some of those with restricted habitat requirements have probably become rarer because of them. The species which have probably suffered most are those confined to bogs and marshes, *I. pumilio*, *C. mercuriale*, *C. armatum* and *Ceriagrion*, since man has drained many of their breeding places. Of these four species *Ceriagrion* prefers the most acid bogs, and since these are less worthwhile to drain from the agricultural point of view, more of them have been left. The other three seem to prefer water with a slightly higher pH and these bogs are potentially more valuable and so have been reclaimed more, to the detriment of the dragonflies.

Similarly the East Anglian species *A. isosceles* was commoner at one time than it is now. There is no reason to believe that *Oxygastra* was ever really common—but new housing estates are fast encroaching on its most famous locality.

Throughout the world man is fast reaching the time when the survival of our larger vertebrates and many invertebrates will depend on whether or not he decides to protect them. Put another way, the distribution of countless animals and plants will depend on where he allows them to remain. For scientific and aesthetic reasons, and in many species for economic reasons too, it is desirable to pass on as much as possible of the biological inheritance which we have received. But the wealth of life that we have inherited will be lost for ever unless active steps are taken to protect it.

Dragonflies in Britain do not yet pose many urgent problems of conservation because most of the British species are fairly abundant and widely distributed. But we must look to the future. The rate of development increases every year: drainage schemes that are impracticable to-day will be easily undertaken when power becomes cheap in the Atomic Age. Competition for land will almost certainly continue to increase, especially in the south of England.

The creation of the Nature Conservancy in 1949 demonstrated the country's recognition that in an age of official destruction there must also be official conservation. It was clear that the valiant efforts of many private landowners and private societies to preserve our biological resources must be given support by the country as a whole. At the time of writing (1958) there are 70 National Nature Reserves. These reserves are selected primarily as the best available examples of the main types of habitat found in Britain to-day to act both as out of door laboratories and living museums. What is important from our present point of view is that some of them include the breeding places of rare dragonfly species, for example the Cairngorms Nature Reserve contains populations of *S. arctica* and *A. caerulea,* and Hartland Moor Nature Reserve in Dorset is the home of large numbers of *Ceriagrion.* But many of the rarer species live in small bogs or streams which, even if their total flora and fauna are of great interest, are too small to be administered as nature reserves. These places can be given some protection by notifying them as "Sites of Special Scientific Interest" to the owners and the Planning Authorities. This means that the Nature Conservancy is informed of any subsequently proposed development affecting the sites and so is given an opportunity to ask the owner to preserve their scientific interest and to advise him on how to do so. Breeding places of *Oxygastra, Leucorrhinia, I. pumilio* and other species have been given this form of protection.

If conservation measures are to succeed they must be based on a full knowledge of the natural history of the species to be protected. We must for example know their habitat requirements and how small an isolated population can be to be strong enough to survive the normal rigours of existence. As we have shown in this book we know very little: it must end on a plea for more study of these fascinating insects, study which will help us to enjoy them increasingly and will enable others to enjoy them in the future.

MAPS SHOWING THE
DISTRIBUTION OF THE DRAGONFLIES
IN THE BRITISH ISLES

THE following maps, compiled by Cynthia Longfield, give the known distribution to the end of the year 1957. When there are any records for a county, then the whole of it is "blacked in." The "hatched" areas show an authentic record (unless with a question mark (?)), but the species is either now extinct, or the status is very uncertain. Breeding has not been established for all the "blacked in" counties.

38. *Agrion virgo* (L.)

39. *Agrion splendens* (Harr.)

40. *Lestes sponsa* (Hans.)

D—N

41. *Lestes dryas* Kirby

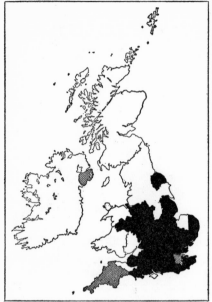

42. *Erythromma najas* (Hans.)

43. *Platycnemis pennipes* (Pall.)

44. *Ischnura elegans* (Lind.)

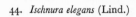

45. *Ischnura pumilio* (Charp.)

46. *Pyrrhosoma nymphula* (Sulz.)

47. *Ceriagrion tenellum* (Vill.)

48. *Coenagrion pulchellum* (Lind.)

49. *Coenagrion puella* (L.)

50. A. *Coenagrion hastulatum* (Charp.)
    B. *Coenagrion mercuriale* (Charp.)

51. A. *Coenagrion armatum* (Charp.)
    B. *Coenagrion scitulum* (Ramb.)

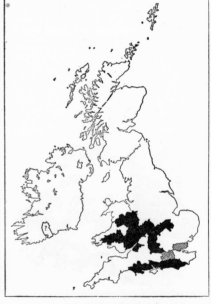

52. *Enallagma cyathigerum* (Charp.)

53. *Gomphus vulgatissimus* (L.)

54. *Cordulegaster boltoni* (Don.)

55. *Brachytron pratense* (Müll.)

56. *Anax imperator* Leach

57. *Aeshna grandis* (L.)

58. *Aeshna cyanea* (Müll.)

59. *Aeshna juncea* (L.)

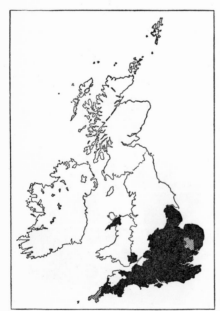

60. *Aeshna mixta* Latr.

61. A. *Aeshna caerulea* (Ström)
    B. *Aeshna isosceles* (Müll.)

62. *Cordulia aenea* (L.)

63. *Somatochlora metallica* (Lind.)

64. A. *Oxygastra curtisi* (Dale)
    B. *Somatochlora arctica* (Zett.)

65. *Orthetrum coerulescens* (Fabr.)

66. *Orthetrum cancellatum* (L.)

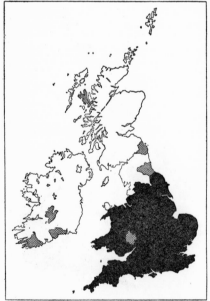

68. *Libellula depressa* L.

67. *Libellula quadrimaculata* L

69. *Libellula fulva* Müll.

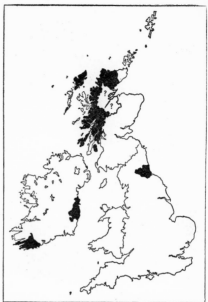

70. *Sympetrum striolatum* (Charp.)

71. *Sympetrum nigrescens* Lucas.

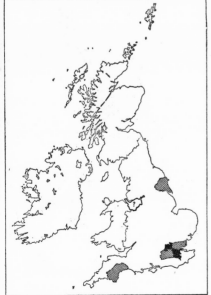

72. *Sympetrum vulgatum* (L.) The hatched records were previous to 1910.

73. *Sympetrum sanguineum* (Müll.)

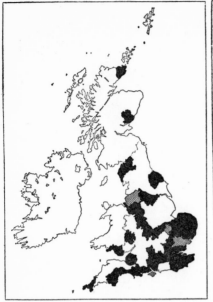

74. *Sympetrum flaveolum* (L.)

75. *Sympetrum fonscolombei* (Selys)

76. *Sympetrum danae* (Sulz.)

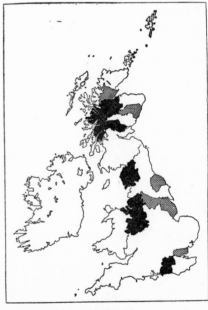

77. *Leucorrhinia dubia* (Lind.)

APPENDIX I

A Key to the Larvae of the British Odonata *

A. E. GARDNER

INTRODUCTION

The separation characters summarized in the following key have been based on those found in the mature larvae. In many species, however, the characters are sufficiently well developed to enable relatively immature specimens to be identified; these species have been indicated in the text.

Although thirty species of the British Odonata have been bred from the egg to the imaginal stage, it is considered necessary to breed the remaining thirteen species before any attempt is made to provide a key for the identification of the very early instars. Indeed, it may well prove impossible to provide a reliable key at specific level. However, some species have been found to exhibit distinctive characters at the 2nd instar and these characters have been included in the keys to the mature larvae.

With most species a sufficient degree of maturity will have been reached for identification if it is found that the wing-sheaths reach beyond the 3rd abdominal segment. It is considered inadvisable to name specimens prior to this stage unless special characters are evident; this applies especially to Zygopterous larvae. The lengths of the mature larvae have been given and in many species will be seen to be very variable. Measurements are in millimetres from the front margin of the head, or forward protuberance of the labium, to the tip of the anal appendages. With spirit-preserved specimens a shrinkage of ten per cent may be expected. The exuvia of the Zygopterous larvae may fall well below the minimum length indicated for a given species on account of the telescoping of the abdominal segments; whilst Anisopterous exuviae may slightly exceed the maximum length indicated on account of the abdominal segments being fully distended. In order to facilitate identification, keys have been constructed for Suborders, families, genera and finally for species, with the sole exception of the

---

Entomologist's Gazette, 1954, 5:157-171, 193-213, with additions to *Sympetrum* Key, 1955, *Entomologist's Gazette,* 6:94-95.

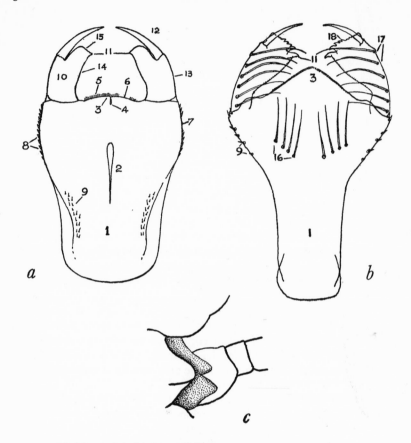

a. Labium of *Aeshna juncea* (L.)
b. Labium of *Coenagrion hastulatum* (Charp.)

1 Prementum	10 Labial palpus
2 Median sulcus	11 End hook
3 Median lobe	12 Movable hook
4 Median cleft	13 Outer margin of palpus
5 Piliform setae	14 Inner margin of palpus
6 Distal margin of median lobe	15 Distal margin of palpus
7 Lateral margin of prementum	16 Premental setae
8 Spines	17 Palpal setae
9 Spiniform setae	18 Intermediate hooks

c. Supracoxal armature of *Aeshna cyanea* (Müll.)

Corduliidae. In this family, the scheme adopted, namely the omission of a key to the genera, is considered easier for the student to follow. Wherever possible characters have been included which will assist the identification of living specimens. Unfortunately, however, this is not possible with all species and it may be found necessary to kill the subject in order to examine the labium or "mask." With exuviae, the labium may either be detached and made into a permanent slide mount, or merely attached to a slip of card and kept with the specimen. With the larger species it is usually sufficient to extend the labium by previously softening the base and labial suture in water for a short time.

Previous authors have relied on the number of premental and palpal setae to provide a sufficient means of identification for a number of species, but the examination of a long series of known larvae and exuviae has proved this character to be seldom reliable as the variation is often considerable. Although the full variation found in the number of premental and palpal setae is given, the character and disposition of small fields of setae have often been found to be more reliable guides. The shape of the labium and distal border of the labial palpi are also important separation characters. All drawings of the labium show the organ as flattened on a slide. The terminology used is that put forward by Corbet (1953).

In the *Aeshnidae* the supracoxal armature (Fig. c) situated on the dorsal surface at the base of the fore-legs, although slightly variable in outline, will help to confirm the identification. The shape of the head, both dorsal and frontal aspect, shape of the abdomen, mid-dorsal and lateral abdominal spines are important characters. Larvae breeding in muddy habitats frequently have the abdominal spines obscured by dirt; this may be cleaned off gently with a camel-hair brush. Any dirt may be cleaned from exuviae by boiling in a weak solution of caustic potash for half-a-minute, followed by careful brushing.

With most Zygopterous larvae the caudal lamellae provide a useful character for identification. A live larva may have a lamella removed without injury to the specimen by placing it in a dish of water and taking hold of the organ with a pair of tweezers, the points of which have been stoned to remove any excessive sharpness which may injure the lamella. When held by the tweezers the larva will cast the organ off. It is generally desirable to remove the median lamella as this is the most distinctive in outline. It may be examined in water as a temporary mount on a slide, or made into a permanent mount using glycerine jelly, a medium which shows up the tracheation well. The distorted lamellae of exuviae may be softened in water, straightened and mounted in a suitable medium. With those species of the *Zygoptera* in which the lamellae have the edge armature differentiated into stout ante- and fine postnodal setae, it must be remembered that the lateral lamellae generally have the greater number of

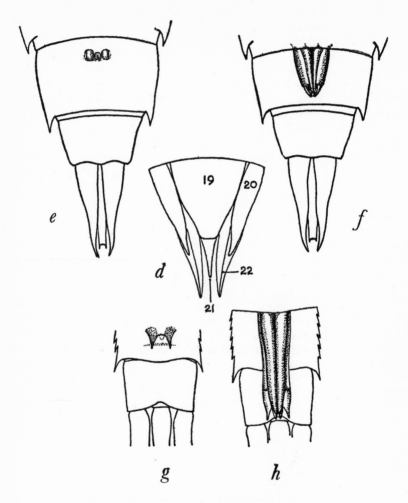

d. Anal appendages of *Cordulia aenea* (L.) male
    19 Male projection   21 Epiproct
    20 Cerci   22 Paraprocts

e. *Aeshna juncea* (L.) male genitalia. *f*. Female genitalia
g. *Lestes sponsa* (Hans.) male genitalia. *h*. Female genitalia.

antenodal setae on the dorsal edge, whereas with the median lamella the position is reversed. *Lamellae* are not infrequently lost and regrown; therefore care must be exercised when examining these organs otherwise confusion may result if a partly regrown organ is mistaken for the fully developed lamella.

Where single lamellae are illustrated they represent the median, the dorsal edge being shown uppermost in all examples excepting Figures 12 and 15 where the dorsal edge is towards the left.

In the *Anisoptera* the anal appendages (Fig. d) also provide a useful character for identification of many species. The terminology adopted in my previous papers is that of Tillyard (1917) but this is held by some experts to be incorrect. It is considered that the appendix dorsalis should be known as the *epiproct;* the cerci as the *paraprocts;* whilst the cercoids developing late in the larval stage should br. referred to as the true *cerci.* I have adopted this latter terminology in all cases where reference is made to the anal appendages.

The sex of even relatively immature larvae may be determined by the following characters:—

In all the *Zygoptera* the male gonapophyses are relatively small and consist of two triangular processes (Fig. g) on the ventral surface of the 9th abdominal segment. The female gonapophyses (Fig. h) are conspicuous and generally extend over the ventral surface of the 9th and 10th segments. Within the *Anisoptera,* females of *Cordulegasteridae* and *Aeshnidae* may be determined by the conspicuous gonapophyses (Fig. f) as in the Zygopterous species; in the remaining families the female gonapophyses are generally inconspicuous. All Anisopterous males possess a male projection (Fig. d19) situated at the base of the epiproct on the dorsal surface; this is additional to the accessory genitalia which are indicated on the ventral surface of the 2nd and 3rd abdominal segments, and the genital pore on the 9th (Fig. e).

*The separation characters employed in the following key
are based entirely on those found in the British species*

KEY TO SUBORDERS

1 Larvae long and slender; abdominal pleurites infolded; abdomen terminating in three caudal lamellae   ZYGOPTERA

— Larvae comparatively shorter and more stoutly built; abdomen with ventral pleurites present; abdomen terminating in five spine-like appendages   ANISOPTERA

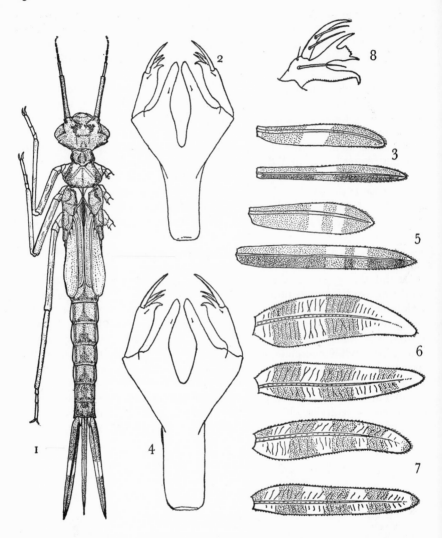

Agrion virgo (L.)   1, larva; 2, labium; 3, median and lateral caudal lamellae. *A. splendens* (Harris) 4, labium,; 5 median and lateral lamella. *Lestes dryas* Kirby 6, median and lateral lamellae. *L. sponsa* (Hans.) 7, median and lateral lamellae; 8, labial palpus.

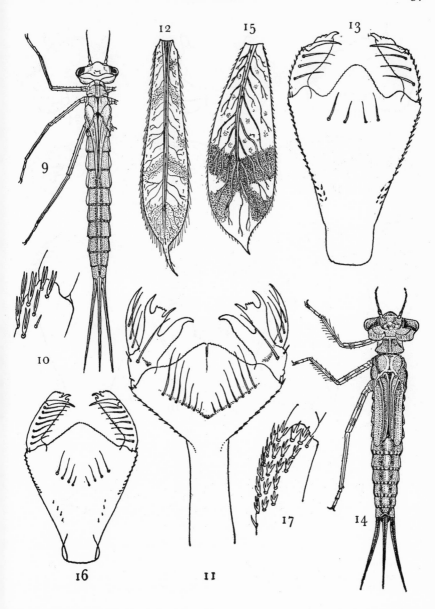

Lestes dryas Kirby 9, larva; 10, apical comb of fore-tibia; 11, labium. *Platyc-nemis pennipes* (Pallas) 12, lamella; 13, labium. *Pyrrhosoma nymphula* (Sulz.) 14, larva; 15, lamella; 16, labium. 17, Apical comb of fore-tibia of *Platyc-nemididae* and *Coenagriidae*.

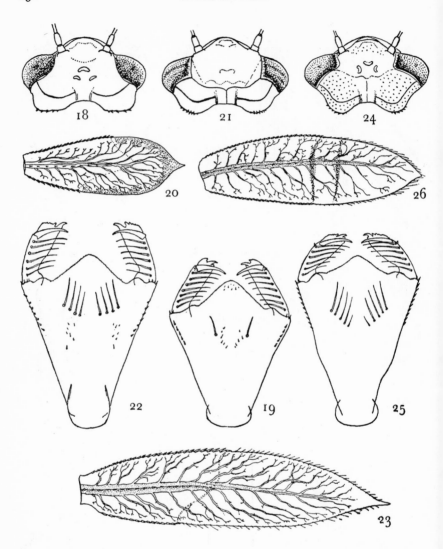

Ceriagrion tenellum (Villers) 18, head; 19, labium; 20, lamella. *Ischnura elegans* (Van der Lind.) 21, head; 22, labium; 23, lamella. *Coenagrion puella* (L.) 24, head. *Enallagma cyathigerum* (Charp.) 25, labium; 26, lamella.

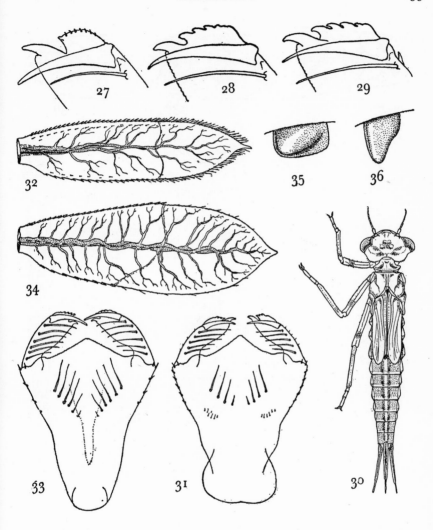

Ceriagrion tenellum (Villers) 27, labial palpus. *Ischnura elegans* (Van der Lind.) 28, labial palpus. *Enallagma cyathigerum* (Charp.) 29, labial palpus. *Coenagrion mercuriale* (Charp.) 30, larva; 31, labium; 32, lamella. *C. scitulum* (Ramb.) 33, labium; 34, lamella. *C. hastulatum* (Charp.) 35, left cercus, male. *C. armatum* (Charp.) 36, left cercus, male.

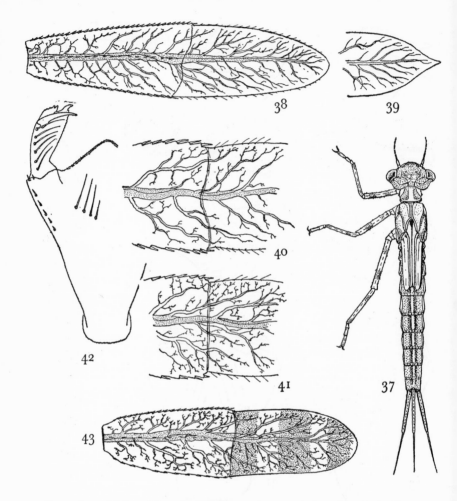

Coenagrion pulchellum (Van der Lind.) 37, larva; 38, lamella. *C. puella* (L.)
39, apex of lamella. *C. armatum* (Charp.) 40, nodal line of lamella. *C. hastulatum* (Charp.) 41, nodal line of lamella. *Erythromma najas* (Hans.) 42, labium,
43, lamella.

S|UBORDER ZYGOPTERA

KEY TO FAMILIES

1. Antennae with scape as long as the remaining six segments taken together. Labium with median cleft wide, extending to nearly half the length of the prementum (Figs. 2, 4). Caudal lamellae with laterals triquetral, median of the lamellar type (Figs. 3, 5). (Apical combs of tibiae consisting of spinate setae)

AGRIIDAE

– Antennae with scape considerably less than the total length of the remaining segments taken together. Labium with median cleft short, slit-like or with medium lobe entire. All caudal lamellae of the lamellar type   2

2. Labium with prementum much contracted basally (ladle-shaped), not triangular in outline, median cleft slit-like (Fig. 11); labial palpi with movable hooks armed with setae. Caudal lamellae with secondary tracheae at right angles to main trunks, running nearly to edge of lamellae before branching. (Apical combs of tibiae consisting mainly of bidentate setae (Fig. 10))   LESTIDAE

– Labium not greatly contracted basally, triangular in outline, median lobe of prementum without median cleft; labial palpi with movable hooks not armed with setae. Caudal lamellae with secondary tracheae at an oblique angle to main trunks, much branched. (Apical combs of tibiae consisting mainly of tridentate setae (Fig. 17))   3

3. Antennae with first segment of flagellum shorter than pedicel. Labial palpi with outer margin armed with spinate setae (Fig. 13). Caudal lamellae denodate, with apices produced into long narrow points, marginal setae long, hair-like and of varying lengths, not differentiated into stout antenodal and fine postnodal setae (Fig. 12)   PLATYCNEMIDIDAE

– Antennae with first segment of flagellum longer than pedicel. Labial palpi with outer margin not armed with spinate setae (except *Coenagrion mercuriale* (Charp.) which has them few in number and of piliform structure). Caudal lamellae denodate to nodate, not produced into long narrow points; marginal setae not relatively long, differentiated into stout antenodal and fine postnodal setae (except *Pyrrhosoma nymphula* (Sulzer))   COENAGRIIDAE

Family *AGRIIDAE*
One genus AGRION Fabricius

KEY TO SPECIES

1. Labium with median cleft of prementum more than four times as long as broad (Fig. 2). Median caudal lamella narrow, nearly as long as laterals; lamellae dark in colour with a narrow pale band at about mid-length (Fig. 3). L. 30-35 mm.
   Breeds in swift clear streams with clean sandy or gravelly bottoms.   A. virgo (Linnaeus)

– Labium with median cleft of prementum less than four times as long as broad (Fig. 4). Median caudal lamella broad, distinctly shorter than laterals (Fig. 5);

lamellae dark, usually with two pale bands at about mid-length. L. 30-45 mm.

A. splendens (Harris)

Breeds in sluggish streams and occasionally ponds with muddy bottoms. As these species occasionally breed in the same stream if the conditions are suitable, and as the larvae are not infrequently found with one or more caudal lamellae missing, or regrown, care should be exercised when using the lamellae as a separation character. Immature specimens of both species may be readily determined by their characteristic appearance (Fig. 1).

Family *LESTIDAE*
One genus LESTES Leach

KEY TO SPECIES

1. Labial palpi with two setae on each movable hook (Fig. 8). Caudal lamellae narrower in proportion to length, of more even width from base to apex (Fig. 7). Female gonapophyses reaching to, or just beyond the 10th abdominal segment. L. 26·5–34·5 mm. *L. sponsa* (Hansemann)

    Breeds in ponds, canals and weedy ditches.

– Labial palpi with three or more setae on each movable hook (Fig. 11). Caudal lamellae broader in proportion to length, of a sharper apical taper and more pronounced curvature (all these characters most distinctive in the median lamella (Fig. 6)). Female gonapophyses reaching well beyond the 10th abdominal segment. L. 29–32 mm. *L. dryas* Kirby

    Breeds in similar habitats to L. sponsa.

    From the 2nd instar onwards, the larvae of *Lestes* can be separated from other genera by the presence of the bidentate setae on the tibial combs.

Family *PLATYCNEMIDIDAE*
One genus PLATYCNEMIS Burmeister

One species recorded from Britain. Labium with premental setae 2+2, labial palpi with 3 setae (Fig. 13). Caudal lamellae (Fig. 12) distinctive in outline, with scattered setae on sides from base to apex; markings variable, sometimes confined to marginal spots. L. 18·5–22 mm. *P. pennipes* (Pallas)

Breeds in weedy streams, rivers and seepages bordering streams.

Family *COENAGRIIDAE*

KEY TO GENERA

1. Caudal lamellae denodate, with distinctive dark pattern (Fig. 15) broad, of convex apical outline, apices acutely pointed; marginal setae not divided into stout antenodal and fine postnodal setae; strong setae few and widely spaced. (Head with postocular region somewhat rectangular in outline.) *Pyrrhosoma* Charpentier

– Caudal lamellae subnodate or nodate, immaculate, blotched or with transverse bands of various outlines; marginal setae divided into stout antenodal and fine postnodal setae

2

2. Caudal lamellae with marginal setae reaching to, or beyond mid-length on one of the two margins only   3

– Caudal lamellae with marginal setae reaching to, or beyond mid-length on both margins   5

3. Head with postocular region rectangular in outline (Fig. 18). Caudal lamellae short, broad, obtusely pointed, marked with marginal blotches (Fig. 20). Labium with premental setae 1 + 1 (rarely 2 + 2); area between premental setae bearing a field of scattered short setae (Fig. 19); distal margin of labial palpi nearly straight and armed with setae (Fig. 27)   *Ceriagrion tenellum* (Villers)

– Head with postocular region of a sweeping curvilinear outline (Fig. 21). Labium with premental setae more than 2 + 2; area between premental setae not bearing a field of short scattered setae; distal margin of labial palpi bearing prominent intermediate hooks without setae (Fig. 28)   4

4. Caudal lamellae of medium length, broad, with apices acutely pointed (Fig. 34)
                                                                    Coenagrion scitulum (Rambur)

– Caudal lamellae relatively long, narrow, with apices usually sharply pointed (Fig. 23)   *Ischnura* Charpentier

5. Larvae usually of more than 30 mm. in length. Caudal lamellae with apices obtusely rounded or convexo-angulate, postnodally marked with three distinctive dark bands and with tracheation prominently dark (Fig. 43)
                                                                    Erythromma Charpentier

– Larvae of less than 30 mm. in length. Caudal lamellae not marked with 3 broad dark bands   6

6. Head without prominent spotting. Labial palpi bearing a short spine on the outer margin in line with the anterior palpal setae (Fig. 29). Caudal lamellae with antenodal and postnodal margins of approximately the same convexity in outline, usually with one to three narrow transverse bands (Fig. 26) *Enallagma* Charpentier

– Head with or without prominent spotting (Fig. 24). Labial palpi without a short spine on the outer margin in line with the anterior palpal setae. Caudal lamellae with antenodal margins generally less convex than the postnodal, without pigmentation. (Sometimes showing a "false" band from the lodgement of foreign matter along the nodal line)   *Coenagrion* Kirby

Genus PYRRHOSOMA Charpentier

One species recorded from Britain. Abdomen of rather stumpy appearance; mid-dorsal line pale, flanked by a dark suffusion, dark spots on each visible segment except 10th. Labium (Fig. 16) with premental setae 3 + 3 to 4 + 4; labial palpi with 6 to 7 setae. Caudal lamellae distinctive in shape and markings (Fig. 15). L. 19–22·5 mm.   *P. nymphula* (Sulzer)
  Breeds in ponds, lakes, canals, streams and marshes.
  Small larvae of about 5·5 mm. (6th instar) can be identified by their stumpy appearance, square heads and the dark markings on the caudal lamellae.

Genus Ischnura Charpentier

1. Labium (Fig. 22) with premental setae varying from 4+4 to 6+5; labial palpi
   with 6 to 7 setae. L. 21·5–25 mm.   *I. elegans* (Van der Linden)
   Breeds in weedy ponds, lakes, slow moving and brackish waters.

– Labium with premental setae 6+6; labial palpi with 5 setae. L. 15–20 mm.
   Breeds in seepages, marshes and bogs.   *I. pumilio* (Charpentier)

Both these species have the labium with prementum bearing a field of short
scattered setae proximal to the main premental setae (Fig. 22). This character is
shared also by *Coenagrion mercuriale* (Charp.) but the larva (Fig. 30) is of such
characteristic appearance that it cannot be confused with *Ischnura*.

Genus Enallagma Charpentier

One species found in Britain. Labium (Fig. 25) with premental setae 3+3 to
5+5; labial palpi with 6 to 7 setae. Caudal lamellae (Fig. 26) sub-nodate. Larvae
generally of some tint of green; abdomen with pale mid-dorsal line flanked by V-
shaped dark suffusions. L. 20–26·5 mm.   *E. cyathigerum* (Charpentier)
   Breeds in ponds, lakes, canals, slow moving streams and in brackish water.

Genus Coenagrion Kirby

1. Head without prominent spotting; caudal lamellae subnodate   2

– Head with prominent spotting (Fig. 24); caudal lamellae nodate   3

2. Caudal lamellae short, boat-shaped (Fig. 32); antenodal marginal setae reaching
   beyond mid-length on both margins, becoming progressively longer and more
   slender towards node; a secondary series of setae on sides of lamellae reaching to,
   or beyond nodal line. Postnodal marginal setae relatively long, very numerous;
   secondary tracheae few in number, inclined at an angle of about 45 degrees to
   main trunks. Labium with prementum nearly as wide as long (Fig. 31), premental
   setae 3+3 to 4+4, a field of short setae proximal to these; labial palpi with 5
   setae, outer margin bearing a few fine setae. L. 15–17 mm.
   Breeds in clear weedy and boggy streams.   *C. mercuriale* (Charpentier)

– Caudal lamellae of medium length, broad, with apices acutely pointed (Fig. 34);
   antenodal marginal setae reaching to mid-length on one margin only, not becoming
   markedly longer towards node, sides of lamellae bearing basal setae only. Postnodal marginal setae very fine, few in number; secondary tracheae numerous,
   inclined at an angle of more than 45 degrees to main trunks. Labium (Fig. 33)
   with prementum elongate, premental setae 4+4 to 5+5, no field of short setae on
   outer margin. L. 20–22 mm.   *C. scitulum* (Rambur)
   *Recorded only from Essex where it has been found breeding in a small weedy pond near a salt
   marsh.*

3. Antennae 6-segmented   4

– Antennae 7-segmented   5

4. Male cerci (Fig. 36) with inner margin concave. Caudal lamellae with nodal line not straight; secondary tracheae with sub-tracheae relatively few in number (Fig. 40). Labium with premental setae 4+4 to 5+5; labial palpi with 6 to 7 setae. L. 21–23 mm. *C. armatum* (Charpentier)

Breeds in shallow pools containing Frogbit Hydrocharis morsusranae in which the female places her eggs. Confined to the Norfolk Broads.

– Male cerci (Fig. 35) with inner margin straight. Caudal lamellae with nodal line straight, secondary tracheae with sub-tracheae numerous (Fig. 41). Labium with premental setae 3+3 to 5+5; labial palpi with 5 to 7 setae. L. 21–23 mm.

C. hastulatum (Charpentier)

Breeds in river shallows and bog-holes. Confined to a few counties in Scotland.

5. A high proportion of larvae with the narrowly-lanceolate caudal lamellae (Fig. 39) having bluntly-pointed apices. Labium with premental setae 5+5; labial palpi with 6 setae. May vary in having premental setae 4+4 and labial palpi with 5 to 7 setae. Larvae generally of some shade of green with wing-sheaths and lamellae brown. L. 22–25.75 mm. *C. puella* (*Linnaeus*)

Breeds in weedy ponds, lakes and canals.

– A high proportion of larvae with the caudal lamellae (Fig. 38) with rounded apices, this most obvious with the median lamella. Labium with premental setae 4+4; labial palpi with 6 setae. May vary in having the premental setae 5+5 labial palpi with 5 setae. Larvae generally of some shade of brown to sepia, rarely green. L. 20–25.25 mm. *C. pulchellum* (Van der Linden)

Breeds in similar habitats to C. puella.

Genus ERYTHROMMA Charpentier

One species found in Britain. Labium (Fig. 42) with premental setae 3+3, 4+4 to 3+5; labial palpi with 6 to 7 setae. Caudal lamellae (Fig. 43) nodate, with dark transverse apical bands and clearly defined tracheation distinctive. L. 29–32 mm. *E. najas* (Hansemann)

Breeds in clear weedy ponds, lakes and canals.

Genus CERIAGRION Selys

One species found in Britain. Labium distinctive (Fig. 19); premental setae 1+1, rarely 2+2; labial palpi with 6 setae. Caudal lamellae (Fig. 20) subnodate. Small larvae generally of a brownish or olivaceous colour. L. 16–17 mm.

Breeds in boggy pools and peaty runnels. *C. tenellum* (Villers)

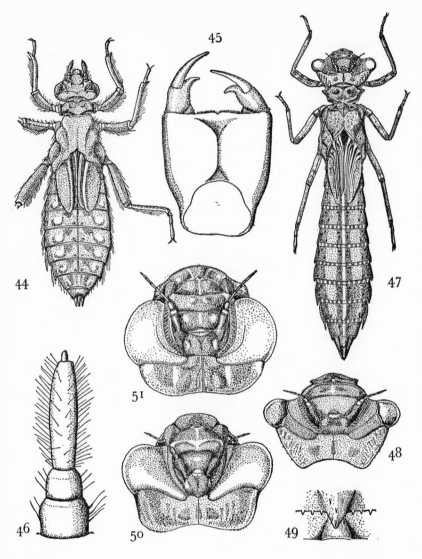

Gomphus vulgatissimus (L.) 44, larva; 45, labium; 46, antenna. *Brachytron pratense* (Müll.) 47, larva; 48, dorsal view of head; 49, spine-like process on 9th abdominal tergite. *Aeshna grandis* (L.) 50, dorsal view of head. *Anax imperator* Leach 51, dorsal view of head.

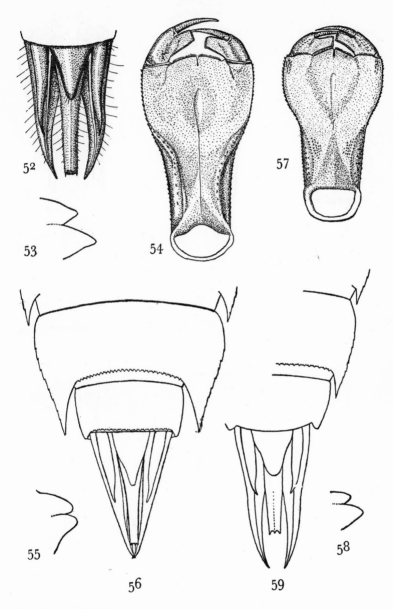

Aeshna isosceles (Müll.) 52, anal appendages male; 53, supracoxal armature.
A. mixta Latr. 54, labium; 55, supracoxal armature; 56, lateral abdominal
spines. *A. caerulea* (Ström) 57, labium; 58, supracoxal armature; 59, lateral
abdominal spines.

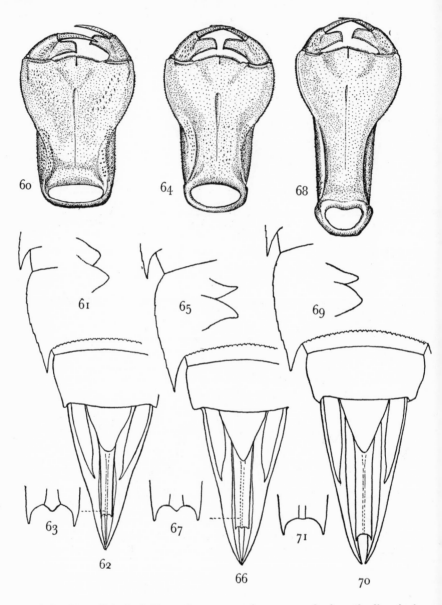

Aeshna juncea (L.) 60, labium; 61, supracoxal armature; 62, lateral adbominal spines; 63, distal margin of epiproct. *A. grandis* (L.) 64, labium; 65, supracoxal armature; 66, lateral abdominal spines; 67, distal margin of epiproct. *A. cyanea* (Müll.) 68, labium; 69, supracoxal armature; 70, lateral abdominal spines; 71, distal margin of epiproct.

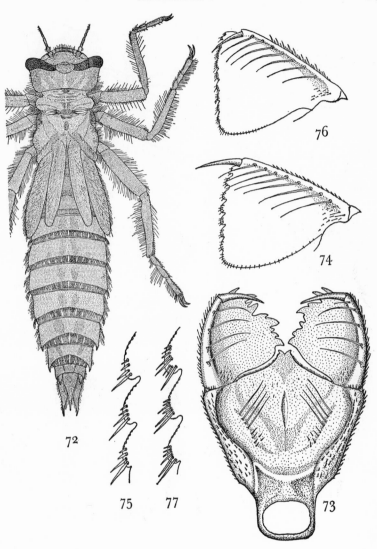

Cordulegaster boltoni (Don.) 72, larva; 73, labium. *Cordulia aenea* (L.) 74, labial palpus; 75, distal margin of palpus. *Somatochlora metallica* (Van der Lind.) 76, labial palpus; 77, distal margin of palpus.

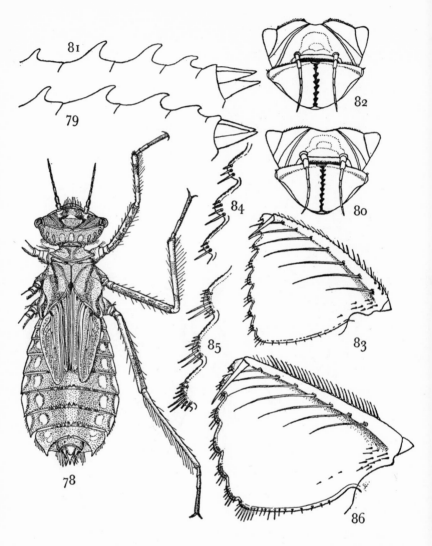

Cordulia aenea (L.) 78, larva; 79, mid-dorsal abdominal spines; 80, head from in front. *Somatochlora metallica* (Van der Lind.) 81, mid-dorsal abdominal spines; 82, head from in front. *S. arctica* (Zett.) 83, labial palpus; 84, distal margin of palpus. *Oxygastra curtisi* (Dale) 85, distal margin of palpus; 86, labial palpus.

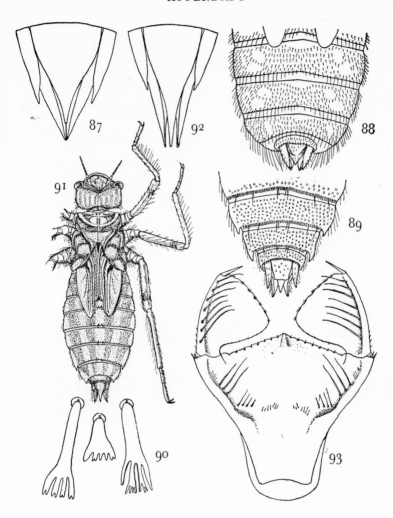

Cordulia aenea (L.) 87, anal appendages female. *Somatochlora arctica* (Zett.) 88, posterior segments of abdomen male. *Oxygastra curtisi* (Dale) 89, posterior segments of abdomen male; 90, abdominal setae. *Orthetrum cancellatum* (L.) 91, larva; 92, anal appendages female; 93, labium.

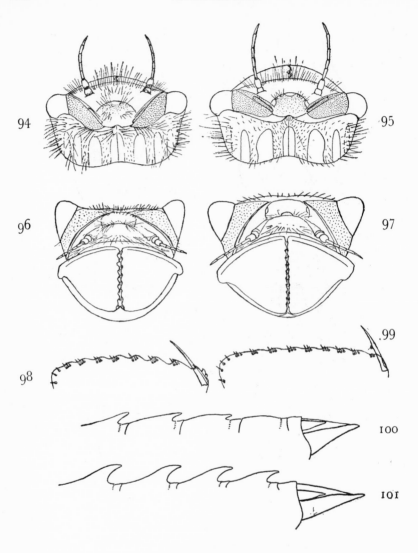

Libellula depressa L. 94, head dorsal view; 96, head from in front; 98, distal margin of labial palpus. *L. quadrimaculata* L. 95, head dorsal view; 97, head from in front; 99, distal margin of labial palpus; 100, mid-dorsal abdominal spines. *L. fulva* Müll. 101, mid-dorsal abdominal spines.

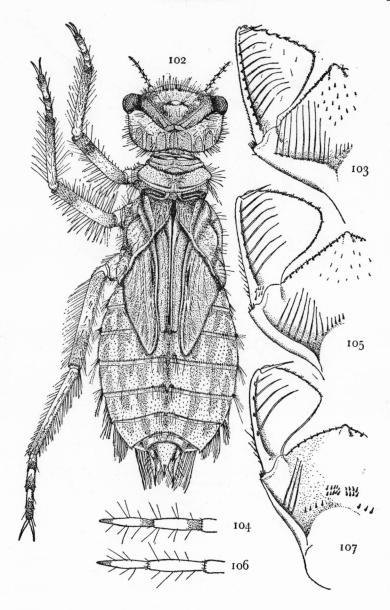

Libellula depressa L. 102, larva; 103, labium; 104, apical segments of antenna.
L. quadrimaculata L. 105, labium; 106, apical segments of antenna. *L. fulva*
Müll. 107, labium.

DRAGONFLIES

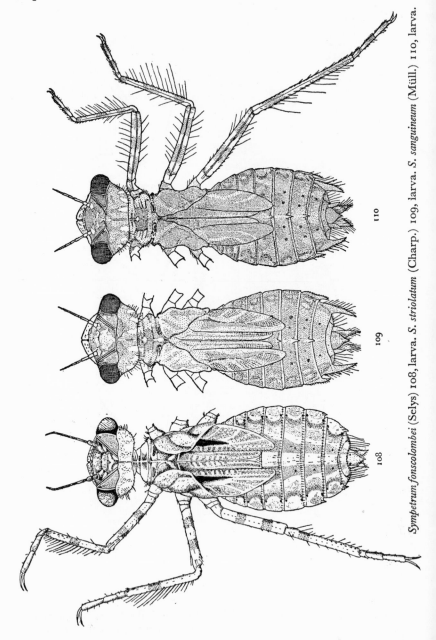

Sympetrum fonscolombei (Selys) 108, larva. *S. striolatum* (Charp.) 109, larva. *S. sanguineum* (Müll.) 110, larva.

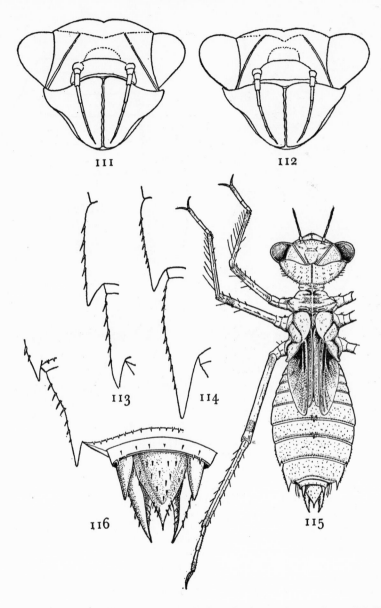

Sympetrum striolatum (Charp.) 111, head from in front. *S. sanguineum* (Müll.) 112, head from in front. *S. flaveolum* (L.) 113, lateral abdominal spines. *S. vulgatum* (L.) 114, lateral abdominal spines. *S. danae* (Sulz.) 115, larva; 116, anal appendages and lateral spines male.

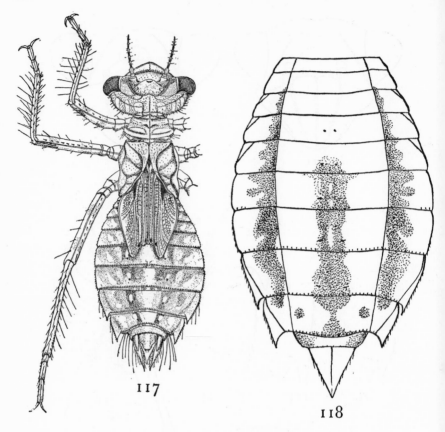

Leucorrhinia dubia (Van der Lind.) 117, larva; 118, markings on
ventral surface of abdomen.

SUBORDER ANISOPTERA

KEY TO FAMILIES

1. Labium with prementum flat, without major premental or palpal setae; distal
   margin of labial palpi without crenations   2

- Labium with prementum spoon-shaped, with major premental and palpal setae;
  distal margin of labial palpi with crenations   3

2. Antennae 4-segmented (Fig. 46). Front and middle tarsi with 2, hind with 3
   segments   GOMPHIDAE

- Antennae 7-segmented. All tarsi with 3 segments   AESHNIDEA

3. Labium with median lobe of prementum bifid, the points ending in beak-like hooks; distal margin of labial palpi deeply serrated (Fig. 73)   CORDULEGASTERIDAE

– Labium with median lobe of prementum not bifid; distal margin of labial palpi not deeply serrated   **4**

4. Cerci notably more than half the length of the paraprocts (Fig. 87). Distal margin of labial palpi with broad deep crenations (Fig. 75)   CORDULIIDAE

– Cerci rarely half, generally less than half the length of the paraprocts (Fig. 92). Distal margin of labial palpi with crenations shallow or much flattened (Figs. 93, 98, 99)   LIBELLULIDAE

Family *GOMPHIDAE*
One genus GOMPHUS Leach

One species found in Britain. Larva (Fig. 44) distinctive in appearance. Head small and heart-shaped. Labium (Fig. 45) rectangular. Abdomen broad and flat, lateral spines on segments 6 to 9. L. 27–30 mm.   *G. vulgatissimus* (Linnaeus)
   Breeds in swift streams with sandy bottoms, also the back-waters of some rivers. Burrows in the sand or silt.
   Relatively immature specimens may be determined by the general outline and the segmentation of antennae and tarsi.

Family *CORDULEGASTERIDAE*
One genus CORDULEGASTER Leach

One species found in Britain. Larva (Fig. 72) large, hairy and distinctive in appearance. Labium (Fig. 73) with distal margin of labial palpi formed into deep asymmetrical dentations. Premental setae 4+4 to 5+5, a field of short setae proximal to these. Labial palpi with 4 to 5 major setae, 0 to 2 short anterior setae. Abdomen with lateral spines on segments 8 and 9. L. 35–42 mm.
                                                                                 C. boltoni (Donovan)
   Breeds in swift streams with sandy or muddy bottoms. The larvae lie in the detritus with only the fore-part of the head and the anal appendages protruding.
   Immature specimens of 18 mm., (and probably less) can be readily determined by their resemblance to the mature larva, also by the form of the labium.

Family *AESHNIDAE*

KEY TO GENERA

1. Eyes small, less than half the length of the lateral margin of the postocular lobes, the latter sloping markedly inwards (Fig. 48). Dorsal surface of abdomen with an obtuse spine-like process on the distal margin of the 9th tergite and a vestigial process on 8th (Fig. 49). Length of the anal appendages less than the combined lengths of the 9th and 10th segments   *Brachytron* Selys

– Eyes large, half, or more than half the length of the lateral margin of the postocular lobes, the latter not sloping markedly inwards. Dorsal surface of abdomen immaculate. Length of the anal appendages as long as, or longer than the combined lengths of the 9th and 10th segments   **2**

2. Eyes markedly flattened dorsally, posterior margins forming a transverse straight line; outline of head of a rounded appearance (Fig. 51). Larvae rarely of less than 49 mm. in length *Anax* Leach

– Eyes not markedly flattened dorsally, posterior margins not forming a transverse straight line; outline of head not of a rounded appearance (Fig. 50). Larvae rarely exceeding 49 mm. in length *Aeshna* Fabricius

Genus BRACHYTRON Selys

One species found in Britain. Head distinctive in appearance (Fig. 48). Abdomen with lateral spines on segments 5 to 9. L. 35–40 mm. Fig. 47. *B. pratense* (Müller)
Breeds in dykes, ponds, lakes and canals. Often found clinging to submerged sticks, roots and broken sedges.

The 2nd instar larva (length about 2·5 mm.) can be identified by means of a spine-like process on the lateral margin of the postocular lobes. These are not absorbed until the 7th instar (length about 8 mm.). From *Aeshna grandis* (Linnaeus), which also exhibits this character in the early instars, separation can be effected by noting the absence of the mid-dorsal abdominal protruberance on the 9th tergite, which is conspicuous in immature specimens of *B. pratense*.

Genus AESHNA Fabricius

KEY TO SPECIES

1. Cerci two-thirds the length of the paraprocts, slender and incurved (Fig. 52). Supracoxal armature as Fig. 53. (Abdomen with lateral spines on segments 6 to 9, those on 9 reaching a little beyond the middle of the 10th segment. Distal margin of epiproct nearly straight.) L. 38–44 mm. *A. isosceles* (Müller)
Breeds in weedy dykes and broads. Confined to the area of the Norfolk Broads.

– Cerci less than two-thirds the length of the paraprocts 2

2. Larvae of not more than 38 mm., in length 3

– Larvae of more than 38 mm., in length 4

3. Lateral abdominal spine on segment 9 reaching nearly to the distal margin of the 10th segment (Fig. 56). Distal margin of epiproct nearly straight. Supracoxal armature as Fig. 55. (Labium as Fig. 54; lateral abdominal spines on segments 6 to 9.) L. 30–38 mm. *A. mixta* Latreille

– Lateral abdominal spine on segment 9 only reaching to about one-third over the 10th segment (Fig. 59). Distal margin of epiproct bifid. Supracoxal armature as Fig. 58. (Labium as Fig. 57; lateral abdominal spines on segments 7 to 9, perhaps sometimes a vestigial one on 6.) L. about 35 mm. *A. caerulea* (Ström)*
Confined to a few districts in Scotland where it breeds in sphagnum bogs.

4. Distal margin of epiproct concave (Fig. 71). Labium (Fig. 68) with length of prementum nearly twice the width of the front margin. Supracoxal armature as Fig. 69. (Lateral abdominal spines on segments 6 to 9.) L. 38–48 mm.
Breeds in ponds, lakes and canals. *A. cyanea* (Müller)

*Has 6-segmented antennae. See *Ent. Gaz.* 1955, 6: 85

- Distal margin of epiproct bifid (Figs. 63, 67). Labium (Figs. 60, 64) with length of prementum markedly less than twice the width of the front margin 5

5. Labium (Fig. 60) somewhat rectangular in outline. Supracoxal armature as Fig. 61. Lateral abdominal spines on segments 7 to 9 (sometimes a vestigial one on 6), that on 9 not reaching more than one-third over the 10th segment (Fig. 62). L. 40–51 mm. *A. juncea* (Linnaeus)
   Breeds in weedy ponds, lakes and peat pools.

- Labium (Fig. 64) less rectangular in outline. Supracoxal armature as Fig. 65. Lateral abdominal spines on segments 6 to 9 (sometimes a vestigial one on 5), that on 9 reaching to the middle of the 10th segment. (Fig. 66). L. 40–46 mm.
   Breeds in ponds, lakes and canals. *A. grandis* (Linnaeus)
   For the identification of the very immature larvae of *A. grandis* see separation characters given for this species and *Brachytron pratense*.

Genus ANAX Leach

One species found in Britain. Larvae of robust appearance, head distinctive in outline (Fig. 51). Abdomen with lateral spines on segments 7 to 9. L. 45–56 mm.
A. imperator Leach
   Breeds in weedy ponds, lakes and canals. It is one of the first species to colonise an almost empty pond or gravel pit.

Family *CORDULIIDAE*

KEY TO SPECIES

1. Abdomen armed with prominent mid-dorsal spines, dorsal surface sparsely covered with hair-like setae 2

- Abdomen not armed with prominent mid-dorsal spines; dorsal surface with hair-like or pectinate setae numerous 3

2. Abdomen with mid-dorsal spine on segment 9 small (sometimes only vestigial) (Fig. 79). Abdomen when viewed dorsally appearing somewhat truncate (Fig. 78). Head viewed from the front as Fig. 80; occiput not bearing short obtuse spine-like processes. Labium with outer margin of prementum immaculate; labial palpi with outer margins armed with short setae, their length being less than the distance between individual setae (Fig. 74); distal margin with crenations armed with 3 to 4 setae (Fig. 75). (Labium with premental setae 12+12 to 15+15; labial palpi with 8 to 9 setae. Abdomen with recurved mid-dorsal spines on segments 4 to 9, lateral spines on 8 and 9.) L. 22.5–25 mm. *Cordulia aenea* (Linnaeus)
   Breeds in weedy ponds, lakes and canals.

- Abdomen with mid-dorsal spine on segment 9 of medium length (Fig. 81). Abdomen viewed dorsally of fusiform outline. Head when viewed from the front as Fig. 82; occiput bearing a pair of obtuse spine-like processes in line with the base of the antennae. Labium with outer margin of prementum armed with setae; labial palpi with setae on outer margins long, shorter setae interspersed, the former as long as the distance between individual setae (Fig. 76); distal margin

with crenations armed with 6 to 9 setae (Fig. 77). (Labium with premental setae 11+11 to 12+12; labial palpi with 6 to 7 setae. Abdomen with recurved mid-dorsal spines on segments 4 to 9 (sometimes a vestigial one on 3), lateral spines on 8 and 9.) L. 24–25 mm.   *Somatochlora metallica* (Van der Lind.)
Breeds in ponds, canals and moorland bog-holes.

2nd instar larvae of *C. aenea* and *S. metallica* have obtuse spine-like processes on the occiput, these persisting in *S. metallica* and becoming progressively shorter. In *C. aenea* they become absorbed at about the 6th instar (length about 6 mm.).

3. Abdomen not armed with lateral spines, sides more parallel, posterior segments obtuse (Fig. 88); abdominal setae spinate or piliform. Male projection with distal margin obtuse. Labial palpi with distal margin consisting of 8 to 11 crenations, each armed with 3 to 5 setae (Figs. 83, 84). (Premental setae 9+9 to 14+14; labial palpi with 7 to 9 setae.) L. 17–22·5 mm.   *S. arctica* (Zetterstedt)
Breeds in sheltered runnels and seepages on moorlands. Confined to a few counties in Scotland, and in Kerry.

– Abdomen bearing lateral spines on segments 8 and 9, fusiform in outline, posterior segments more acutely tapered to anal appendages (Fig. 89). Setae on dorsal surface of head, thorax and abdomen consisting mainly of scale-like pectinate setae (Fig. 90). Male projection with distal margin truncate. Labial palpi with distal margin consisting of 6 to 8 crenations, each armed with 5 to 9 setae (Figs. 85, 86). (Premental setae 11+11 to 12+12; labial palpi with 7 to 8 setae.) L. 19–22 mm.   *Oxygastra curtisi* (Dale)
Breeds in one, possibly two sluggish but well oxygenated streams in the S. of England.
From the 6th instar (6 mm.) larvae may be determined by the scale-like setae on the dorsal surface of the abdomen.

Family *LIBELLULIDAE*

KEY TO GENERA

1. Larvae of distinctive appearance (Figs. 108, 109, 110, 117). Head with outer margin of postocular lobes of a sweeping curvilinear outline. Legs long and slender, hind when fully extended reaching to well beyond the apex of abdomen. Abdomen with lateral spines on segments 8 and 9 generally prominent   2

– Head with outer margin of postocular lobes not of a sweeping curvilinear outline (Fig. 91). Legs of moderate length, stout, hind when fully extended barely reaching beyond apex of abdomen. Abdomen with lateral spines on segments 8 and 9 not prominent   3

2. Ventral surface of abdomen with distinctive markings (Fig. 118)
                                        Leucorrhinia Brittinger

– Ventral surface of abdomen immaculate   *Sympetrum* Newman

3. Abdomen without mid-dorsal spine on segment 8. Labium with premental armature consisting of 2 to 4 long setae inserted near each lateral margin and 2 medial fields of short spiniform setae, these latter flanked by 4 to 7 setae of medium length (Fig. 93). (*Libellula fulva* Müller, which has the premental setae disposed

in a somewhat similar manner, may be readily identified by the prominent mid-dorsal abdominal spines on segments 4 to 9) *Orthetrum* Newman

– Abdomen with mid-dorsal spine on segment 8. Premental setae arranged as Figs. 103, 105, 107 *Libellula* Linnaeus

Genus ORTHETRUM Newman

KEY TO SPECIES

1. Abdomen with mid-dorsal spines on segments 4 to 7 and a smooth and slightly raised mid-dorsal area on segments 8 and 9. Labium with premental setae consisting of 2 long setae inserted near each lateral margin and 2 medial fields of from 10 to 12 short spiniform setae, these latter flanked by from 4 to 7 setae of medium length. Labial palpi with 3 setae (rarely 4 to 5). Male projection with distal margin obtuse. (Short lateral spines on segments 8 and 9). L. 17–23 mm.
   Breeds in streams, weedy ponds, bogs and marshes. *O. coerulescens* (Fabricius)

Abdomen with mid-dorsal spines on segments 3 to 6, without a smooth and slightly raised mid-dorsal area on segments 8 and 9. Labium with premental setae consisting of 3 (rarely 2 or 4) long setae inserted near each lateral margin and 2 medial fields of from 7 to 8 short spiniform setae, these latter flanked by 4 setae of medium length (Fig. 93). Labial palpi with 7 (rarely 6) setae. Male projection with distal margin acute. (Short lateral spines on segments 8 and 9.) L. 23–25.5 mm. (Fig. 91) *O. cancellatum* (Linnaeus)
   Breeds in ponds and lakes, shows a marked liking for clay and gravel pits.

Genus LIBELLULA Linnaeus

KEY TO SPECIES

1. Abdomen with long recurved mid-dorsal spines on segments 4 to 9 (Fig. 101). Labium (Fig. 107) with premental setae consisting of 3 long setae inserted near each lateral margin, slightly anterior to these a chain of from 2 to 5 short spiniform setae extending forwards to 2 medial fields of about 10 short spiniform setae. Labial palpi with 4 (rarely 5) setae. (Abdomen with short lateral spines on segments 8 and 9.) L. 22–25 mm. *L. fulva* Müller
   Breeds in slow-moving muddy streams, canals, dykes and bog-pools.
   From the 6th instar (5 mm.), larvae may be determined by the disposition of the premental setae and the mid-dorsal abdominal spines on segments 4 to 9.

– Abdomen with obtuse mid-dorsal spines on segments 4 to 8. Labium with premental setae not arranged in 6 distinct fields 2

2. Head when viewed dorsally appearing somewhat rectangular in outline, labium with only a slight forward protrusion, prolongation of eyes directed diagonally backwards (Fig. 94). Head when viewed from in front with eyes strongly upraised, epicranium markedly below a line taken across the top of the eyes (Fig. 96). Antennae with segments 6 and 7 of almost equal length (Fig. 104). Labial palpi with crenations of distal margin moderately deep and rounded in outline (Fig. 98). Premental setae $9+9$ to $11+11$, slightly anterior to these 2 medial fields of 3 to 5 short setae (Fig. 103). Abdomen marked with alternate light and dark suffusions (Fig. 102), apical segments truncate. (Labial palpi with 9 to 11 setae. Abdomen

with obtuse mid-dorsal spines on segments 4 to 8 (sometimes a vestigial one on 3), short lateral spines on 8 and 9.)   L. 22.5–25 mm.   *L. depressa* Linnaeus
   Breeds in ponds, lakes and canals.

– Head when viewed dorsally appearing pentagonal in outline, labium with a strong forward protusion, prolongation of eyes more transverse (Fig. 95). Head when viewed from in front with eyes less strongly upraised, epicranium in line with, or slightly above the level of the top of the eyes (Fig. 97). Antennae with segment 7 markedly shorter than 6 (Fig. 106). Labial palpi with crenations of distal margin shallow and flattened in outline (Fig. 99). Premental setae 10+10 to 13+13, in alignment (Fig. 105). Abdomen of a uniform sepia tint, apical segments not truncate. (Labial palpi with 7 to 11 setae, usually 7 to 8). Abdomen with mid-dorsal spines on segments 4 to 8 (Fig. 100), short lateral spines on 8 and 9.)   L. 22–26 mm.   *L. quadrimaculata* Linnaeus
   Breeds in ponds, lakes, canals, brackish water, bog-holes and occasionally slow-moving streams.

Genus SYMPETRUM Newman

KEY TO SPECIES

1. Abdomen without mid-dorsal spines (Fig. 108). (Labium with premental setae 18+18; labial palpi with 14 setae (both premental and palpal setae may be found to vary in number). Abdomen with short lateral spines on segments 8 and 9.) L. about 18 mm.   *S. fonscolombei* (Selys)
   An infrequent immigrant which has been recorded as breeding in S. England. Weedy ponds and lakes would be suitable habitats.

   Immature specimens of over 6 mm. in length may be determined by the lack of mid-dorsal spines.

– Abdomen with mid-dorsal spines   2

2. Lateral spine on segment 9 of abdomen with inner margin half, or nearly half the length of the outside margin of spine and segment taken together (Figs. 109, 110, 114)   3

– Lateral spine on segment 9 of abdomen with inner margin markedly less than half the length of the outside margin of spine and segment taken together (Figs. 113, 116)   5

3. Abdomen with mid-dorsal spines on segments 3 to 8, that on 3 small. Labium with premental setae 14+14 to 15+15; labial palpi with 10 to 12 setae (usually 11). L. 17-18 mm.   *S. vulgatum* (Linnaeus)
   A rare immigrant. Would breed in similar habitats to S. striolatum (Charp.). The larva has not been found in Britain.

– Abdomen without a mid-dorsal spine on segment 3   4

4. Abdomen with almost straight mid-dorsal spines on segments 4 to 8. Lateral spines straight or only slightly incurved. Labium with premental setae 15+16 to 16+16; labial palpi with 11 setae. L. 16·5–17·5 mm.   *S. nigrescens* Lucas
   Appears to favour waters close to, or not far removed from the coast. Generally of a more northern distribution than the succeeding species.

– Abdomen with mid-dorsal spines on segments 5 to 8 (rarely a vestigial one on 4) 4a

4a. Abdomen with recurved mid-dorsal spines on segments 4 to 8 (rarely a vestigial one on 4). Lateral spines generally incurved. Head viewed dorsally as Fig. 109; viewed from in front as Fig. 111. (Larvae approaching metamorphosis with head pattern (Fig. 109) having "bulges" posterior to the lateral branches of the epicranial suture with a linear posterior margin.) Labium with premental setae 14+14 to 15+15 (more rarely 13 to 18); labial palpi with 11 to 12 setae. L. 15·5–18 mm.
Breeds in ponds, lakes and canals.   *S. striolatum striolatum* (Charpentier)

– Head viewed dorsally as Fig. 110; viewed from in front as Fig. 112. (Larvae approaching metamorphosis with head pattern (Fig. 110) with "bulges" posterior to the lateral branches of the epicranial suture inevident or vaguely defined by a diffuse border.) Labium with premental setae 12+12 to 14+14; labial palpi with 9 to 11 setae. L. 15–17 mm.   *S. sanguineum* (Müller)
    Breeds in ponds and lakes, favouring sites occupied by the Great Reedmace (Typha latifolia L.) *and Horsetails* (Equisetum spp.), *where the larvae lurk under the tangle of roots.*
    On an average the nymphs of *S. striolatum* are larger and the lateral abdominal spine on segment 9 longer than that of *S. sanguineum,* but as these characters are subject to variation they cannot be completely relied upon.

5. Abdomen with mid-dorsal spines on segments 5 to 7 (sometimes a vestigial one on 8). (Labium with premental setae 10+10 to 15+15 (usually 13+13 to 14+14); labial palpi with 10 to 12 setae (usually 11).) Abdomen with short lateral spines on segments 8 and 9 (Fig. 116). L. 14-16 mm.   *S. danae* (Sulzer)
    Breeds in rushy pools and moorland bog-holes.

– Abdomen with mid-dorsal spines on segments 6 to 8. (Labium with premental setae 10+10 to 15+15 (usually 13+13 to 14+14)); labial palpi with 11 setae. Abdomen with short lateral spines on segments 8 and 9 (Fig. 113). L. about 16·5 mm.   *S. flaveolum* (Linnaeus)
    A more frequent immigrant than S. fonscolombei *and would breed in similar habitats.*

GENUS LEUCORRHINIA Brittinger

One species found in Britain (Fig. 117). Abdomen with mid-dorsal spines on segments 4 to 6 (sometimes a vestigial one on 7); lateral spines on 8 and 9. Ventral surface marked with distinctive dark bands (Fig. 118). Labium with premental setae 12+12 to 15+15; labial palpi with 10 to 11 setae. L. 18–20 mm.
    Breeds in sphagnum pools and marshes.   *L. dubia* (Van der Lind.)
    Immature larvae of 11 mm., may be determined by the dark markings on the ventral surface of the abdomen.

Figs. 9, 72, 109 and 110 have been reproduced from drawings by Colonel Niall MacNeill, M.R.I.A., F.R.E.S.

RECORDING INFORMATION ABOUT LARVAE

A valuable contribution to our knowledge of dragonfly ecology can be made by recording certain particulars after larvae have been identified. As mentioned on page 81 (Chap. 6), the larvae of some species are found so seldom that it is only by pooling our information that we can hope to reach conclusions about their rate of growth in nature.

Therefore it is well worth while recording even single specimens—in fact, it will be necessary to do this if the problem is to be tackled properly. In this way even the smallest collection can be turned to good account, and everyone able to identify a dragonfly larva will be in a position to make a useful contribution to knowledge.

Information on any species will be of value, but it can be seen from the table in Chapter 6 that we need to know much more about some species than others.

Those who are able to help in this way are asked to send their records to

The Warden,
Flatford Mill Field Centre,
East Bergholt, Colchester, Essex.

The type of information needed is given below, but the final analysis will be made much easier if printed record cards are used. These cards can be obtained, free of charge, by applying to the Warden of Flatford Mill Field Centre, and it is suggested that collectors may find it convenient to keep a small number of these available for ready use.

Measurements should be made on fresh specimens, using a pair of dividers and a millimetre scale (as on an ordinary ruler). Lengths should be recorded to the nearest whole millimetre *below:* thus a larva 24·7 mm. long will be given as 24. On no account should the caudal lamellae be included in lengths of Zygoptera.

If identification is certain, it is best to return larvae, alive, to the habitat from which they were collected. (They should not be released in a different place!) But if the identity is uncertain, and appropriate facilities are available, it is advisable to preserve the material in a labelled tube of alcohol, so that it can be examined later.

DRAFT OF PRINTED CARD

Records of Larval Odonata

(Delete words not required)

SPECIES   IDENTITY $\begin{cases} \text{Certain} \\ \text{Uncertain} \end{cases}$

DATE COLLECTED

LOCALITY: COUNTY

NAT. GRID REF.   HABITAT $\begin{cases} \text{Pond} & \text{Stream} & \text{Canal} \\ \text{Lake} & \text{River} & \text{Marsh} \\ \text{Bog} & \text{Ditch} \end{cases}$

Instars other than final	Final instar	Total
No. of larvae		
Lengths in mm.		
No. final instar with *a*. Swollen wing-sheaths		
b. Adult labium within postmentum		

MATERIAL AVAILABLE FOR EXAMINATION   Yes/No

COLLECTOR'S NAME

ADDRESS

APPENDIX II

Venation: Systems, Origins, Terminology
and Table of Notation
(C.L.)

THE classification of the dragonflies (Odonata) has been based on the wing venation, and over the course of time, several systems of notation have been in use. Owing to the wide divergences of opinion as to the origins of some primary veins and the sequence, in geological time, of others, fundamental differences have arisen in the interpretation of many of them. In addition to this question of phylogeny, is that of the ontogeny of the veins, which also has a considerable bearing on their identification. Which came first, the veins, or the tracheae that nourished them in the larval wing? Those believing in the Comstock-Needham "pre-tracheation" theory say the latter, and those of the British school believing in the "pre-determination" theory, say the former.

The holders of both theories agree on the names and positions of the six primary veins (and their corresponding larval tracheae) at the base of the wing. The systems begin to differ at the level of the arculus and become acutely divergent at the nodus and beyond. The table on page 230 gives the equivalent notations for the veins, which will enable the reader to compare the various descriptions by British, Continental and American writers. Odonatists however, even experienced taxonomists, may still find difficulty in determining the correct veins in the very divergent types of dragonfly wings which exist.

During countless millenia of evolution from Protodonate ancestors, the Odonata have gone through a phase of drastic reduction of wing size, and as early as Lower Permian times, they had virtually lost two important veins, the posterior media and the anterior cubitus. Some of the most primitive forms of existing venation are to be found in the present day *Zygoptera,* and these differ in many respects astonishingly little from some of the Permian fossils. The pterostigma was well formed in the latter, but none of them had a fully formed nodus or discoidal cell. There are two genera still to be found in the Old World, which have "open" discoidal cells, and there are many more with other archaic characters.

For the purpose of recognising the positions of the primary longitudinal veins, it is best to distinguish the *Cubitus* at its start (Fig. 119, p. 229). There is only the one, the posterior cubital vein (Cu2) and it always has its origin at the base of the wing, and is the fourth from the upper wing border or costal edge. It always runs apically, past the lower strut of the arculus and along the lower edge of the discoidal cell (*Zygoptera*), or forms the basal side of the triangle (*Anisoptera*). The vein below it, if able to be seen, is the Analis (IA), but in many of the zygopterid genera it is not visible, being fused with the wing border or even atrophied altogether. In other genera there is more than one anal vein present.

Immediately above the *Cubitus*, but separated from it by the discoidal cell (triangle), lies the *Media* (MA), which is also the lower sector of the arculus. Trace it upwards, at that position, along the upper half of the arculus, and you will find it fused to the *Radius* for the entire length of its base. The *Radius*, the third vein from the upper wing border, and the strongest, begins from the base with a stout section fused to the *Media*, and branches into two at the arculus. R1 goes straight out to the wing tip in every odonata wing. The second branch, the *Radial sector* (RS), also always begins in the same way from the base, but turns down the upper half of the arculus, together with the *Media*. After straightening out, it starts off towards the wing tip as R2, but within variable distances between the arculus and the nodus, branches again into R4 and, from anywhere between the nodus and halfway to the pterostigma, into R3. These branches of the *Radial sector* are all concave veins and parts of RS itself, and they have moved their points of origin back towards the wing base as evolution proceeded. In addition to the above are two important intercalary convex veins, IR2 and IR3, and in some genera, several other less important intercalaries. All these veins make identification far from easy and it will be a help to the reader to remember the following points.

In the most primitive forms of the true *Zygoptera*, the vein R4 comes off R2 just basal to the nodus, with IR3 from the position of the nodus, and R3 a long way further forward towards the pterostigma. This is the position in all our *Coenagriidae*, which shows us their extremely ancient origin. This is known from the extensive fossil records. In the *Protozygoptera*, Lower Permian ancestors, all three veins lay apical to the nodus and can be traced stage by stage, in the fossils, as they moved backwards to the base of the wing.

In the only known fossils of *Protanisoptera*, R4 is at the nodus with IR3 just apical to it, and there are existing genera in the *Zygoptera* with the veins still in this position. The next stage, described above for the *Coenagriidae*, is the one found in a vast number of genera all over the world today. All the same, owing to the confluence of the postnodal (and other) veins, noticeable in all present-day *Coenagrioidea*, it can be seen that they have come a long way from the fossil ancestors.

Still early in their history, came a big alteration, and the *Lestes* type of venation appeared; this still remains in many and widespread genera today. Here IR3 has moved back towards the arculus, together with R4, and R3 has moved back towards the nodus. It appears from larval evidence that the big recession of IR3 has been accomplished by means of a secondary back-growth of the vein, called the "bridge," which has not yet received a direct tracheal supply of oxygen.

The next advance came with a widening of the wings again, as in the *Agriidae*. Here IR3 is as in the *Lestes* but with an even longer "bridge," R3 is back to the nodus or nearly so, and R4 is either right back to the arculus, or very nearly so. The number of small intercalary veins in the closely netted wings of the *Agriidae* make if far from easy to distinguish the primary veins, IR2 being particularly difficult to locate. But at any rate it can be seen that R3 has now changed places with IR3 at the nodus, and this is the position in which it will be found in all the *Anisoptera*. All of these have a short "bridge," with a conspicuous, oblique cross-vein leaving the sub-nodus, or R3, and most of them a short, down-curved R4.

This oblique cross-vein beneath the sub-nodus, and another important cross-vein at the base of all wings, the anal crossing (Ac), mark the positions where the tracheae in the larvae descend from primary tracheae to nourish the veins that have developed during the course of evolution. The anal trachea had, some time in the Carboniferous during a period of great reduction in wing size, been pressed sharply upwards against the cubital trachea, but later returned towards the wing border and the anal vein, at the position of the Ac.

The *Radial sector* and its primary branches are nourished directly from their origins, but IR2 has no trachea and that of IR3 varies in origin throughout the Order. In the *Coenagrioidea* it comes off R2 from the position of the sub-nodus. In the *Lestidae* it comes from R3 well apical to the nodus, and the long, basal lestine bridge is unsupplied with oxygen. In the *Agriidae* the trachea of IR3 has come back all the way to the origin of the vein near the arculus. In the *Anisoptera*, the trachea of IR3 leaves the short basal bridge unsupplied as in the *Lestidae*, but branches from the trachea R1 near the position of the sub-nodus, crossing in its descent the two tracheae of R2 and R3. In all these cases an oblique vein in the adult wing marks the course now taken, or formerly taken, by the larval trachea of IR3. There is, therefore, extremely strong evidence that IR3 was a vein added to the simpler venation of the original pre-odonate ancestors. IR3, being a very

---

Fig. 119. Wings of Zygoptera: *a*, *Coenagrion puella*; *b*, *Lestes sponsa*. Wings of Anisoptera: *c*, *Sympetrum striolatum*, hindwing; *d*, *Gomphus vulgatissimus*, forewing. *A2*, *A3*, branches of the anal vein. *Ac*, anal crossing. *Ans*, antenodal cross-veins. *Arc*, arculus. *Aspl*, anal supplement. *b*, bridge. *C*, costa. *Cu2*, cubitus or posterior cubital vein. *Dc*, discoidal cell. *IA*, analis or 1st anal vein. *IR2*, *IR3*, intercalary radial veins. *M*, media. *MA*, anterior media. *Mspl*, median supplement. *N*, nodus. *O*, oblique vein. *Pns*, postnodal cross-veins. *pr.An*, primary antenodals. *Pt*, pterostigma. *R*, radius. *R1*, *R2*, *R3*, *R4*, branches of the radius. *RS*, radial sector. *Rspl*, radial supplement. *Sc*, sub-costa. *Sn*, sub-nodus. *St*, sub-triangle. *T*, triangle.

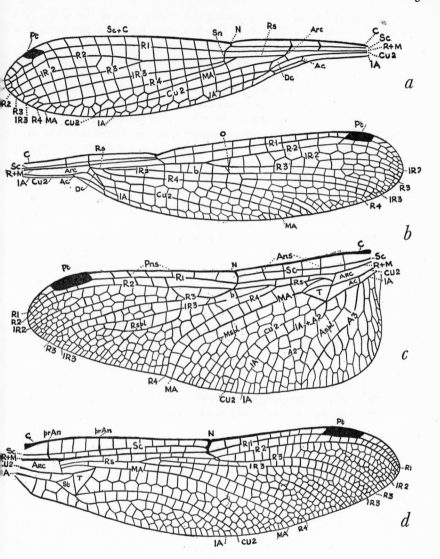

long and important vein, strengthening the middle area of the wings, had to receive an oxygen supply (which IR2 has never had), and the method of getting its tracheal supply has varied considerably.

The term "sector" should be used only for veins that are extra to the main six, but nourished by tracheae in the larvae. The term "supplement" is used for extra veins for which there are no tracheae in the larvae. "Oblique veins," that persist in certain positions throughout the Order, mark the path taken by a few tracheae, during the long course of evolution.

Dr. Needham and others who disagree with the above theories, deny that the anterior cubitus (Cui) has been lost and that the *Media* has only one branch left. In Dr. Needham's view the larval tracheation precedes the formation of the veins. But this theory leaves him without satisfactory explanations for those veins without corresponding tracheae. The belief that the *Media* has four branches leaves the notation in the unhappy position of the *Radial sector* having to cross over M1 and M2, surely an impossible thing for a vein to do. The larval trachea, in the *Anisoptera*, does indeed cross over two tracheae, but this is not an infrequent happening with tracheae. It does not do so, however, in the *Zygoptera* wing, and Needham finds it hard to explain this. In his interpretation, the RS is in the place of our IR3, and he loses sight of this latter vein's obvious secondary origin. Why he persists in the "pre-tracheation" theory, I fail to understand, as in several paragraphs in his 1935 and 1951 papers, he acknowledges both the dominance of the hypodermis in building the veins, and the fact that the latter begin to develop in the "wing bud" before the tracheae arrive there.

The differences in the vein notations are a rather different matter and an unfortunate and confusing one for all taxonomists. It may well be that further "labels" may be given to the veins in the future and that none of us, so far, are altogether correct in our interpretation.

Names of veins	C.L. (1957)	Fraser (1949)	Tillyard (1926)	Tillyard (1917)	Needham (1903-54)	Ris (1908-30)
Costa	C	C	C	C	C	C
Sub-costa	Sc	Sc	Sc	Sc	Sc	Sc
Radius+Media	R+M	R+M	R_1+Rs	R+M	R+M	R+M
Radius	Ri	Ri	R_1	R	R	R
Branches of Radius	R_2 R_3 R_4	Rii Riii Riv-v	R_2 R_3 R_{4+5}	M_1 M_2 M_3	M_1 M_2 M_3	M_1 M_2 M_3

Names of veins	C.L. (1957)	Fraser (1949)	Tillyard (1926)	Tillyard (1917)	Needham (1903-54)	Ris (1908-30)
Radial sector (Upper sector of arculus)	RS	RS	Rs	M_{1+3}	M_{1+3}	M_{1+3}
Intercalary vein ,, ,,	$IR2$ $IR3$	IRii IRiii	IR_2 IR_3	M_{1a} Rs & Ms	M_{1a} Rs	M_{1a} Rs
Radial supplement	Rspl	Rspl	Rspl	Rspl	Rspl	Rspl
Media or anterior media (Lower sector of arculus)	MA	MA	MA	M_4	M_4	M_4
Medial supplement	Mspl	Mspl	Mspl	Mspl	Mspl	Mspl
Cubitus or posterior cubital	Cu2	CuP*	Cu_2	Cu_1	Cu_1	Cu_1
Analis or 1st anal vein	IA	IA	IA	Cu_2	Cu_2	Cu_2
Arculus	Arc	Arc	arc	Arc	ar	Arc
Anal crossing	Ac	Ac	Ac	Ac	Ac	Cuq

REFERENCES

Only a few of the many papers on this controversial question are given below.

COMSTOCK, J. H. (1918). The wings of insects. Ithaca, N.Y.

FRASER, F. C. (1938). A note on the fallaciousness of the theory of pretracheation in the venation of Odonata. *Proc. R. ent. Soc. Lond.* (A) *13:* 60–70.

FRASER, F. C. (1944). The significance of vestigial oblique veins in the evolution of intercalated veins in the odonate wing, with the description of a new genus. *Proc. R. ent. Soc. Lond.* (B) *13:* 58–67.

FRASER, F. C. (1954). The origin and descent of the Order Odonata based on the evidence of persistent archaic characters. *Proc. R. ent. Soc. Lond.* (B) *23:* 89–94.

NEEDHAM, J. G. (1903). Genealogic study of dragonfly wing venation. *Proc. U.S. nat. Mus., 26:* 703–64.

NEEDHAM, J. G. (1935). Some basic principles of insect wing venation. *J.N.Y. ent. Soc., 43:* 113–29.

NEEDHAM, J. G. (1951). Prodrome for a Manual of the Dragonflies of North

*This is a notation which it is better not to use for the 2nd Cubitus, owing to the fact that it may get mixed with the *Postcubitus* (Pcu) of Snodgrass (1935) and Smart (1951) in the Blattidae, with which it may not be homologous.

America, with extended comments on wing venation systems. *Trans. Amer. ent. Soc., 77:* 21–62.

SMART, J. (1951). The wing-venation of the American Cockroach *Periplaneta americana* Linn. (Insecta: Blattidae). *Proc. zool. Soc. Lond., 121:* 501–9.

SNODGRASS, R. E. (1935). Principles of Insect Morphology. New York and London.

TILLYARD, R. J. (1926). The Insects of Australia and New Zealand. Sydney.

TILLYARD, R. J. (1928). The evolution of the Order Odonata. Part I. Introduction and early history of the Order. *Rec. Indian. Mus., 30:* 151–72.

TILLYARD, R. J. and FRASER, F. C. (1938-1940). A reclassification of the Order Odonata, based on some new interpretations of the venation of the dragonfly wing. *Aust. Zool., 9:* 125–69 (1938, Part I), 195–221 (1939, Part II), 359–96 (1940, Part III).

APPENDIX III

Methods for Preservation of Colours
(C.L.)

ALL THE "metallic" species: *Cordulia, Oxygastra, Somatochlora, Agrion* and *Lestes,* are best dried naturally in the air. The other *Zygoptera* are quite successfully preserved by the solvent drying method. For this method set the specimens on small cards, using cotton. Place in a one pound preserving jar with tight-fitting snap-on lid and containing ethyl-acetate. Leave in all night and after removing, leave exposed to the air for a time, before removing from the cards.

For those collectors without adequate facilities, there are two methods which give moderately good results for the *Anisoptera.*

1. *Degutting and quick-drying by external heat:*—Cut a slit, with sharp scissors, beneath the fourth segment of the abdomen. Take care not to damage the genitalia on 2-3 and 8-9 segments. Grasp the intestines by a pair of forceps and pull out. Paper the insect in the ordinary way and place it on a plate or tray over a low spirit lamp, plate warmer, stove or whatever heat is available. Take care not to scorch the specimen, which should be completely dried within a very short time. It can also be dried in an oven at not more than 110°F.

2. *Setting on a cork mat and immersing in methylated spirit:*—Set the dragonfly on its back on a cork mat. Pierce the thorax between the legs, and the abdomen near the base. Float for not more than four hours upside down in a bowl of methylated spirit. Remove and leave to dry thoroughly before removing setting pins, etc.

For those collectors with home or laboratory facilities, the following two methods give excellent results.

*1. *Dr. B. P. Moore's Vacuum drying method.* Apparatus needed: Glass vacuum desiccator, fitted with a ground-glass lid carrying a stopcock. Glass or metal water pump. Length of rubber pressure tubing. Phosphorus pentoxide (the drying agent).

a. All dragonflies for vacuum drying need to be punctured at the membranes

---

*Moore, B. P., (1951), *Proc. S. Lond. ent. nat. Hist. Soc., 1951*:179. On preserving the colours of dragonflies and other insects.

separating the abdominal sternites. This is necessary to prevent contortions during evacuation and it also facilitates drying.

b. Several insects may be dried at one session, but *Anisoptera* and *Zygoptera* should not be mixed.

c. *Anisoptera* are given the full vacuum, *i.e.* exhausted until the note of the pump has attained constant pitch and then for a further five minutes.

d. Plenty of drying agent should be used. The spent material forms a viscous layer which can be lifted off entire, leaving un-reacted material ready for further use. Do not use a metal container for the agent; a glass or china dish is the most satisfactory.

e. Twenty-four hours is usually sufficient for drying, but large batches of *Anisoptera* may require a little longer. The eyes are always the last to dry and the appearance of these affords a ready means of determining when the process is complete. During drying these organs change from the pellucid translucence of life to an opaque appearance characteristic of this method of preservation.

f. When drying is complete the vacuum is released by opening the stopcock carefully until the sound of the entering air can just be heard. Do not open further until equilibrium is established, or the rush of air may cause damage to the specimens.

g. The abdomens of some specimens, particularly female *Aeshnidae*, are very liable to be marred by grease. Detach the abdomen, soak in ethyl-acetate for a few hours, dry off and refix with gum arabic.

Zygoptera can also be dried as above, but in a partial vacuum only, the time of exhaustion being determined by experiment.

Naturally the insects must be freshly killed and the drying begun immediately. Dr. Moore recommends killing all red, yellow and black and yellow-brown species with sulphur dioxide. This mixture to be made of equal small parts of powdered potassium metabisulphite and powdered citric acid, in the bottom of a glass tube, covered with a wad of blotting paper kept moist by a few drops of water. All blue and green species to be killed in ethyl-acetate vapour.

†2. *Dr. D. A. L. Davies' Low-temperature drying method.* Apparatus needed: Ice box. Glass vacuum desiccator. Concentrated sulphuric acid (the drying agent).

Bring specimens home alive and allow to evacuate their last meal. Kill with cyanide and set on small cork blocks. Cool immediately to 2-3°C. by placing in ice box at minus 10°C. Next put blocks into glass desiccator and evacuate to a pressure of less than 0·5 mm. Hg.

After five hours, slowly release the vacuum, take the insects off the

†Davies, D. A. L., (1954), *Entomologist*, 87:34. On the preservation of insects by drying *in vacuo* at low temperature.

blocks and they are ready for the cabinet. (Five years later, Dr. Davies' specimens remained perfectly set and in their natural colours.)

Both large and small species can equally well be dried by this method which has a great advantage over heat, really quite the wrong approach to insects containing labile pigments. A further conspicuous advantage is the natural condition of the colour of the compound eyes of specimens dried by the low-temperature method.

APPENDIX IV

Marking

(N.W.M.)

A. GENERAL

Much can be learned about the behaviour and ecology of dragonflies by marking them. They are particularly suitable subjects for this technique because they are large robust insects and do not possess scales which rub off when handled.

Several methods of marking dragonflies have been used with varying degrees of success. The method to be used of course largely depends on the problem to be tackled. In particular the investigator must decide:—

1. Whether he wishes to be able to identify individuals or only groups (*e.g.* dragonflies caught at a certain date at a certain locality).
2. Whether it is essential or merely desirable that the identification mark should be permanent.

In all marking experiments it must be remembered that one is dealing with complex living organisms. Even if the greatest care is taken the process of being caught in a net, marked and released is bound to cause considerable disturbance to the insect. If insufficient care is taken the results of the marking experiment are liable to be meaningless or even misleading. The main snags are mentioned below.

B. METHODS FOR MARKING LARVAE

1. *Cellulose paint*
   Advantages
   > Quick, possible to have many colour combinations, and so especially suitable when individuals must be recognisable.

   Disadvantages
   > Not permanent.
   > Cuticle must be dry when painted; therefore only applicable to larvae which can stand about 10 minutes out of water.

   Method
   > Apply with needle, or painted stick, rush point etc. Avoid eyes,

spiracles, joints, and wing-sheaths (because latter swell at meta-morphosis).

Femora of legs provide best places.

Oil paint could possibly also be used.

2. *Wire or tinfoil*

Advantages

Permanent if carefully done.

Insect need not be taken out of water for long period before marking.

Disadvantages

Slow.

Different combinations less easy to achieve than with paint.

Only suitable for marking femora of robust species.

Method

a. Wire

Tie thin copper wire round femur in a reef knot, cut ends close. Do not pull too tight or leg will be severed.

b. Tinfoil

Cut foil into narrow (less than 1 mm. wide) strips, *c.* 1 cm. long and wind obliquely round a femur. Milk bottle tops are excellent material because they have the right thickness, are often coloured differently on both sides and can be cut with scissors. Trim off projecting ends. Pinch leg with forceps slightly so that foil does not form a regular cylinder which would work off owing to the distally pointing spines on legs.

If possible when using wire or tinfoil it is best to paint leg first to make it rigid. It is essential to do this if larva is teneral.

N.B. No external mark will survive a moult.

C. METHODS FOR MARKING ADULT INSECTS

Adult insects are much more easily damaged than larvae and their be-haviour therefore correspondingly more likely to be affected by marking. The following points must be borne in mind:—

1. If the insect hits a net when travelling fast the delicate head suspension, and therefore the balancing mechanism, is usually damaged—this applies particularly to the heavier Anisoptera.

2. The wings are easily broken if the insect is allowed to struggle in the net. Partial breaks in the veins which can prevent the insect from flying properly are often not obvious.

3. Any paint on the head (especially on the eyes) or on the legs is liable to cripple the insect. Care also should be taken not to cover spiracles with paint.

4. If the wings are marked, great care must be taken not to put too much paint—as this seriously affects the flying power of the insect.

5. It is almost impossible to mark a teneral damselfly without damaging it. If it is essential to mark teneral insects do so very delicately on femur.

6. When releasing a dragonfly it is essential to let it go as gently as possible. Individuals of most species will fly away from their captor on release. They are much less likely to fly away immediately if their legs are made to grasp a plant before being let go, and if they are released when the sun is not shining.

No method in which wire, tinfoil, cotton etc., is tied to the adult insect is suitable since it is bound to affect the insect's flight, or feeding or mating. None of the following methods is permanent but all are fairly adequate for the short time a dragonfly spends as an adult insect.

1. *Indian Ink*
   Advantages
     Minimal effect on insect (thin film only).
   Disadvantages
     Rather slow drying.
     Colours not very brilliant.

2. *Oil paint*
   Advantages
     Adheres well.
     Bright colour.
   Disadvantages
     Heavy.
     Dries slowly.

3. *Cellulose paint* (Quick drying brands)
   Advantages
     Bright colours.
     Dries very quickly especially if use is made of paints like Aerocar Brushing cellulose enamel (Valay Industries Product). Brushing Belco (Rawlplug Paint Co.). Cellulose spotting enamel X9384 (British Domolac Co.).

Disadvantages
>   Liable to flake off and so is less permanent than Indian Ink or Oil paint.

Method
>   Apply paint with needle, rush or pointed stick, as thinly as possible. Avoid spiracles, leg bases and head, and dorsal region of thorax because here it may be dislodged by anal appendages of male during precopulation behaviour. From the point of view of the paint sticking it is best to mark the sides of the thorax, but marks here are not easily seen during flight and marking may obscure colour patterns which are of importance in mating. If one wishes to be able to identify an insect without catching it, the wings should be used. They should be marked near the base, and as little paint used as possible. Anisoptera are unable to rub off paint on the wings but the cleaning movement of Zygopterans shown in Fig. 27, p. 113, sometimes succeeds in removing paint.

D.   MISCELLANEOUS NOTES

1. Catching Anisoptera adults so as not to damage them needs considerable skill and knowledge of their behaviour. To catch big samples special opportunities have to be sought, *e.g.* species with a synchronised emergence provide excellent opportunities for marking before their maiden flight. At this time (early in the morning) a large proportion of the total annual population may be easily caught and marked in a short time. This method has the great advantage that the exact adult age is known when the insect is recaptured.

2. For larvae radio-active tracers cannot be used to label individuals because they are cannibals. This technique might have a limited use in studying the roosting habits of adult Zygoptera.

3. If larvae are marked in the final instar they can be recaptured again as larvae or as exuviae left behind after emergence.

4. Finally, a word of warning should be given concerning sampling populations. There are a number of pitfalls for the unwary. For example the capture-recapture method (Lincoln Index) of estimating population size can only be used if certain conditions are fulfilled. Would-be experimenters are urged to consult the literature before embarking on such schemes.

E.   REFERENCES

Larvae
CORBET, P. S. (1957). The life-history of the Emperor Dragonfly, *Anax imperator* Leach (Odonata, Aeshnidae). *J. Anim. Ecol.* 26: 1–69.

Adults

BORROR, D. J. (1934). Ecological studies of *Argia moesta* Hagen (Odonata, Coenagrionidae) by means of marking. *Ohio J. Sci.* 34: 97–108.

CORBET, P. S. (1952). An adult population study of *Pyrrhosoma nymphula* (Sulzer) (Odonata, Coenagrionidae). *J. Anim. Ecol.* 21: 206–22.

JACOBS, M. E. (1955). Studies on territorialism and sexual selection in dragonflies. *Ecology,* 36: 566–86.

MOORE, N. W. (1952). On the so-called "territories" of dragonflies (Odonata-Anisoptera). *Behaviour,* 4: 85–100.

REFERENCES

ALVERDES, F. (1924). Beobachtungen an Ephemeriden und Libellenlarven. *Biol. Zentralblatt, 43:* 577–605.

ANDREWARTHA, H. G. (1952). Diapause in relation to the ecology of insects. *Biol. Rev. 27:* 50–107.

ASAHINA, S. (1954). A morphological study of a relic dragonfly *Epiophlebia superstes* (Selys) (Odonata, Anisozygoptera). Tokyo, The Japan Society for Promotion of Science.

BALDUS, K. (1924). Experimentale Untersuchungen über die Entfernungs-lokalisation der Libellen (*Aeschna cyanea*). *Zeit. vergl. Physiol. 3:* 475–505.

BALFOUR-BROWNE, F. (1909). The life-history of the agrionid dragonfly. *Proc. zool. Soc. Lond. 1909:* 253–85.

BALL, K. M. (1926). Decorative Motives of Oriental Art. London, New York.

BORROR, D. J. (1934). Ecological studies of *Argia moesta* (Hagen) (Odonata, Coenagrionidae) by means of marking. *Ohio J. Sci. 34:* 97–108.

BREDER, C. M. (1948). Observations on coloration in reference to behavior in tide-pool and other marine shore fishes. *Bull. Amer. Mus. nat. Hist. N.Y. 92:* 281–312.

BUCHHOLTZ, C. (1951). Untersuchungen an der Libellen—Gattung *Calopteryx* Leach—unter besonderer Berücksichtigung ethologischer Fragen. *Z. Tierpsychol. 8:* 274–93.

BUCHHOLTZ, C. (1955). Eine vergleichende Ethologie der orientalischen Caloptery-giden (Odonata) als Beitrag zu ihrer systematischen Deutung. *Z. Tierpsychol. 12:* 364–86.

BUCHHOLTZ, C. (1956). Eine Analyse des Paarungsverhaltens und der dabei Wirkenden Reizauslöser bei den Libellen *Platycnemis pennipes* Pall. und *Pl. dealbata* Klug. *Z. Tierpsychol. 13:* 14–25.

BURMEISTER, H. (1836). Manual of Entomology. London.

CORBET, P. S. (1951). The development of the labium of *Sympetrum striolatum* (Charp.) (Odon., Libellulidae). *Ent. mon. Mag. 87:* 289–96.

CORBET, P. S. (1952). An adult population study of *Pyrrhosoma nymphula* (Sulzer) (Odonata, Coenagrionidae). *J. Anim. Ecol. 21:* 206–22.

CORBET, P. S. (1953). A terminology for the labium of larval Odonata. *Entomologist, 86:* 191–96.

CORBET, P. S. (1954). Seasonal regulation in British dragonflies. *Nature, Lond. 174:* 655.

CORBET, P. S. (1955). A critical response to changing length of day in an insect. *Nature, Lond. 175:* 338–39.

CORBET, P. S. (1955). The immature stages of the Emperor Dragonfly, *Anax imperator* Leach (Odonata, Aeshnidae). *Ent. Gaz. 6:* 189–204.

CORBET, P. S. (1955). The larval stages of *Coenagrion mercuriale* (Charp.) (Odonata, Coenagriidae). *Proc. R. ent. Soc. Lond. (A), 30:* 115–26.

CORBET, P. S. (1956). Environmental factors influencing the induction and termination of diapause in the Emperor Dragonfly, *Anax imperator* Leach (Odonata, Aeshnidae). *J. exp. Biol. 33:* 1–14.

CORBET, P. S. (1956). The influence of temperature on diapause development in the dragonfly, *Lestes sponsa* (Hansemann) (Odonata, Lestidae). *Proc. R. ent. Soc. Lond. (A), 31:* 45–48.

CORBET, P. S. (1956). The life-histories of *Lestes sponsa* (Hansemann) and *Sympetrum striolatum* (Charp.) (Odonata). *Tijdschr. Ent. 99:* 217–29.

CORBET, P. S. (1957). The life-histories of two summer species of dragonfly (Odonata, Coenagriidae). *Proc. zool. Soc. Lond. 128:* 403–18.

CORBET, P. S. (1957). The life-histories of two spring species of dragonfly (Odonata, Zygoptera). *Ent. Gaz. 8:* 79–89.

CORBET, P. S. (1957). The life-history of the Emperor Dragonfly, *Anax imperator* Leach (Odonata, Aeshnidae). *J. Anim. Ecol. 26:* 1–69.

CORBET, P. S. (1958). Temperature in relation to seasonal development of British dragonflies (Odonata). *Trans. Xth Int. Congress of Entomology, Montreal, 2:* 755–57.

CORBET, P. S. and S. A. (1958). Emergence of a summer species of dragonfly. *Nature, Lond. 182:* 194.

COTTAM, C. 1939). Food habits of North American diving ducks. *U.S.D.A., Tech. Bull. 643:* 1–139.

COWLEY, J. (1940). Ceratopogonidae (Diptera) as parasites of Odonata in the Japanese Empire. *Trans. Nat. Hist. Soc. Formosa, 30:* 1–7.

CROZIER, W. J. *et al.* (1937). Critical illumination and critical frequency for response to flickered light, in dragonfly larvae. *J. Gen. Physiol. 20:* 363–410.

DALE, J. C. (1834). Cordulia Curtisii Dale, a species hitherto undescribed, characterised by Mr. Dale. *Mag. Nat. Hist. (I), 7:* 60–61.

DANNREUTHER, T. (1951). Dragonfly Migrations. *Countryside.* Summer 1951.

EVANS, W. F. (1845). British Libellulinae. London.

FISHER, R. A. and FORD, E. B. (1947). The spread of a gene in natural conditions in a colony of the moth *Panaxia dominula* (L.) *Heredity, 1:* 143–74.

FRASER, F. C. (1939). The evolution of the copulatory process in the Order Odonata. *Proc. R. ent. Soc. Lond. (A), 14:* 125–29.

FRASER, F. C. (1945). Migration of Odonata. *Ent. mon. Mag. 81:* 73–74.

FRASER, F. C. (1949 and 1956). Handbooks for the identification of British Insects. Vol. I, (10), Odonata. *Roy. ent. Soc. Lond.*

FRASER, F. C. (1953). A new variety of *Leucorrhinia dubia*. *Ent. mon. Mag. 89:* 138.

FRASER, F. C. (1954). The origin and descent of the Order Odonata based on the evidence of persistent archaic characters. *Proc. R. ent. Soc. Lond. (B), 23:* 89–94.

FRASER, F. C. (1957). A reclassification of the Order Odonata. Roy. zool. Soc. N.S.W.

FROST, W. E. and SMYLY, W. J. P. (1952). The brown trout of a moorland fishpond. *J. Anim. Ecol. 21:* 62–86.

GAMBLES, R. M. (1956). Eggs of *Lestinogomphus africanus* Fraser. *Nature, Lond. 177:* 663.

GARDNER, A. E. (1950-58). Numerous papers on larval Odonata in the *Ent. Gaz.*

GARDNER, A. E. (1955). A study of the genitalia of the two species *Sympetrum nigrescens* Lucas and *S. nigrifemur* (Selys) with notes on their distribution. *Ent. Gaz. 6:* 86–108.

GARDNER, A. E. and MACNEILL, N. (1950). The life-history of *Pyrrhosoma nymphula* (Sulzer) (Odonata). *Ent. Gaz. 1:* 163–82.

GRASSÉ, P. P. (1932). Observations et remarques sur les migrations d'Odonates. *Soc. ent. Livre du cent:* 657–68.

HINMAN, E. H. (1934). Predators of the Culicidae 1. The predators of larvae and pupae exclusive of fish. *J. trop. Med. & Hyg. 37:* 129–34, 145–50.

HINTON, H. E. (1948). On the origin and function of the pupal stage. *Trans. R. ent. Soc. Lond. 99:* 395–409.

JACKSON, C. H. N. (1948). The analysis of a tsetse-fly population, III. *Ann. Eugen. London, 14:* 91–108.

JACOBS, M. E. (1955). Studies on territorialism and sexual selection in dragonflies. *Ecology, 36:* 566–86.

JONSTON, J. (1657). Historiae naturalis de Insectis Libri III. Amsterdam, Schipper.

KENNEDY, C. H. (1950). The relation of American dragonfly-eating birds to their prey. *Ecological Monographs, 20:* 103–42.

KINGSBURY, O. R. (1937). Foes encountered in the rearing of smallmouth bass. *Trans. Amer. fish Soc. 66:* 267–74.

LACK, D. (1954). The Natural Regulation of Animal Numbers. Oxford Clarendon.

LACK, D. and E. (1951). Migration of insects and birds through a Pyrenean pass. *J. Anim. Ecol. 20:* 63–67.

LAMBORN, R. (1890). Dragonflies versus Mosquitoes. New York.

LEES, A. D. (1953). Environmental factors controlling the evocation and termination of diapause in the fruit tree red spider mite *Metatetranychus ulmi* (Koch) (Acarina, Tetranychidae). *Ann. appl. Biol. 40:* 449–86.

LEES, A. D. (1953). The significance of the light and dark phases in the photoperiodic control of diapause in *Metatetranychus ulmi* (Koch). *Ann. appl. Biol. 40:* 487–97.

LONGFIELD, C. (1948). A vast immigration of dragonflies into the south coast of Co. Cork. *Irish Nat. J. 9:* 133–41.

LONGFIELD, C. (1949). The breeding status of *Aeshna mixta* Latreille (Odonata) and notes on the evidence of breeding in *Sympetrum flaveolum* (L.) and *S. fonscolombii* (Selys). *J. Soc. Brit. Ent. 3:* 84–88.

LONGFIELD, C. (1949). The Dragonflies of the British Isles. London, Warne.

LUCAS, W. J. (1900). British Dragonflies (Odonata). London, Upcott Gill.

LUCAS, W. J. (1930). The Aquatic (Naiad) Stage of the British Dragonflies (Paraneuroptera). London, Ray Society.

MAY, E. (1933). Libellen oder Wasserjungfern (Odonata), in: DAHL, F. *Die Tierwelt Deutschlands, 27,* Jena: 1–124.

MOORE, N. W. (1952). On the so-called "territories" of dragonflies (Odonata—Anisoptera). *Behaviour, 4:* 85–100.

MOORE, N. W. (1952). Notes on the oviposition behaviour of the dragonfly *Sympetrum striolatum* (Charpentier). *Behaviour, 4:* 101–3.

MOORE, N. W. (1952). On the length of life of adult dragonflies (Odonata—Anisoptera) in the field. *Proc. Bristol Nat. Soc. 28:* 267–72.

MOORE, N. W. (1953). Population density in adult dragonflies (Odonata—Anisoptera). *J. Anim. Ecol. 22:* 344–59.

MOORE, N. W. (1954). On the dispersal of Odonata. *Proc. Bristol Nat. Soc. 28:* 407–17.

MOORE, N. W. (1957). Territory in dragonflies and birds. *Bird Study, 4:* 125–30.

MÜNCHBERG, P. (1931). Zur Biologie der Odonatengenera *Brachytron* Evans und *Aeshna* Fbr. *Z. Morph. Ökol. Tiere, 20:* 172–232.

MÜNCHBERG, P. (1935). Zur Kenntnis der Odonatenparasiten mit ganz besonderer Berücksichtigung der Ökologie der in Europa an Libellen schmarotzenden Wassermilbenlarven. *Arch. Hydrobiol. 29:* 1–120.

NEEDHAM, J. G. (1900). The fruiting of the Blue Flag (*Iris versicolor* L.). *Amer. Nat. 34:* 361–86.

NEEDHAM, J. G. and HEYWOOD, H. B. (1929). A Handbook of the Dragonflies of North America. Springfield, Illinois, Thomas.

PIERRE, ABBÉ (1904). L'éclosion des oeufs du *Lestes viridis* (Van der Lind.). *Ann. Soc. ent. France, 73:* 477—84.

RÉAUMUR, R. A. (1734–42). Mémoires pour servir à l'histoire naturelle et à l'anatomie des insectes. Paris.

ROSTAND, J. (1935). La Vie des Libellules. Paris, Delamain et Boutelleau.

ST. QUENTIN, D. (1934). Beobachtungen und Versuche an Libellen in ihren Jagdrevieren. *Konowia, 13:* 275–82.

SÄLZLE, K. (1932). Untersuchungen an Libellenlarven über das Sehen bewegter Objekte. *Z. vergl. Physiol. 18:* 347–68.

SCHAFER, G. D. (1923). The growth of dragonfly nymphs at the moult and between moults. *Stanford Univ. Publ. Biol. Sci. 3:* 307–37.

SCHMIDT, E. (1929). Libellen, Odonata. *Die Tierwelt Mitteleuropas, IV.,* Leipzig: 1–66.

SØMME, S. (1937). Contributions to the biology of Norwegian fish food animals, III., Odonaten. *Avh. norske Viden-Akad.* Oslo: 1–133.

SOTAVALTA, O. (1954). On the thoracic temperature of insects in flight. (Contributions to the problem of insect flight IV.) *Ann. zool. Soc. zool. bot. Fenn. Vanamo, 16:* 1–22.

STEINER, H. (1948). Die Bindung der Hochmoorlibelle *Leucorrhinia dubia* Vand., an ihr Biotop. *Zool. Jb. Jena Syst. 78:* 65–96.

STRAUB, E. (1943). Stadien und Darmkanal der Odonaten in Metamorphosen und Häutung, sowie die Bedeutung des Schlüpfaktes für die systematische Biologie. *Arch. Naturgesch. Berlin, 12:* 1–93.

TILLYARD, R. J. (1917). The Biology of Dragonflies (Odonata or Paraneuroptera). Cambridge.

TINBERGEN, N. (1951). The Study of Instinct. Oxford, Clarendon.

TINBERGEN, N. (1957). The functions of territory. *Bird Study, 4:* 14–27.

TJØNNELAND, A. (1951). Odonatene—en baktalt insektgruppe. *Naturen, Bergen 1951:* 109–16.

TJØNNELAND, A. (1953). A contribution to the zoogeography of Norwegian dragonflies. *Arbok 1952. Univ. Bergen, naturv. rekke Nr. 15:* 1–44.

VALLE, K. J. (1952). Die Verbreitungsverhältnisse der ostfennoskandischen Odonaten. *Acta ent. fenn. 10:* 1–87.

VOINOV, D. N. (1898). Recherches physiologiques sur l'appareil digestif et le tissu adipeux des larves des Odonata. *Bull. Soc. Bucharest, 7:* 49–52, 473–93.

WESENBERG-LUND, C. (1943). Biologie der Süsswasserinsekten. Kopenhagen.

WIGGLESWORTH, V. B. (1953). The Principles of Insect Physiology. (5th edition) London, Methuen.

WILLIAMS, C. B. (1958). Insect Migration. London, Collins.

WILSON, C. B. (1918). Dragonflies and damselflies in relation to pond-fish culture, with a list of those found near Fairport, Iowa. *Bull. U.S. Bureau Fisheries 36:* 181–264.

WOLFE, L. S. (1953). A study of the genus *Uropetala* (Selys) (Order Odonata) from New Zealand. *Trans. Roy. Soc. N.Z. 80:* 245–75.

WRIGHT, M. (1946). The economic importance of dragonflies (Odonata). *J. Tennessee Acad. Sci. 21:* 60–71.

GLOSSARY

Accessory genitalia	The genital apparatus found on the ventral surface of the second and third segments of the abdomen of male dragonflies.
Anal clasper	The appendages at the end of the abdomen of the male dragonfly which are used in holding the head or pronotum of the female during mating and in the tandem position.
Anisopteran	A dragonfly belonging to the Anisoptera, one of the main divisions of living Odonata. In this group the wings are held open while the insect is at rest. The eyes either touch or are close together. The larvae have internal rectal gills. Most of the larger and more robust species belong to this group.
Base-rich	Containing a relatively large amount of alkaline salts, such as calcium and magnesium.
Bivoltine	Completing two generations in one year.
Chain reaction	A series of instinctive actions, each action being triggered off by the preceding one.
Clypeus	That part of the face between the upper lip and the frons.
Coxa	First (from base) segment of leg.
Damselfly	A popular name for Zygoptera.
Diapause	A state of interrupted development which arises spontaneously and which is not brought about by unfavourable environmental conditions.
Display	Movements whose function is to elicit an instinctive response in another animal.
Dormancy	An interruption of development brought about by unfavourable environmental conditions.
Ecdysis	The moulting of the chitinous cuticle of an insect.
Emergence	The processes associated with the moult from larva to adult.
Ethology	Objective comparative study of animal behaviour.
Expectation of life	The average life, or the age at which half the individuals under consideration will have died.
Exuvia	The skin cast by an insect during a moult. Plural: exuviae.
Face	The front of the head.
Facultative	The opposite of obligate. An obligate diapause invariably recurs once in each generation, but a facultative diapause can be averted by certain environmental conditions.
Femur	Third (from base) segment of leg.

Flying season	The period between the arrival of the first mature adult dragonflies over water and the disappearance of the last.
Frons	The forehead or upper part of the face, usually rounded in Zygoptera and ridged in Anisoptera.
Genitalia	The external organs of reproduction.
Heat budget	Accumulated temperature received by a habitat during a specified period (usually a year).
Instar	A stage in development between two successive ecdyses.
Interspecific	Between individuals of different species.
Intraspecific	Between individuals of the same species.
Labium	Lower lip—consists of a pair of fused head appendages.
Larva	The post-embryonic aquatic stage in the life-history of a dragonfly. It is sometimes referred to as the nymph or naiad, but such names are liable to lead to misunderstanding.
Maiden flight	The first flight made by a dragonfly after emergence.
Mandible	Biting mouthpart.
Mass emergence	A term best used to describe a condition in which a substantial proportion of the annual population of a certain species emerges from a given habitat on a single day. The absolute numbers emerging are immaterial; it is the degree to which emergence is synchronised that is important. In some species, a mass emergence may involve more than 30 per cent of the annual population emerging on a single day.
Maturation period	The first part of the life of an adult dragonfly, spent away from water while it is becoming sexually mature.
Maximum life-span	The greatest period that an individual of a certain species has been observed to live.
Melanism	A condition in which an animal becomes unusually dark in colour.
Metamorphosis	The changes taking place inside the larval skin in preparation for the moult from larva to adult.
Niche	The place of an animal in its living environment. The term implies its relationship to food and enemies.
Obligate	See *Facultative*.
Occiput	Posterior and upper part of the head.
Ovipositor	Organ at hind end of abdomen of female insects through which eggs are laid. To oviposit—to lay eggs with this organ.
Per collum	See *Tandem position*.
Photoperiod	The duration of uninterrupted light during a 24-hour period. An 8-hour photoperiod involves a dark interval of 16 hours.
Phylum	One of the major groups used in classifying animals. Consists

of one or more classes. *E.g.* Phylum Vertebrata which is subdivided into classes Mammalia, Aves, Reptilia etc.

Pronotum   The dorsal plate covering the prothorax.

Prothorax   The anterior segment of the thorax. It bears a pair of legs but no wings.

Pterostigma   The opaque chitinised cell near the apex of the wing on the costal border.

Releaser   Sign-stimulus peculiar to a given species which releases an instinctive reaction in other members of that species.

Rheophilic   Adapted to life in running water.

Sign-stimulus   Part of any object (*e.g.* of mate, prey, predator, etc.) which alone or in conjunction with other sign-stimuli elicits an instinctive action.

Seasonal regulation   The means by which animals and plants maintain a periodicity in reproduction and growth associated with certain seasons of the year.

Semivoltine   Requiring two years to complete a single generation.

Spiracle   External opening of a trachea.

Spring species   Dragonflies with a diapause in the final larval instar. Such species usually have a synchronised emergence in spring or early summer, and a relatively short adult life. In Britain, most spring species require a minimum of two years in which to complete the life-history.

Sub-optimal stimulus   A stimulus which under normal conditions would be insufficient to evoke a particular reaction.

Summer species   Dragonflies without a diapause in the final larval instar. Such species tend to have emergence spread over a long time, and to have a relatively long adult life. Two types of summer species can be recognised, depending upon whether or not the life-history is univoltine.

Tandem position   The position in which the male leads and holds the head or the pronotum of the female with his anal claspers. It is adopted by all dragonflies before mating and by many during oviposition. (See Fig. 2, p. 9.)

Tarsus   Fifth (from base) segment of leg.

Temperature coefficient   The relationship between change in temperature and the change this brings about in the rate of growth or of some other developmental process. If an animal possesses a high positive temperature coefficient for growth, this means that a small rise in temperature causes a rapid increase in the rate of growth.

Temperature threshold   The lowest or highest temperature at which a given process can take place.

Teneral	The condition of a larva or an adult soon after ecdysis, before the cuticle has hardened completely.
Territory	An area defended by an animal.
Thorax	The group of three segments behind the head which bears the legs and wings.
Tibia	Fourth (from base) segment of leg.
Tracheae	Tubes which ramify throughout the body and conduct air from the spiracles to the tissues.
Trochanter	Second (from base) segment of leg.
Univoltine	Completing one generation in a single year.
Zygopteran	A dragonfly belonging to the Zygoptera, one of the main divisions of living Odonata. In this group the wings are held closed or nearly closed over the back when the insect is at rest. The eyes are widely separated. The larvae have external caudal gills. Most of the smaller and weaker species belong to this group. They are sometimes called damselflies.

INDEX

FIGURES in bold type refer to pages opposite which plates will be found. Distribution maps are likewise indexed according to the pages on which they occur.

Dragonflies recognised as British are indexed under their full scientific names, with cross references both from the specific trivial name and the English name.

The Key to Larvae, being itself systematically arranged, has not been indexed.